B

Maths Links

Dave Capewell
Mike Heylings
Pete Mullarkey
Nina Patel

9

OXFORD
UNIVERSITY PRESS

Great Clarendon Street, Oxford OX2 6DP

Oxford University Press is a department of the University of Oxford.
It furthers the University's objective of excellence in research, scholarship, and education by publishing worldwide in

Oxford New York

Auckland Cape Town Dar es Salaam Hong Kong Karachi
Kuala Lumpur Madrid Melbourne Mexico City Nairobi
New Delhi Shanghai Taipei Toronto

With offices in

Argentina Austria Brazil Chile Czech Republic France Greece
Guatemala Hungary Italy Japan South Korea Poland Portugal
Singapore Switzerland Thailand Turkey Ukraine Vietnam

Oxford is a registered trade mark of Oxford University Press in the UK and in certain other countries

First published 2009.

British Library Cataloguing in Publication Data

Data available

ISBN 978 0 19 915303 9

10 9 8 7 6 5 4 3 2 1

Printed in Spain by Cayfosa (Impresia Iberica)

Paper used in the production of this book is a natural, recyclable product made from wood grown in sustainable forests. The manufacturing process conforms to the environmental regulations of the country of origin.

Acknowledgements

The publisher would like to thank Pete Crawford for his work in creating the case studies.

The publisher is grateful for permission to reproduce the following photographs;

P1: Chris Price/I-stock; **P5:** Paul Lampard/I-stock; **P7:** Mypokcik/Dreamstime.com; **P15:** I stock; **P21:** Martin Mcelligott/I-stock; **P37:** Andrew Cribb/I-stock; **P45:** Donall O Cleirigh/I-stock; **P52:** Absolut_photos/Dreamstime.com; **P57:** Steve Rosset/Dreamstime.com; **P61:** Breenicole/Dreamstime.com; **P75:** Enis Izgi/I-stock; **P77:** Adisa/Dreamstime.com; **P80:** Max Blain/Shutterstock; **P83:** Andrey Khrolenok/Shutterstock; **P88:** OUP/South West Images Scotland; **P91:** Krzysztof Zmij/I-stock; **P92:** Ashley Whitworth/Shutterstock; **P94t:** Gneesam/I-stock; **P94b:** ICP/Alamy; **P99t:** OUP/Jon Arnold Images; **P99b:** Marbo/Dreamstime.com; **P105:** Dennis Guyitt/I-stock; **P108t:** OUP/Photodisc; **P108b:** Sebastien Burel/Shutterstock; **P109:** Kletr/Shutterstock; **P118:** Rob Wallis/Alamy; **P121:** Texas Intruments; **P127:** Guy Erwood/I-stock; **P149:** David Joyner/I-stock; **P150:** The Photolibrary Wales/Alamy; **P151:** Keith Wheatley/Shutterstock; **P155:** OUP/Photodisc; **P165:** OUP; **P168:** OUP/Photodisc; **P172:** OUP/Photodisc; **P173:** OUP/Mike Chinery; **P173:** OUP; **P179:** Cci Archives / Science Photo Library; **P201:** Michel de Nijs/I-stock; **P204:** OUP/Image Source; **P206:** Lane Erickson/Dreamstime.com; **P210:** Wallenrock/Shutterstock; **P211:** trucic/Shutterstock; **P212&213:** World Health Organisation; **P217tl:** Kyle Froese/I-stock; **P217tr:** Donald Erickson/I-stock; **P217br:** Frank van Haalen/I-stock; **P217bl:** I-stock; **P218:** OUP/Digital Vision; **P219:** Craig Barhorst/Shutterstock; **P221:** Viktoriya/Shutterstock; **P231:** shock/Dreamstime.com; **P232l:** beltsazar/Shutterstock; **P232r:** Simon Krzic/Shutterstock; **P237:** Colton Stiffler/Shutterstock. **CASE STUDY 1: ONLINE AUCTION** Mats Tooming/I-stock; Bronwyn8/Dreamstime.com; Alexander Ostrijchuk/I-stock; **CASE STUDY 2: INVESTIGATING CRIME** Dreamstime/Scol22; Stefan Klein/I-stock; Mark Evans/I-stock; Mikhail Kokhanchikov/I-stock; Kmitu/I-stock; Juri Samsonov/Dreamstime.com; Terraxplorer/I-stock; Timothy Large/I-stock; Martin Applegate/Dreamstime.com; Lisa F. Young/Dreamstime.com; blackred/I-stock; Robert Mizerek/Dreamstime.com; Jf123/Dreamstime.com; Andy Brown/Dreamstime.com; Jf123/Dreamstime.com.
CASE STUDY 3: WHY DO BIKES HAVE GEARS? Heather Down/I-stock; Hulton Archive/I-stock; James Davidson/Dreamstime.com; Brianna May/I-stock; Stefanie Leuker/Dreamstime.com; Viktor Pravdica/Dreamstime.com; Karam Miri/I-stock; Giorgio Fochesato/I-stock; Greenwales/Alamy; Mehmet Salih Guler/I-stock; Mediagfx/Dreamstime.com; Dušan Zidar/Dreamstime.com.
CASE STUDY 4: KART RACE Engraver/Dreamstime.com;Jan Greune/Getty Images.

Figurative Artwork is by: Peter Donnelly and Matt Latchford

Contents

1 Algebra

Sequences and graphs

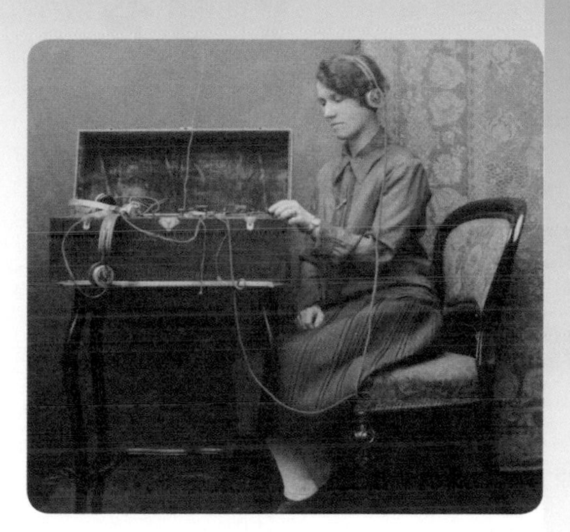

Morse code uses a sequence of 'dots and dashes' to represent letters, numbers and punctuation. It has been used for more than 160 years and in the early 20th century was the most common way of transmitting information quickly between countries using radio, telegraph lines or undersea cables.

What's the point? Morse code is still used today by the Armed Forces, people with various disabilities and to send a distress signal with only a torch!

Check in

Level 4

1 The total cost £C of buying n shirts by mail order is given by this rule.
Multiply by 15 and then add 3.
Find C when

a $n = 4$ **b** $n = 10$.

2 A rule is given as '*divide by 5 and then subtract 4*'.
Find the output when the input is

a 30 **b** 200.

Level 5

3 Use this function machine to calculate the value of y when

a $x = 6$ **b** $x = \frac{1}{2}$.

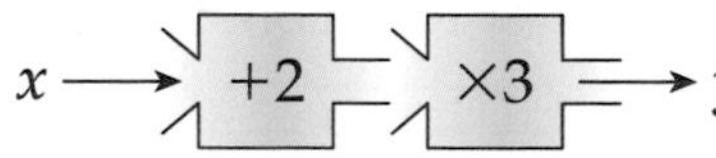

4 A builder charges £2 for each paving slab that he lays when making a patio.
He then adds on a further £30 for travelling costs.

a Write a formula in terms of x and y for the total cost £C of laying this patio.

b Find the cost when $x = 6$ and $y = 5$.

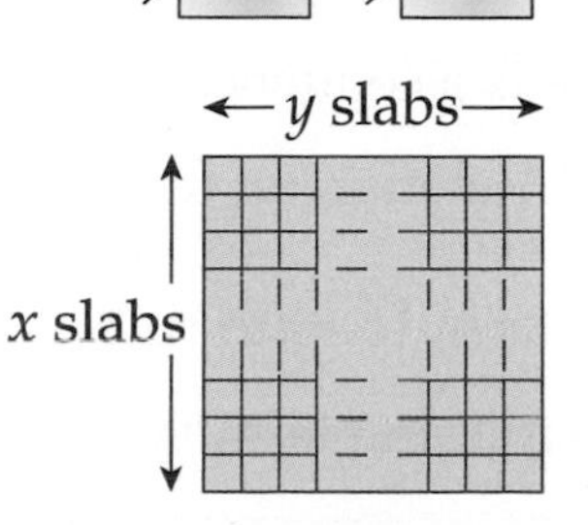

1a Sequences and terms

LEVEL 6

- Find the term-to-term rule for a sequence
- Apply the term-to-term rule for a sequence in different situations

Keywords
Consecutive Sequence
Generate Term
Rule

- A **sequence** is a set of numbers, or **terms**. Each term can be found using a **rule**.

Emma plants a flower bed with two kinds of plants.
She starts with five plants and keeps adding four more plants.

The sequence for the **total** number of flowers begins 5, 9, 13, ….
The rule is *'start with 5 and add 4 each time'*.
The next two terms are 17 and 21.

- The term-to-term rule of a sequence gives the first term and tells you how to find each consecutive term from the previous one.

Consecutive terms follow on one after the other.

example

The first term of a sequence is 5.
The term-to-term rule is given by this function machine.

Term → $\times 3$ → -9 → Next term

Generate the first four consecutive terms of the sequence.

The first term of the sequence is 5.
The second term is $5 \times 3 - 9 = 15 - 9 = 6$.
The third term is $6 \times 3 - 9 = 18 - 9 = 9$.
The fourth term is $9 \times 3 - 9 = 27 - 9 = 18$.
The first four consecutive terms are 5, 6, 9, 18.

example

Here is a sequence. 2 3 5 9 ☐ 33

Find the missing term.

The term-to-term rule is *'start with 2, double and subtract 1'*.

The missing term is $9 \times 2 - 1 = 18 - 1 = 17$.

Check the next term:
$2 \times 17 - 1 = 34 - 1 = 33$

Exercise 1a

1 You can use straws to make this sequence of patterns.

a Draw the next pattern of the sequence.

b Write the first four terms to give the sequence of the number of straws.

c Find the term-to-term rule.

d Write the next three consecutive terms.

2 Two sequences both start with a first term of 7.
Use these two function machines to generate the first five consecutive terms of each sequence.

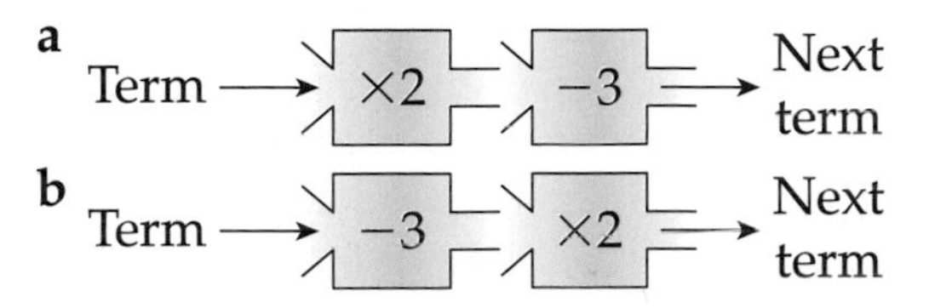

3 Generate the first five terms of the sequences with these rules.

a *Start with 4, double and subtract 2.* **b** *Start with 600, halve and subtract 20.*

c *Start with 0, treble and add 1.* **d** *Start with 0, add 1 and treble.*

e *Start with $\frac{1}{4}$, double and add 1.* **f** *Start with 4, multiply by three and subtract 8.*

4 Use this flow diagram to generate consecutive terms of the sequence when **a** $x = 2$ **b** $x = 50$ **c** $x = -30$.

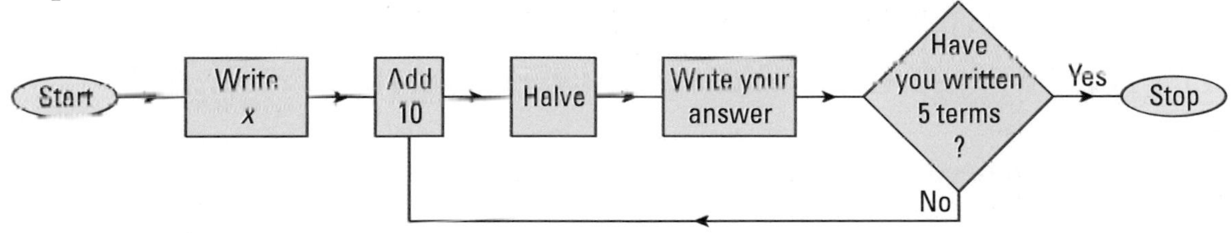

5 For each of these sequences, describe the term-to-term rule in words and find the next three consecutive terms.

a 7, 10, 13, 16, … **b** 20, 17, 14, 11, … **c** 3, 7, 15, 31, …

d 3, 5, 9, 17, … **e** 1, 4, 13, 40, … **f** 1, 2, 5, 14, …

g 200, 100, 50, 25, … **h** $\frac{1}{2}$, 3, 8, 18, … **i** 3, 4, 6, 10, …

ICT challenge

Use a spreadsheet to generate a sequence with the rule *'start with 3, double and add 4'.*

	A	B	C	D
1	3	=2*A1+4	=2*B1+4	=2*C1+4
2				

Invent some sequences of your own. Write the rule you use in each case.

1b Position-to-term rules

- Find and use the position-to-term rule of a sequence

Keywords
Function machine
Position
Position-to-term rule

Anwar makes a sequence of patterns using hexagonal tiles.
He adds three extra tiles each time to make the next pattern.

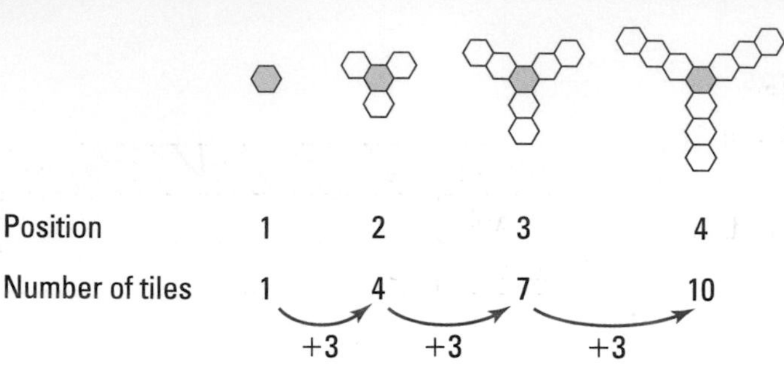

To find a rule he uses the three times table to construct a table of values.

Position	1	2	3	4
3× table	3	6	9	12
No. of tiles (term)	1	4	7	10

(×3, −2)

Position → ×3 → −2 → Term

- A **position-to-term rule** gives you the value of any term if you know its position in the sequence.

Anwar's position-to-term rule is '*multiply the position by 3 and then subtract 2*'.
The 100th position needs $100 \times 3 - 2 = 300 - 2 = 298$ tiles.

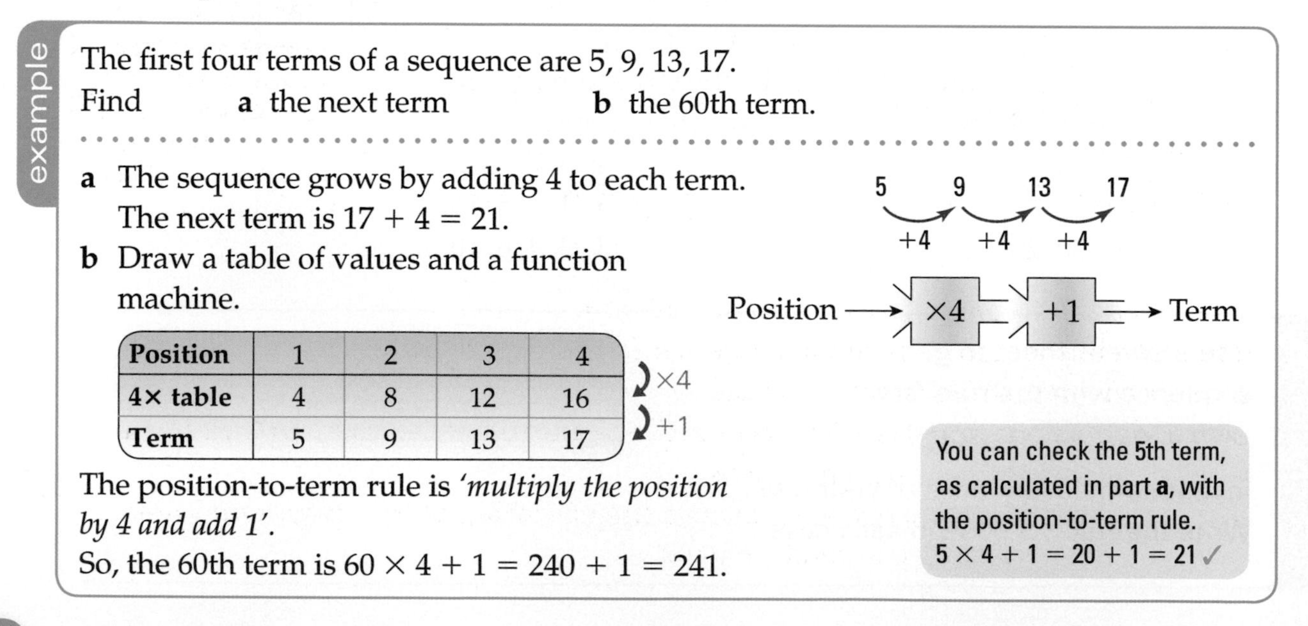

example

The first four terms of a sequence are 5, 9, 13, 17.
Find **a** the next term **b** the 60th term.

a The sequence grows by adding 4 to each term.
The next term is $17 + 4 = 21$.

5 9 13 17 (+4 +4 +4)

b Draw a table of values and a function machine.

Position → ×4 → +1 → Term

Position	1	2	3	4
4× table	4	8	12	16
Term	5	9	13	17

(×4, +1)

The position-to-term rule is '*multiply the position by 4 and add 1*'.
So, the 60th term is $60 \times 4 + 1 = 240 + 1 = 241$.

You can check the 5th term, as calculated in part **a**, with the position-to-term rule.
$5 \times 4 + 1 = 20 + 1 = 21$ ✓

Exercise 1b

1 This sequence of parallelograms is made using short sticks.

Position 1 2 3 4

a How many extra sticks are needed to make the next position?

b Draw the diagram for position 5.

c Write the term-to-term rule in words.

d Copy and complete this table and use it to find the position-to-term rule.

Position	1	2	3	4	5
...× table					
Term	4				

e How many sticks are needed to make the 50th position?

2 For each of these sequences,

i draw the diagram for position 4

ii make a table of values for the number of sticks in positions 1 to 4

iii use the table to find the position-to-term rule

iv find how many sticks are needed for the 100th position.

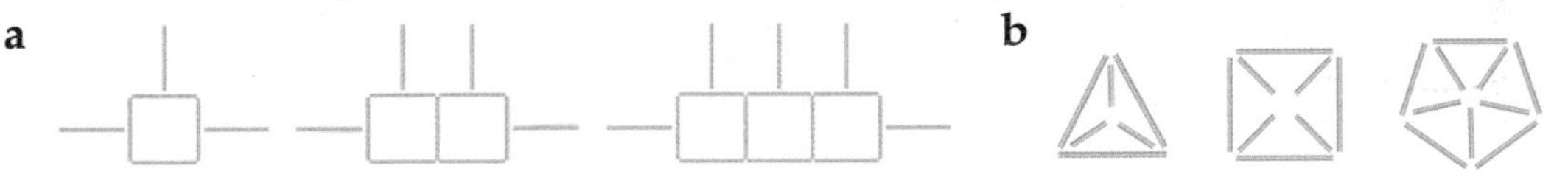

3 For each of these sequences,

i use a table of values to find the position-to-term rule

ii find the next two terms and the 100th term.

a 2, 6, 10, 14, 18, …

b 5, 8, 11, 14, 17, …

c 1, 7, 13, 19, 25, …

d 9, 11, 13, 15, 17, …

e 2, 11, 20, 29, 38, …

f 2, 10, 18, 26, 34, …

g $3\frac{1}{2}$, 4, $4\frac{1}{2}$, 5, $5\frac{1}{2}$, …

h 6, 4, 2, 0, -2, …

4 Find the missing terms and the 50th term of each of these sequences.

a 5, 11, □, 23, 29, □

b $3\frac{1}{2}$, □, $6\frac{1}{2}$, 8, □, 11

Did you know?

The number of petals and leaves that a flower has is often a Fibonacci number. Perhaps that is why four-leaf clovers are so rare.

investigation

The sequence 0, 1, 1, 2, 3, 5, 8, ... starts with 0, 1.

You make further terms by adding together the two previous terms.

a Write the next three terms of the sequence.

This sequence is called the *Fibonacci sequence* after an Italian (born in 1170 AD) who studied with Arab mathematicians.

b Investigate how this sequence relates to the branching of tree, leaves on a stem and patterns in pineapples and sunflowers.

1c The general term

LEVEL 6

- Find and use the general term or formula for the *n*th term of a sequence

Keywords
General term
Generate
nth term

- You can use the **general term** to calculate the value of any term. It is written using n and is often called the ***n*th term.**

This sequence of squares is made from coloured dots.

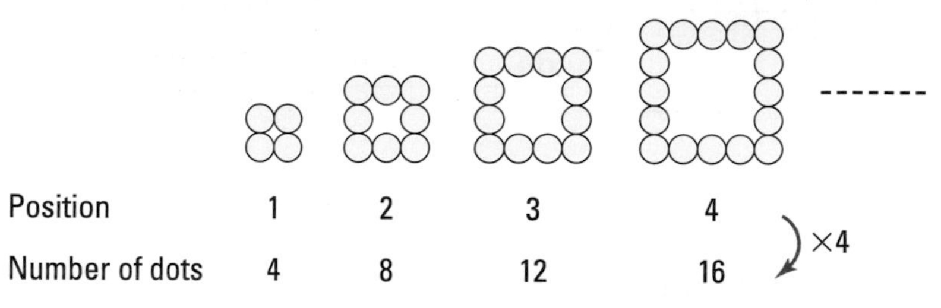

Position	1	2	3	4
Number of dots	4	8	12	16

$\times 4$

The position-to-term rule is *'multiply the position by 4'*.
You can continue the sequence to find this table of values.

The 5th term is $4 \times 5 = 20$.
The nth term is $4 \times n = 4n$.

Position	1	2	3	4	5	...	n
Term	4	8	12	16	20	...	$4n$

$\times 4$

The terms increase by 4 each time because the square has four sides and each side increases by one dot.

example

Find the general term and the 80th term of the sequence 1, 4, 7, 10, ...

1 → 4 → 7 → 10 (+3 +3 +3)

Draw a table of values and a function machine.
The general term is $3n - 2$.
The 80th term is $3 \times 80 - 2 = 240 - 2 = 238$.

Position	1	2	3	4	...	n
3× table	3	6	9	12	...	$3n$
Term	1	4	7	10	...	$3n - 2$

$\times 3$, -2

Position → $\times 3$ → -2 → Term

example

The nth term of a sequence is $T(n) = 40 - 5n$.
Generate the first three terms of the sequence.

T stands for Term.
T(n) stands for *n*th term.

The 1st term has $n = 1$, so $T(1) = 40 - 5 \times 1 = 40 - 5 = 35$.
The 2nd term has $n = 2$, so $T(2) = 40 - 5 \times 2 = 40 - 10 = 30$.
The 3rd term has $n = 3$, so $T(3) = 40 - 5 \times 3 = 40 - 15 = 25$.
So, the sequence begins 35, 30, 25, ...

Exercise 1c

1 Here is a sequence made from square tiles.

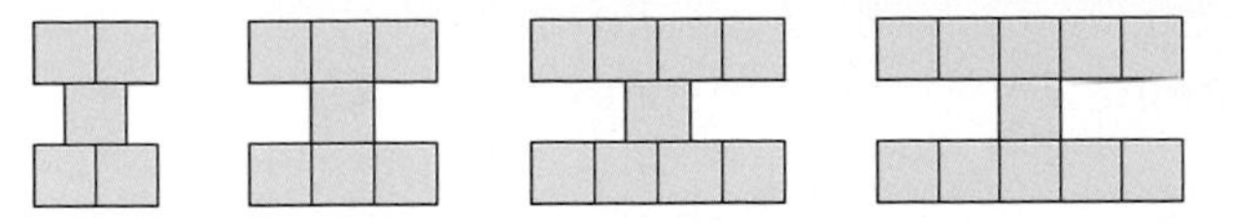

a How many squares are added to get from one term to the next?

b Copy and complete this table of values.

Position	1	2	3	4	5	…	n
…× table							
Term							

)……
)……

c Write the nth term of the sequence.

d Find the 5th term and the 50th term.

Did you know?

Islamic art is famous for its tiling patterns.

2 For each of these sequences,

i construct a table of values

ii write the position-to-term rule in words

iii find the nth term

iv find the 6th term and the 40th term.

a 6, 8, 10, 12, 14, …
b 0, 2, 4, 6, 8, …
c 5, 8, 11, 14, 17, …
d 3, 8, 13, 18, 23, …
e 7, 13, 19, 25, 31, …
f 5, 13, 21, 29, 37, …
g 10, 17, 24, 31, 38, …
h -1, 3, 7, 11, 15, …
i -4, -1, 2, 5, 8, …
j 8, 6, 4, 2, 0, …

Substitute $n = 1$ to $n = 6$ into the expression for T(n).

3 Generate the first six terms of the sequences with these general terms.

a $T(n) = 2n + 5$
b $T(n) = 3n - 2$
c $T(n) = 4n + 1$
d $T(n) = 10n - 7$
e $T(n) = 6n + 3$
f $T(n) = 2n - 5$
g $T(n) = 2(n + 1)$
h $T(n) = 3(n - 1)$
i $T(n) = 4(2n - 1)$
j $T(n) = \frac{1}{2}n + 2$
k $T(n) = 30 - 2n$
l $T(n) = 6 - 4n$

4 Find the missing term, the next term and the 100th term of each of these sequences.

a 6, 11, 16, □, 26, …
b 12, 22, □, 42, 52, …
c 3, 7, 11, □, 19, …
d 5, 13, 21, □, 37, …

investigation

A flower bed is surrounded by square slabs.
The surround is always three slabs wide but it can be any length.
Make a table of values for different lengths of the flower bed from 3 to 7 slabs long and the total number of slabs used in each case.
Then find the general term for the sequence of the number of slabs.

flowers

1d Sequences in context

- Use term-to-term rules and position-to-term rules in different situations
- Use the general term in practical situations

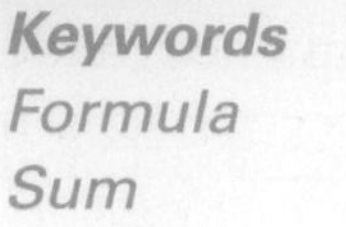

Keywords
Formula
Sum

Kim is given a dog for her birthday.
She has one tin of dog food to start with.
She then buys three tins every day.
She wants to know how many tins she will need to buy in the first 120 days.

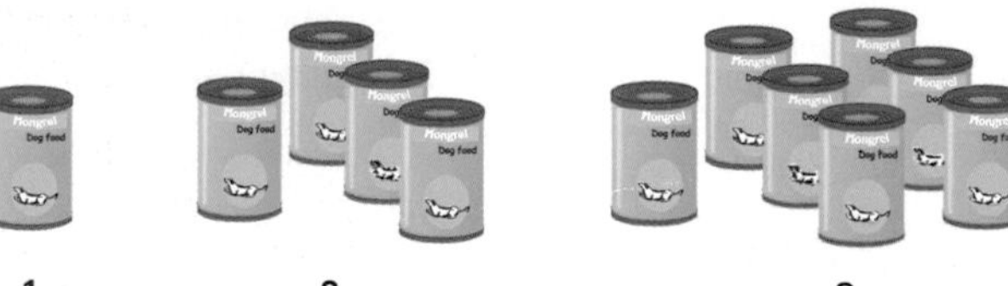

Day 1 2 3

The total number of tins make the sequence 1, 4, 7, 10, ….
The term-to-term rule is *'start with 1 and add 3 each time'*.

Day	1	2	3	4	5	…	n
3× table	3	6	9	12	15	…	$3n$
Tins	1	4	7	10	13	…	$3n - 2$

(×3, −2)

The position-to-term rule is *'multiply by 3 and then subtract 2'*.
The **formula** for the total number of tins is $3n - 2$.
In the first 120 days Kim will need to buy $3 \times 120 - 2 = 360 - 2 = 358$ tins.

Substitute $n = 120$ into the formula.

example

In week 1, Stephen has £10 in his bank account.
His grandma adds £6 each week to help him save.
How much is in his account after a year?

BANK STATEMENT			
Date	**In**	**Out**	**Balance**
04/3/09	10.00	–	10.00
11/3/09	6.00	–	16.00

The term-to-term rule is *'start with £10 and then add £6 each week'*.

Week	1	2	3	4	…	n
6× table	6	12	18	24	…	$6n$
Sum (£)	10	16	22	28	…	$6n + 4$

(×6, +4)

The position-to-term rule is *'multiply by 6 and then add 4'*.
The **sum** in his account after n weeks is £$(6n + 4)$.
A year is 52 weeks.
So, after a year, he will have $6 \times 52 + 4 = 312 + 4 = £316$.

Exercise 1d

1 Holly covers a wall with square tiles.
She starts with two tiles and then she has four tiles in every column.

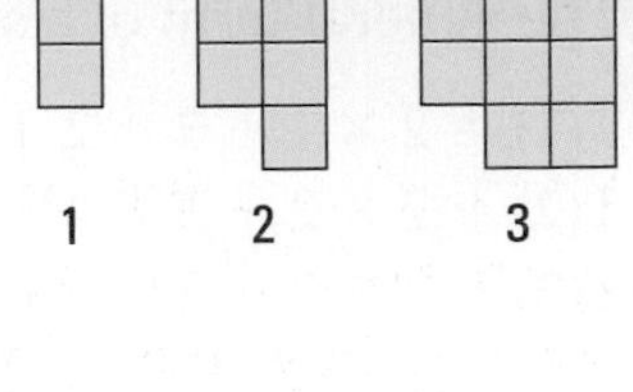

a Write the term-to-term rule and find the next term.

b Construct a table of values and write the position-to-term rule.

c Find an expression for the number of tiles in the nth position.

d How many tiles does Holly need for the 20th position?

2 Safraz buys a new bike. He travels 100 miles on the first day.
He then averages 15 miles every day.

a Generate a sequence for the total miles he has travelled after 1, 2, 3, 4 and 5 days.

b Write the term-to-term rule and find the next two terms.

c Construct a table of values and write the position-to-term rule.

d Find an expression for $T(n)$, the total mileage travelled after days.

e How far has he travelled in total after 2 weeks?

3 A machine punches holes into metal sheet.
In the first second it punches 10 holes.
In every further second it punches 4 holes.

a Write the total number of holes punched after 1, 2, 3, 4 and 5 seconds.

b Find the term-to-term rule and the position-to-term rule.

c How many holes has it punched after

i n seconds **ii** 1 minute?

4 In a science experiment, a beaker contains a liquid chemical.
The volume of liquid, in millilitres, in the beaker after n seconds is $T(n) = 2n + 48$.

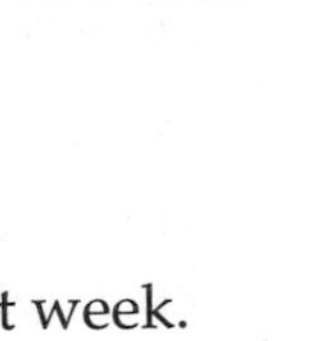

a Write a sequence for the volume of liquid in the beaker after 1, 2, 3, 4 and 5 seconds.

b How many millilitres are added to the beaker each second?

5 The volume of oil, in litres, in a tank at the end of each day is $T(n) = 1000 - 5n$.

a Write a sequence for the volume of oil at the end of each day during the first week.

b How much oil is left in the tank after 3 weeks?

ICT

Use a spreadsheet to generate the sequence with the general term $T(n) = 5n + 3$.

Invent some sequences of your own.

	A	B	C	D	E
1	Position, n	1	2	3	4
2	Term, $T(n)$	=5*B1+3			

1e Graphs of sequences

LEVEL 6

- Draw graphs of sequences

Keywords
Axes *Plot*
Integer *Straight line*
Linear sequence
Linear expression

The general term of a sequence is $T(n) = 2n + 3$.

$T(1) = 2 \times 1 + 3 = 2 + 3 = 5$
$T(2) = 2 \times 2 + 3 = 4 + 3 = 7$
$T(3) = 2 \times 3 + 3 = 6 + 3 = 9$, and so on.

T(1) means term 1.

Position	1	2	3	4	...	n
Term	5	7	9	11	...	$2n + 3$

You can **plot** these values on **axes** as coordinate points.

(1, 5), (2, 7), (3, 9), ...

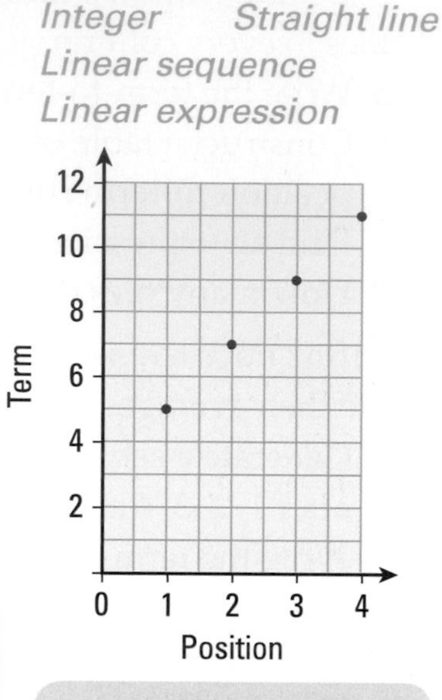

- The points on the graph are all in the same **straight line.** The sequence is a **linear sequence.** The general term, $2n + 3$, is a **linear expression.**

Linear means 'arranged in a straight line'.

example

A sequence has the position-to-term rule *'multiply by 5 and then subtract your answer from 80'*.

- Construct a table of values.
- Find an expression for the nth term.
- Write the term-to-term rule in words.
- Draw a graph of the sequence.

For position 1, the term is $80 - 5 \times 1 = 80 - 5 = 75$.
For position 2, the term is $80 - 5 \times 2 = 80 - 10 = 70$.
For position 3, the term is $80 - 5 \times 3 = 80 - 15 = 65$, ...

Position	1	2	3	4	...	n
Term	75	70	65	60	...	$80 - 5n$

The nth term $= 80 - 5n$.
Each term is 5 less than the previous term, so the term-to-term rule is *'start with 75 and subtract 5 each time'*.

The graph of the sequence has points (1, 75), (2, 70), (3, 65), (4, 60), ...

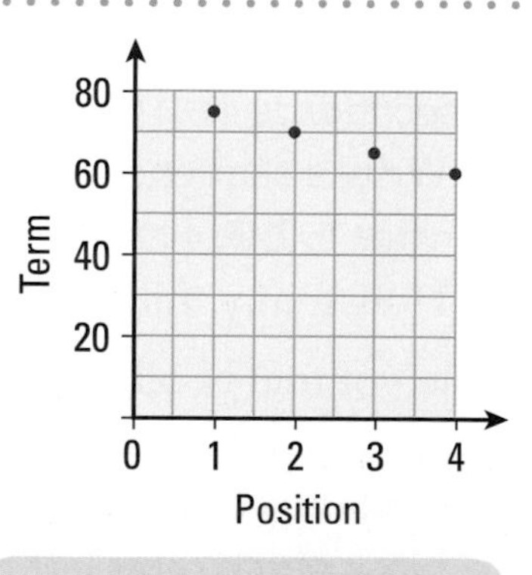

Do not join the points because 'position' on the horizontal axis can only have whole number (**integer**) values.

Exercise 1e

1 Here are the first five terms of some linear sequences.
Draw the graph of each sequence on a copy of these axes.

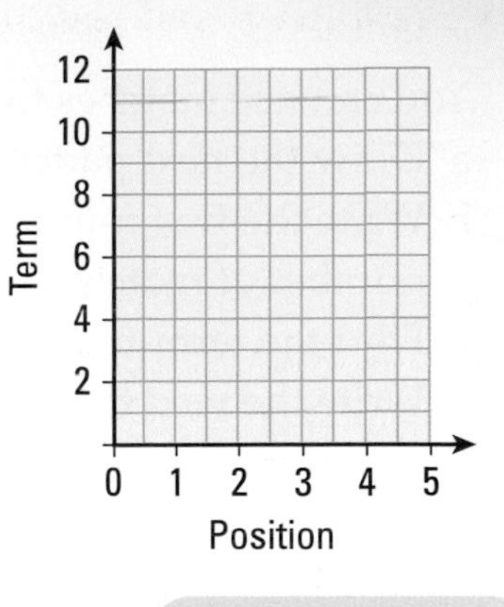

a

Position	1	2	3	4	5
Term	1	3	5	7	9

b 8, 9, 10, 11, 12, … **c** 0, 3, 6, 9, 12, …
d 10, 8, 6, 4, 2, … **e** 7, 6, 5, 4, 3, ….

2 Here are the general terms of some linear sequences.
In each case, construct a table of values for the first five positions and terms.
Draw a graph of each sequence on axes like those in question **1**.

a $T(n) = 2n + 1$ **b** $T(n) = 3n - 3$ **c** $T(n) = 2n - 4$
d $T(n) = n + 5$ **e** $T(n) = n - 2$ **f** $T(n) = \frac{1}{2}n + 6$
g $T(n) = 6 - n$ **h** $T(n) = 12 - 2n$ **i** $T(n) = \frac{20 - n}{2}$

You can use this symbol on the vertical axis to show that the scale does not start at zero.

3 Generate the first five terms of these sequences with the given rules.
Decide how to label the axes and draw the graph of each sequence.

a Start with 6 and add 1 each time. **b** Start with 4 and add $\frac{1}{2}$ each time.
c Start with 0 and add 2 each time. **d** Start with 12 and subtract 3 each time.
e Multiply the position by 2 and then add 2.
f Multiply the position by 3 and then subtract 1.
g Multiply the position by 5 and subtract your answer from 30.
h Multiply the position by 10 and subtract your answer from 160.

4 At the end of January Joe has £100 in the bank.
Each month, he draws out £15 and deposits £10.

a Write a linear sequence for how much is in his account at the end of every month from January to June.
b Draw a graph of the sequence.
c Find an expression for the nth term of the sequence.
d How long does it take before he has no money left?

investigation

Not all sequences are linear.

a Try to find the term-to-term rules for these sequences and so find which of the sequences are linear and which are not.
i 8, 12, 16, 20, 24, … **ii** 2, 5, 10, 17, 26, …
iii 0, 3, 8, 15, 24, … **iv** 0, 2, 6, 12, 20, …

b Draw the graphs of all four sequences to check your answers to part **a**.
c Invent some sequences of your own. Decide which are linear and which are not.

1a

1 You can use matches to make this sequence of patterns.

a Draw the next pattern of the sequence.

b Write the first four terms of the sequence that gives the number of matches.

c Find the term-to-term rule.

d Write the next three consecutive terms of the sequence.

2 Use this flow diagram to generate the terms of a sequence.

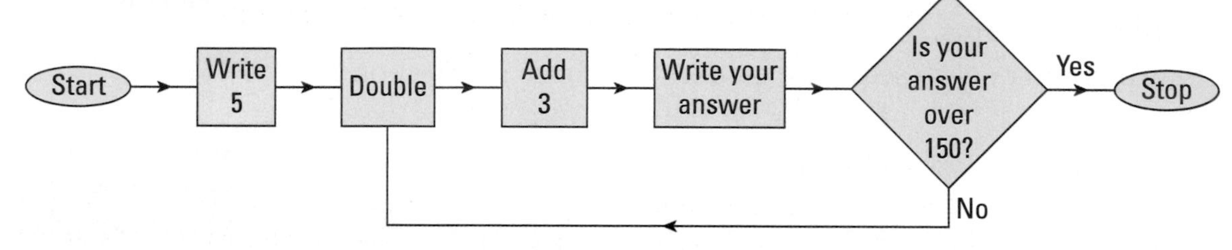

3 For each of these sequences, describe the term-to-term rule in words and find the next three consecutive terms.

a 3, 7, 15, 31, … **b** 4, 7, 13, 25, … **c** 30, 27, 24, 21, …

d $\frac{1}{2}$, 2, 8, 32, … **e** 400, 200, 100, 50, … **f** 1, 11, 111, 1111, …

1b

4 This sequence of crosses is made using square tiles.

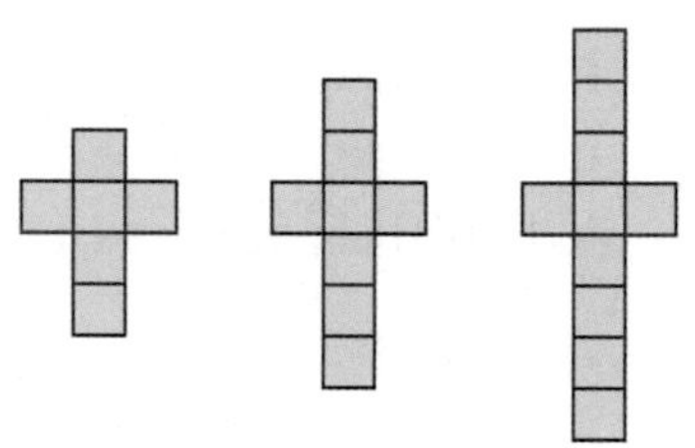

a How many extra tiles are added to make the next position in the sequence?

b Draw the diagram for position 4.

c Copy and complete this table and use it to find the position-to-term rule.

Position	1	2	3	4	5	…	n
…× table							
Term							

d How many squares are needed to make the 20th position?

5 For each of these sequences,

i use a table of values to find the position-to-term rule

ii find the next two terms and the 50th term.

a 4, 7, 10, 13, 16, … **b** 6, 11, 16, 21, 26, …

c 2, 5, 8, 11, 14, … **d** 98, 96, 94, 92, 90, …

6 Find the missing terms and the 100th terms of each of these sequences.

a 5, 8, 11, □, 17, 20 **b** 1, 4, 7, 10, □, 16, …

1c

7 For each of these sequences,

i construct a table of values

ii write the position-to-term rule in words

iii find the nth term

iv find the value of the 6th term and the 100th term.

a 5, 7, 9, 11, 13, … **b** 13, 16, 19, 22, 25, …

c 2, 7, 12, 17, 22, … **d** 1, 5, 9, 13, 17, …

8 Generate the first six terms of the sequences with these general terms.

a $T(n) = 2n + 10$ **b** $T(n) = 5n - 5$ **c** $T(n) = 4n + 6$

d $T(n) = 50 - 2n$ **e** $T(n) = 15 - 5n$ **f** $T(n) = 2(3n - 2)$

9 Here is part of a spreadsheet.
Column A gives the position of each term.
Column B gives the actual terms of a sequence.

a Write the position-to-term rule in words.

b Write the nth term.

c Write the first six terms of the sequence.

	A	B
1	Position	Term
2	1	=3*A2−1
3	=A2+1	=3*A3−1
4	=A3+1	=3*A4−1

1d

10 A kitchen wall has three rows of tiles.
The two end columns have tiles with floral patterns.
There are n central columns of plain white tiles.

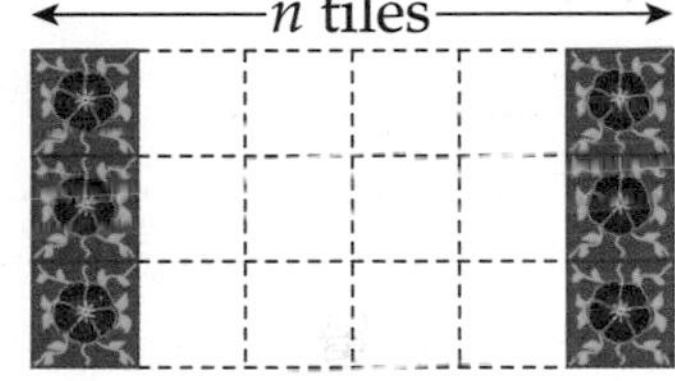

a Find the total number of tiles used when $n = 3$.

b Find an expression $T(n)$ for the total number of tiles.

c Write the sequence of the values of $T(n)$ for $n = 40$ to $n = 45$.

11 David is saving for his summer holiday.
He starts with £20 and then he saves £8 each week.

a How much has he saved after

i 2 weeks ii 5 weeks?

b Find an expression for $T(n)$, the amount, in pounds, he has saved after n weeks.

c How much has he saved after 20 weeks?

1e

12 For each of these sequences

i construct a table of values for the first five terms.

ii draw a graph of the sequence on a copy of these axes.

a $T(n) = 2n - 1$ **b** $T(n) = 3n - 2$

c $T(n) = \frac{1}{2}n + 3$

1 Summary

Assessment criteria

- Construct functions arising from sequences and plot their corresponding graphs **Level 6**
- Generate terms of a sequence **Level 6**

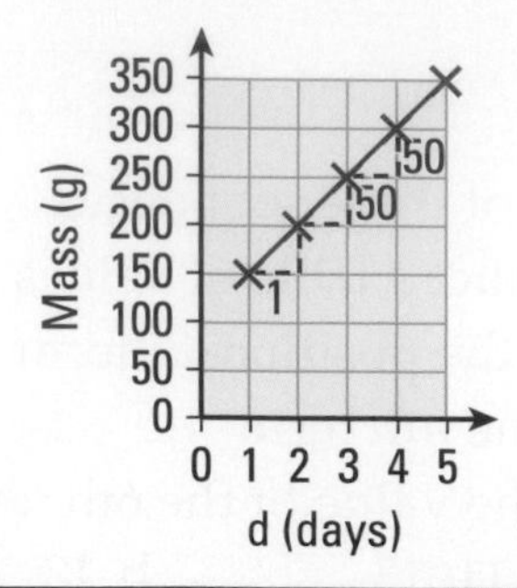

Level 6

1 A baby octopus is born with a mass of 100 g.
Each day the octopus increases its mass by 50 g.

a Copy and complete the table.

b Write an equation linking d and m.

c Plot the graph for your equation.

Day (d)	1	2	3	4	5
Mass (m)	150				

Andrew's answer ✔

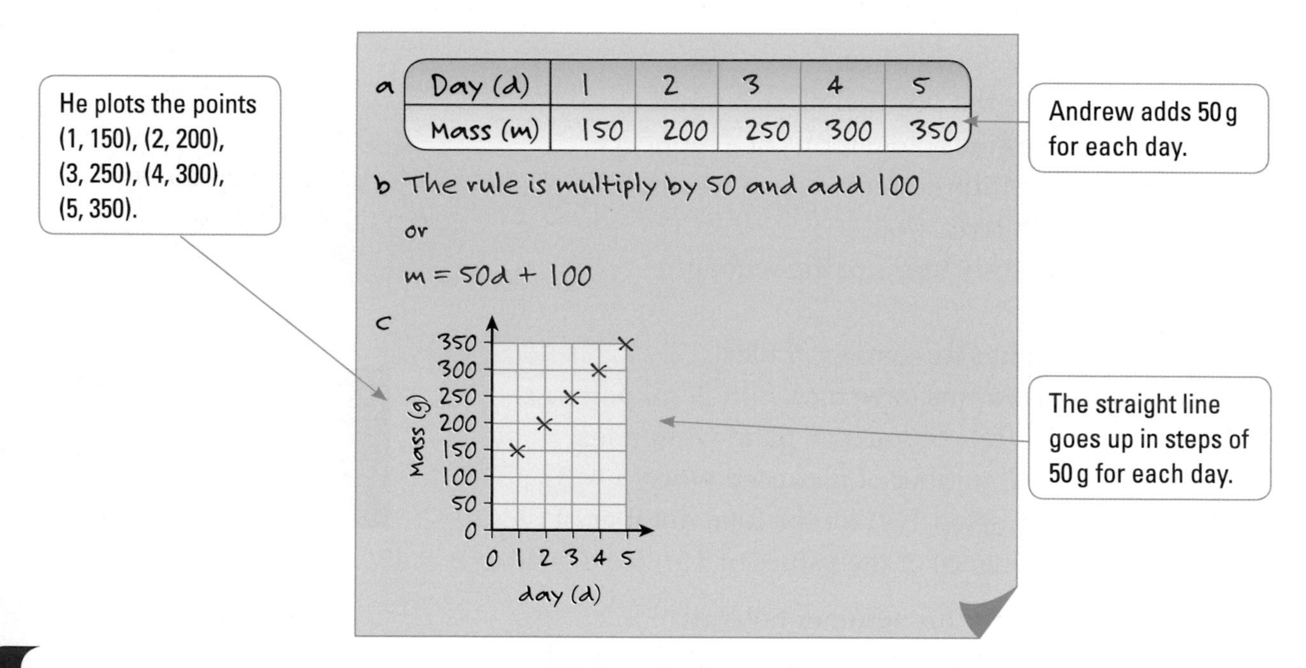

Level 6

2 To find the nth triangular number, you can use this rule.

nth triangular number $= \frac{n}{2}(n + 1)$

Example: 3rd triangular number $= \frac{3}{2}(3 + 1)$

$= 6$

a Work out the 10th triangular number.

b Now work out the 100th triangular number.

Key Stage 3 2008 5–7 Paper 2

2 Number

Proportional reasoning

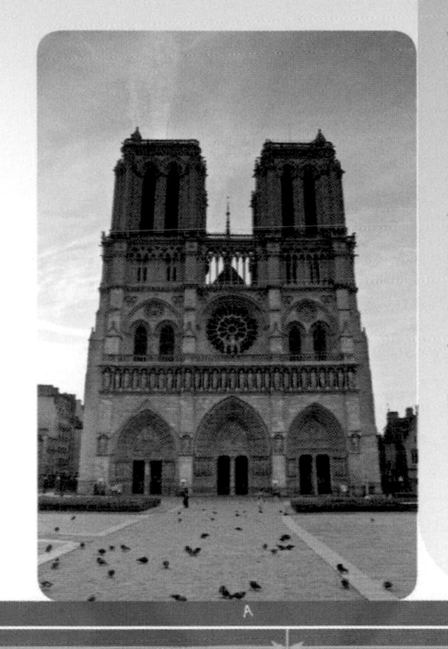

These lines show the Golden Ratio. The ratio of A to B is the same as the ratio of B to C. The Golden Rectangle uses the same proportions so the ratio of length to width is about 1:1.6.

The Golden Rectangle is used in many works of art and architecture, for example, the Notre Dame in Paris, the Parthenon in Athens and the Egyptian pyramids.

What's the point? Mathematical ratios appear all around us in buildings, art, music and nature.

Check in

Level 5

1 Copy and complete these equivalent fractions.

a $\frac{3}{10} = \frac{\square}{40}$ b $\frac{7}{8} = \frac{\square}{40}$ c $\frac{15}{25} = \frac{3}{\square}$

2 Calculate these using a suitable method.

a 15% of £30 b 55% of 40 km c 18% of £128

3 Copy and complete this table using a calculator where appropriate.

Fraction	Decimal	Percentage
$\frac{13}{20}$		
	0.625	
		8%

4 At a running club the ratio of boys to girls is 7 : 4.
There are 28 boys at the club.
How many girls are there?

2a Adding and subtracting fractions

LEVEL 6

- Add and subtract fractions
- Convert between mixed numbers and improper fractions

Keywords
Denominator
Equivalent fraction
Fraction

- You can add or subtract **fractions** with different **denominators** by first writing them as **equivalent fractions** with the same denominator.

example

Calculate

a $\frac{3}{5} + \frac{1}{4}$ **b** $\frac{7}{9} - \frac{5}{12}$

Re-write as equivalent fractions with the same denominator.

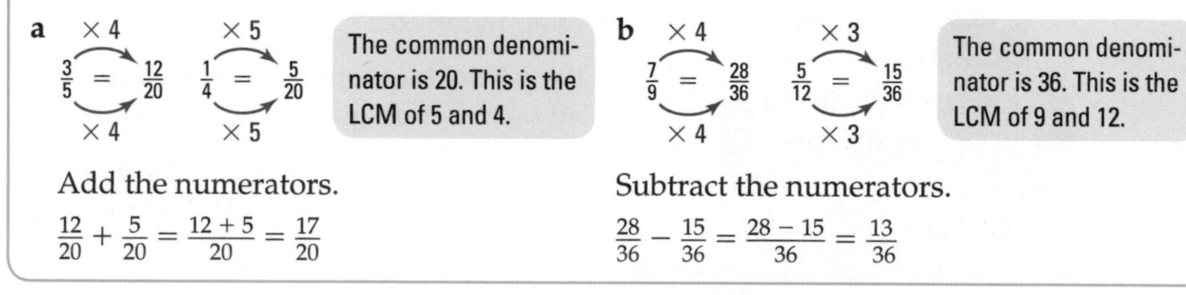

- You can add or subtract mixed numbers by changing them into improper fractions.

example

Calculate $1\frac{3}{8} - \frac{5}{6}$.

Re-write as an improper fraction.

$1\frac{3}{8} = \frac{11}{8}$

Re-write as equivalent fractions with the same denominator.

$\frac{11}{8} \xrightarrow{\times 3} \frac{33}{24}$ $\frac{5}{6} \xrightarrow{\times 4} \frac{20}{24}$

The common denominator is 24. This is the LCM of 8 and 6.

Subtract the numerators.

$\frac{33}{24} - \frac{20}{24} = \frac{33 - 20}{24} = \frac{13}{24}$

You change the mixed number into an improper fraction using multiplication.

$1\frac{3}{8} = \frac{1 \times 8 + 3}{8} = \frac{11}{8}$

Exercise 2a

Did you know?

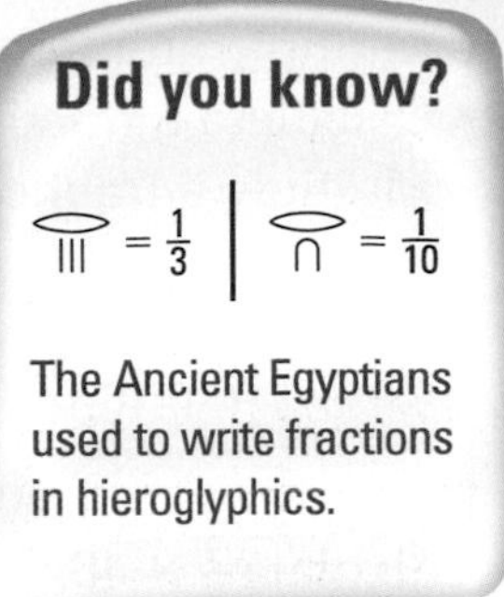

The Ancient Egyptians used to write fractions in hieroglyphics.

1 Find the missing number in each of these pairs of equivalent fractions.

a $\frac{1}{4} = \frac{\square}{20}$ **b** $\frac{5}{6} = \frac{\square}{24}$ **c** $\frac{3}{7} = \frac{12}{\square}$ **d** $\frac{7}{9} = \frac{\square}{54}$

2 Calculate these.
Give your answer as a fraction in its simplest form.

a $\frac{3}{5} + \frac{1}{5}$ **b** $\frac{7}{12} - \frac{3}{12}$ **c** $\frac{20}{13} - \frac{3}{13}$ **d** $\frac{4}{5} + \frac{4}{5}$

e $\frac{1}{5} + \frac{1}{2}$ **f** $\frac{2}{3} + \frac{1}{4}$ **g** $\frac{3}{8} - \frac{1}{3}$ **h** $\frac{3}{7} + \frac{1}{3}$

3 Work out these.
Give your answer as a fraction in its simplest form.

a $\frac{2}{5} + \frac{5}{10}$ **b** $\frac{5}{6} - \frac{3}{4}$ **c** $\frac{5}{6} - \frac{7}{12}$ **d** $\frac{5}{8} + \frac{7}{12}$

e $\frac{5}{18} + \frac{5}{24}$ **f** $\frac{7}{15} + \frac{3}{20}$ **g** $\frac{11}{16} - \frac{5}{8}$ **h** $\frac{17}{24} + \frac{3}{16}$

4 **a** Jacques needs $\frac{5}{8}$kg of flour to make a loaf of bread.
He tips $\frac{2}{5}$kg of white flour onto a weighing scale.
How much more flour does he need to add?

b Kalid runs $\frac{3}{7}$ of a race in pair of trainers.
For the next $\frac{8}{15}$ of the race he runs in bare feet.
Has Kalid completed the race?
Explain your answer.

You can add the integers separately in additions.

5 Work out these.
Give your answer as a fraction in its simplest form.

a $1\frac{3}{4} + 1\frac{1}{2}$ **b** $1\frac{1}{4} - \frac{5}{8}$ **c** $1\frac{2}{3} + 1\frac{2}{5}$ **d** $2\frac{3}{5} - 1\frac{4}{5}$

e $2\frac{3}{5} + 1\frac{5}{6}$ **f** $2\frac{3}{4} + 1\frac{2}{5}$ **g** $1\frac{5}{8} - \frac{3}{5}$ **h** $1\frac{3}{7} + 1\frac{2}{3}$

6 A rectangular mobile phone has a length of $5\frac{3}{4}$cm and a width of $2\frac{2}{5}$cm.
Calculate the perimeter of the phone.

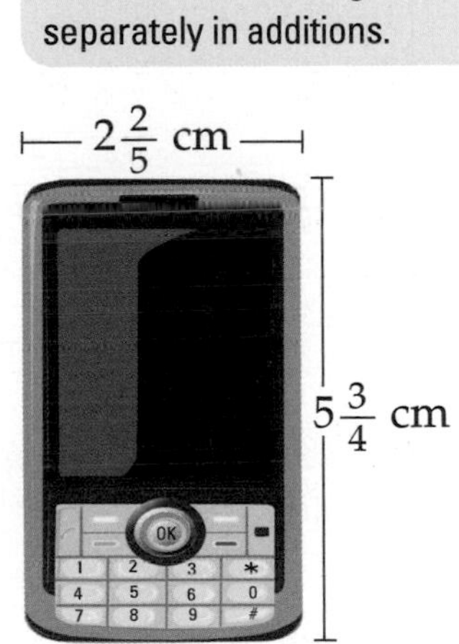

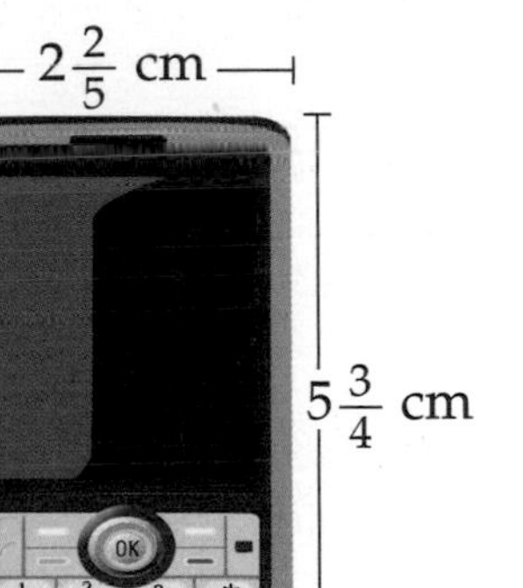

investigation

Ancient Egyptians only used fractions which had 1 as the numerator (unit fractions). Fractions were written as sums of unit fractions.

They would write $\frac{3}{4}$ as $\frac{1}{2} + \frac{1}{4}$ and $\frac{5}{12}$ as $\frac{1}{3} + \frac{1}{12}$.

a Write these fractions in the Egyptian way.
$\frac{5}{8}$ $\frac{7}{10}$ $\frac{7}{12}$

b Find more fractions that can be made by adding pairs of different unit fractions.

c Investigate adding three or more unit fractions.

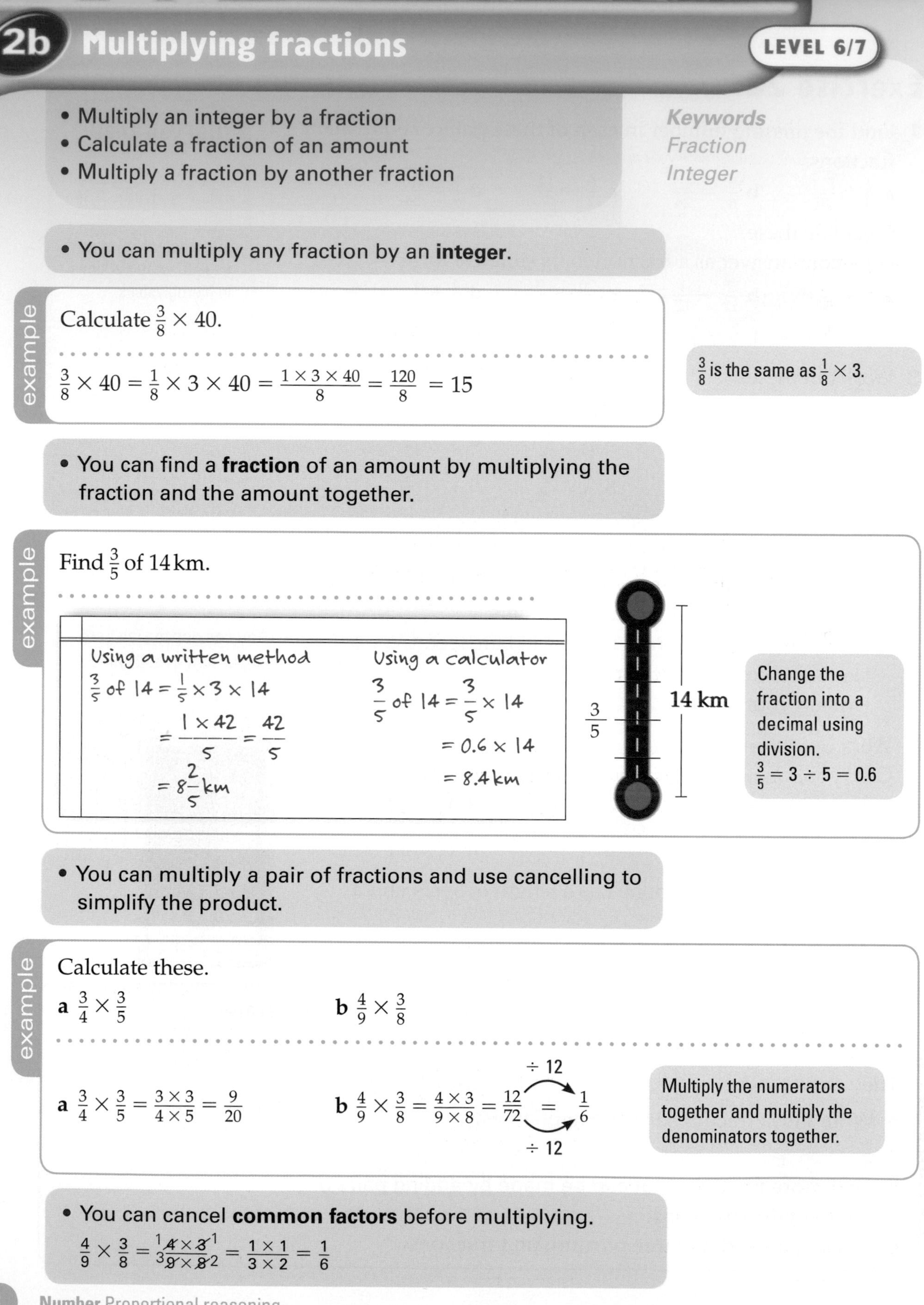

2b Multiplying fractions

LEVEL 6/7

- Multiply an integer by a fraction
- Calculate a fraction of an amount
- Multiply a fraction by another fraction

Keywords
Fraction
Integer

- You can multiply any fraction by an **integer**.

example

Calculate $\frac{3}{8} \times 40$.

$\frac{3}{8} \times 40 = \frac{1}{8} \times 3 \times 40 = \frac{1 \times 3 \times 40}{8} = \frac{120}{8} = 15$

$\frac{3}{8}$ is the same as $\frac{1}{8} \times 3$.

- You can find a **fraction** of an amount by multiplying the fraction and the amount together.

example

Find $\frac{3}{5}$ of 14 km.

Using a written method

$\frac{3}{5}$ of $14 = \frac{1}{5} \times 3 \times 14$

$= \frac{1 \times 42}{5} = \frac{42}{5}$

$= 8\frac{2}{5}$ km

Using a calculator

$\frac{3}{5}$ of $14 = \frac{3}{5} \times 14$

$= 0.6 \times 14$

$= 8.4$ km

Change the fraction into a decimal using division.
$\frac{3}{5} = 3 \div 5 = 0.6$

- You can multiply a pair of fractions and use cancelling to simplify the product.

example

Calculate these.

a $\frac{3}{4} \times \frac{3}{5}$ **b** $\frac{4}{9} \times \frac{3}{8}$

a $\frac{3}{4} \times \frac{3}{5} = \frac{3 \times 3}{4 \times 5} = \frac{9}{20}$

b $\frac{4}{9} \times \frac{3}{8} = \frac{4 \times 3}{9 \times 8} = \frac{12}{72} = \frac{1}{6}$ (÷ 12 numerator and denominator)

Multiply the numerators together and multiply the denominators together.

- You can cancel **common factors** before multiplying.

$\frac{4}{9} \times \frac{3}{8} = \frac{{}^{1}\cancel{4} \times \cancel{3}^{1}}{{}^{3}\cancel{9} \times \cancel{8}^{2}} = \frac{1 \times 1}{3 \times 2} = \frac{1}{6}$

Exercise 2b

1 Calculate these. Give your answer in its simplest form and as a mixed number where appropriate.

a $3 \times \frac{1}{7}$ **b** $3 \times \frac{2}{7}$ **c** $4 \times \frac{3}{13}$ **d** $\frac{3}{5} \times 12$

e $\frac{2}{3} \times 16$ **f** $\frac{5}{8} \times 20$ **g** $\frac{3}{4} \times 28$ **h** $\frac{5}{7} \times 12$

2 Calculate these. Give your answer in its simplest form and as a mixed number where appropriate.

a $\frac{4}{5}$ of 8 cm **b** $\frac{3}{7}$ of 19 kg **c** $\frac{3}{4}$ of 24 m **d** $\frac{4}{9}$ of 30 mins

e $\frac{7}{10}$ of 50 kg **f** $\frac{5}{12}$ of 7 feet **g** $\frac{4}{11}$ of 28 tonnes **h** $\frac{5}{8}$ of 36 km

3 Copy and complete these equivalents.

a $\frac{3}{4}$ of $60 = \frac{1}{2}$ of $\square$ **b** $\frac{1}{8}$ of $40 = \frac{1}{4}$ of $\square$

c $\frac{3}{5}$ of $40 = \frac{\square}{4}$ of 32 **d** $\frac{4}{7}$ of $28 = \frac{2}{\square}$ of 24

4 Use an appropriate method to calculate these amounts. Where necessary give your answer to 2 decimal places.

a $\frac{2}{5}$ of 134 km **b** $\frac{7}{12}$ of £400 **c** $\frac{4}{7}$ of 20 km

d $\frac{3}{8}$ of 275 m **e** $\frac{4}{13}$ of 50 kg **f** $\frac{5}{9}$ of 45 g

g $\frac{3}{11}$ of 1000 ml **h** $\frac{5}{16}$ of 180°

5 a A computer game normally costs £18.
In a sale all prices are reduced by $\frac{2}{5}$.
What is the sale price of the computer game?

b Astra buys a car for £22 500.
Two years later the car has gone down in value by $\frac{2}{7}$.
What is the new value of her car?

6 Calculate these.

a $\frac{2}{3} \times \frac{4}{5}$ **b** $\frac{3}{4} \times \frac{5}{6}$ **c** $\frac{1}{8} \times \frac{4}{7}$ **d** $\frac{3}{5} \times \frac{5}{12}$

e $\frac{4}{7} \times \frac{5}{8}$ **f** $\frac{3}{10} \times \frac{5}{6}$ **g** $\frac{5}{8} \times \frac{4}{15}$ **h** $\frac{6}{13} \times \frac{5}{12}$

Remember sometimes you can cancel common factors first to make the calculation easier.

investigation

Jack and Jermaine are trying to work out $\frac{3}{5}$ of $\frac{2}{3}$ of £60.
Jack says they should calculate $\frac{2}{3}$ of £60 and then calculate $\frac{3}{5}$ of their answer.

a Use Jack's method to work out $\frac{3}{5}$ of $\frac{2}{3}$ of £60.

b Jermaine says that he can improve Jack's method.
Investigate how to improve Jack's method.

c Work out **i** $\frac{3}{8}$ of $\frac{2}{5}$ of £40 **ii** $\frac{5}{7}$ of $\frac{2}{3}$ of 63 kg

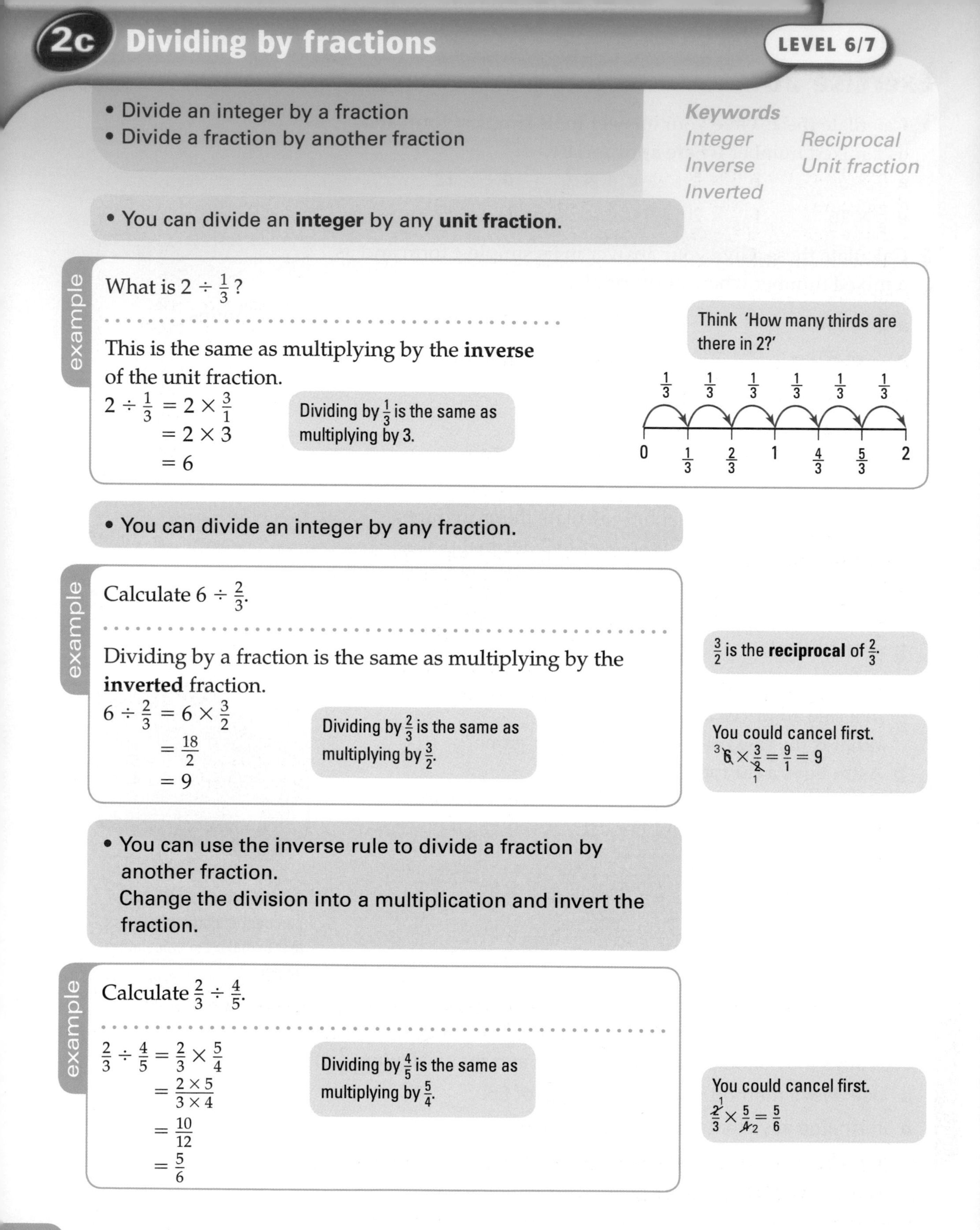

2c Dividing by fractions

LEVEL 6/7

- Divide an integer by a fraction
- Divide a fraction by another fraction

Keywords
Integer *Inverse* *Inverted* *Reciprocal* *Unit fraction*

- You can divide an **integer** by any **unit fraction**.

example

What is $2 \div \frac{1}{3}$?

This is the same as multiplying by the **inverse** of the unit fraction.

$$2 \div \frac{1}{3} = 2 \times \frac{3}{1}$$
$$= 2 \times 3$$
$$= 6$$

Dividing by $\frac{1}{3}$ is the same as multiplying by 3.

Think 'How many thirds are there in 2?'

- You can divide an integer by any fraction.

example

Calculate $6 \div \frac{2}{3}$.

Dividing by a fraction is the same as multiplying by the **inverted** fraction.

$$6 \div \frac{2}{3} = 6 \times \frac{3}{2}$$
$$= \frac{18}{2}$$
$$= 9$$

Dividing by $\frac{2}{3}$ is the same as multiplying by $\frac{3}{2}$.

$\frac{3}{2}$ is the **reciprocal** of $\frac{2}{3}$.

You could cancel first.
$^{3}\cancel{6} \times \frac{3}{\cancel{2}_{1}} = \frac{9}{1} = 9$

- You can use the inverse rule to divide a fraction by another fraction.
  Change the division into a multiplication and invert the fraction.

example

Calculate $\frac{2}{3} \div \frac{4}{5}$.

$$\frac{2}{3} \div \frac{4}{5} = \frac{2}{3} \times \frac{5}{4}$$
$$= \frac{2 \times 5}{3 \times 4}$$
$$= \frac{10}{12}$$
$$= \frac{5}{6}$$

Dividing by $\frac{4}{5}$ is the same as multiplying by $\frac{5}{4}$.

You could cancel first.
$\frac{\cancel{2}^{1}}{3} \times \frac{5}{\cancel{4}_{2}} = \frac{5}{6}$

Exercise 2c

1 a How many fifths are there in 2?
b How many quarters are there in 3?
c How many eighths are there in 4?
d How many eighths are there in one-quarter?
e How many sixths are there in one-half?
f How many fifths are there in one-half?

2 Calculate these.
a $2 \div \frac{1}{4}$ b $5 \div \frac{1}{2}$ c $4 \div \frac{1}{3}$ d $3 \div \frac{1}{5}$
e $5 \div \frac{1}{4}$ f $6 \div \frac{1}{10}$ g $8 \div \frac{1}{7}$ h $7 \div \frac{1}{3}$

3 Calculate these.
Give your answer in its simplest form.
a $3 \div \frac{3}{4}$ b $4 \div \frac{2}{3}$ c $4 \div \frac{2}{5}$ d $6 \div \frac{3}{8}$
e $10 \div \frac{5}{6}$ f $6 \div \frac{3}{5}$ g $12 \div \frac{4}{7}$ h $15 \div \frac{5}{8}$

4 Calculate these.
Give your answer as a mixed number in its simplest form.
a $5 \div \frac{3}{4}$ b $7 \div \frac{4}{5}$ c $5 \div \frac{2}{3}$ d $8 \div \frac{3}{7}$
e $2 \div \frac{7}{9}$ f $5 \div \frac{4}{7}$ g $10 \div \frac{3}{8}$ h $9 \div \frac{7}{11}$

5 a Harriet makes 5 kg of jam. She puts the jam into jars. Each jar can hold $\frac{3}{8}$ kg. How many jars does she need?
b To make one giant muffin Andreas needs $\frac{4}{25}$ kg of flour. How many muffins can he make with 2 kg of flour?

6 Calculate these.
a $\frac{3}{4} \div \frac{2}{3}$ b $\frac{2}{3} \div \frac{4}{5}$ c $\frac{3}{7} \div \frac{3}{5}$ d $\frac{5}{6} \div \frac{1}{3}$
e $\frac{3}{7} \div \frac{2}{9}$ f $\frac{4}{9} \div \frac{2}{3}$ g $\frac{3}{12} \div \frac{5}{8}$ h $\frac{3}{4} \div \frac{15}{16}$

7 Calculate these.
Give your answer in its simplest form.
a $1\frac{1}{2} \div \frac{3}{4}$ b $3\frac{1}{3} \div \frac{5}{6}$ c $2\frac{2}{5} \div \frac{3}{5}$ d $1\frac{1}{4} \div \frac{2}{5}$

Did you know?

Some people use fractions all the time in their jobs. Chefs must make different quantities of food, so they have to reduce or increase all the ingredients by the same fraction.

investigation

Copy and complete the next three lines of each of these fraction division patterns.

a i $1 \div \frac{1}{3} = 3$
$2 \div \frac{1}{3} = 6$
$3 \div \frac{1}{3} = 9$
…

ii $1 \div \frac{1}{4} = 4$
$2 \div \frac{1}{4} = 8$
$3 \div \frac{1}{4} = 12$
…

iii $1 \div \frac{1}{5} = 5$
$2 \div \frac{1}{5} = 10$
$3 \div \frac{1}{5} = 15$
…

b Describe a quick way of dividing an integer by a unit fraction.
c Investigate dividing by $\frac{2}{3}, \frac{2}{4}, \frac{2}{5}, \ldots$.

2d Direct proportion

LEVEL 6

- Recognise when two quantities are in direct proportion
- Use different methods to solve problems involving direct proportion

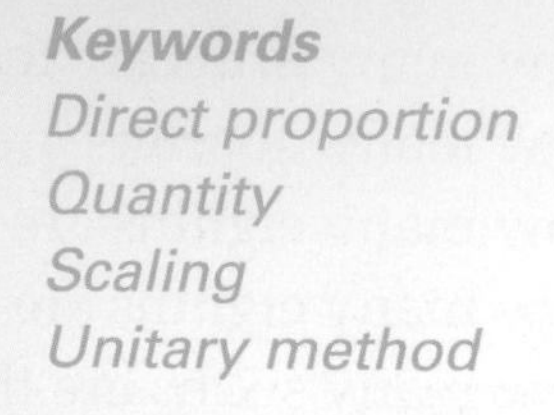

- When two **quantities** are in **direct proportion**, if one of them increases, the other one increases by the same proportion.

Number of text messages	Cost (£)
10	£0.40
20	£0.80
40	£1.60

$\times 2$ (10 → 20, £0.40 → £0.80) $\times \frac{1}{2}$ (40 → 20, £1.60 → £0.80)

The number of text messages is in direct proportion to the cost.

If you double the number of messages, you double the cost.
If you halve the number of messages, you halve the cost.

- You can use the **unitary method** to solve problems involving direct proportion. You find the value of one unit of a quantity.

example

5 litres of petrol cost £5.75. What is the cost of 18 litres of petrol?

$\div 5$	5 litres	£5.75
	1 litre	£1.15
$\times 18$	18 litres	£20.70

5 litres £5.75 → $\div 5$ → 1 litre £1.15 → $\times 18$ → 18 litres £20.70

18 litres cost £20.70.

Find the cost of 1 litre by dividing by 5.

Multiply the cost of 1 litre by 18 to find the cost of 18 litres.

- You can also use a **scaling** method. You multiply both quantities by the same fraction.

example

Five litres of water cost 80 p. What is the cost of 18 litres of water?

5 litres 80p → $\times \frac{18}{5}$ → 18 litres £2.88

18 litres of water cost £2.88.

The number of litres of water has been multiplied by $18 \div 5 = \frac{18}{5}$.

The cost must be multiplied by the same fraction, $\frac{18}{5}$.

Exercise 2d

1 Use direct proportion to solve these problems.

a 4 kg of apples cost £1.20.
What is the cost of 8 kg of apples?

b 50 g of breakfast cereal contain 120 calories.
How many calories are there in 75 g of breakfast cereal?

c A recipe for eight people uses 400 ml of milk.
What amount of milk is needed for six people?

d 250 g of cheese costs £3.80.
What is the cost of 375 g of cheese?

2 Here are two offers for text messages on a mobile phone.
In which of these offers are the numbers in direct proportion?
In each case explain and justify your answers.

Offer A

Number of text messages	Cost (pence)
20	24
50	60
175	210

Offer B

Number of text messages	Cost (pence)
20	26
50	62
175	192

3 Solve these problems using direct proportion.

a 5 litres of oil cost £3.65. What is the cost of 3 litres of oil?

b There are 15 biscuits in a packet. The packet weighs 225 g.
What is the weight of a packet of 20 biscuits?

c 5 miles is approximately 8 km.

i How many kilometres are equal to 35 miles?

ii How many miles are equal to 76 km?

d A 400 g jar of mayonnaise contains 275 g of fat.
How many grams of fat are there in 250 g of mayonnaise?

e A recipe for an apple drink for six people uses 300 g of apples.
Re-write the recipe for 10 people.

challenge

a Sarah's car can hold 45 litres of petrol when it is full.
On a full tank of petrol she can drive 750 km.

i How far can Sarah's car travel on 20 litres of petrol?

ii How much petrol would she need to travel 200 km?

b Use this data to construct a graph showing the number of litres of petrol Sarah's car uses and the number of kilometres she can drive.

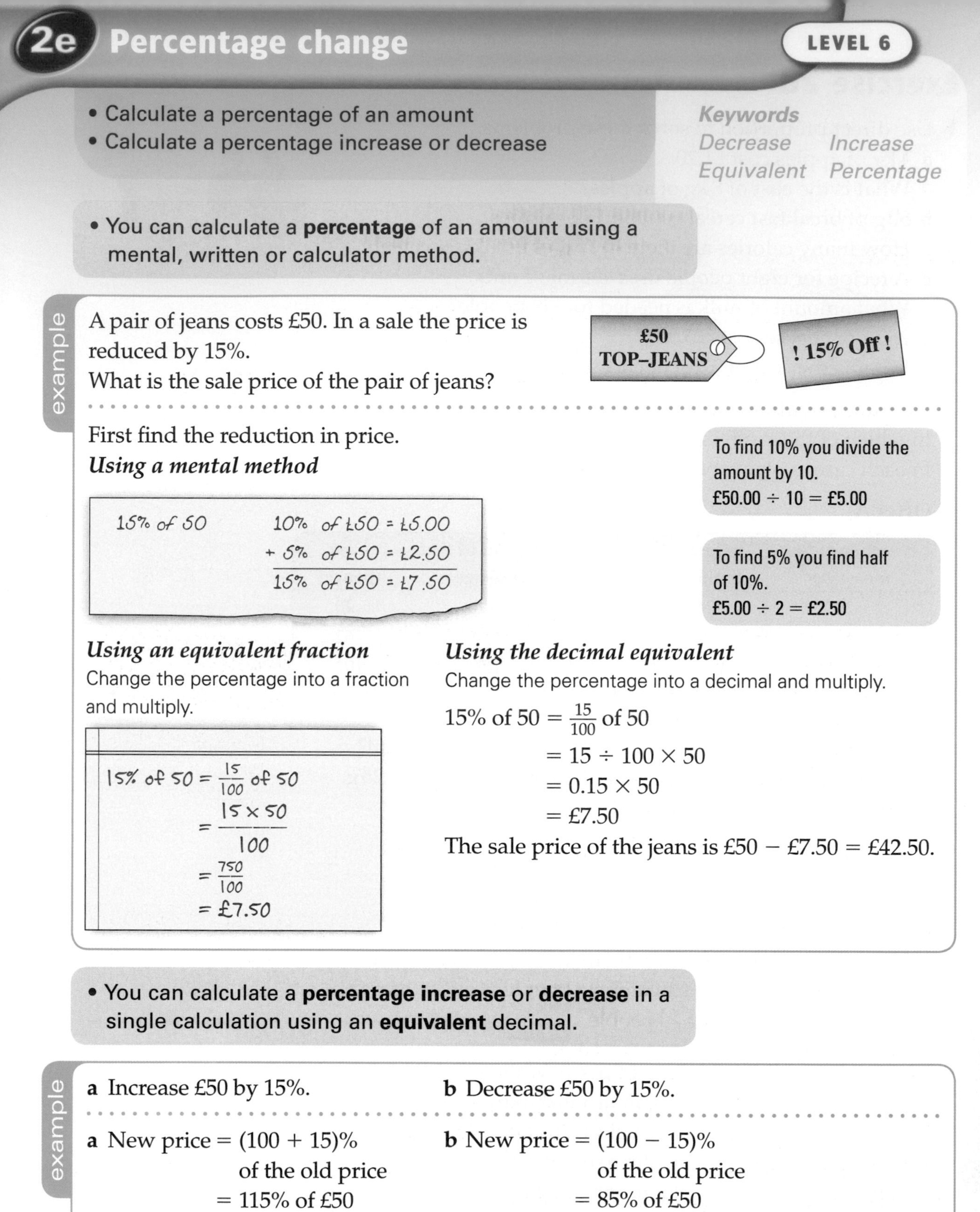

2e Percentage change

LEVEL 6

- Calculate a percentage of an amount
- Calculate a percentage increase or decrease

Keywords
Decrease, Increase, Equivalent, Percentage

- You can calculate a **percentage** of an amount using a mental, written or calculator method.

example

A pair of jeans costs £50. In a sale the price is reduced by 15%.
What is the sale price of the pair of jeans?

First find the reduction in price.

Using a mental method

15% of 50   10% of £50 = £5.00
+ 5% of £50 = £2.50
15% of £50 = £7.50

To find 10% you divide the amount by 10.
£50.00 ÷ 10 = £5.00

To find 5% you find half of 10%.
£5.00 ÷ 2 = £2.50

Using an equivalent fraction

Change the percentage into a fraction and multiply.

$$15\% \text{ of } 50 = \frac{15}{100} \text{ of } 50 = \frac{15 \times 50}{100} = \frac{750}{100} = £7.50$$

Using the decimal equivalent

Change the percentage into a decimal and multiply.

$$15\% \text{ of } 50 = \frac{15}{100} \text{ of } 50$$
$$= 15 \div 100 \times 50$$
$$= 0.15 \times 50$$
$$= £7.50$$

The sale price of the jeans is £50 − £7.50 = £42.50.

- You can calculate a **percentage increase** or **decrease** in a single calculation using an **equivalent** decimal.

example

a Increase £50 by 15%.

b Decrease £50 by 15%.

a New price = (100 + 15)% of the old price
= 115% of £50
= 1.15 × £50
= £57.50

b New price = (100 − 15)% of the old price
= 85% of £50
= 0.85 × £50
= £42.50

Exercise 2e

1 Calculate these using a suitable method.

a 15% of £80 b 45% of 350 kg c 11% of 65 m
d 36% of $12 e 19% of 625 cm f 17% of £145
g 6% of 128 MB h 99% of 33 kg

2 a Increase £80 by 15%. b Decrease £80 by 15%.
c Increase 22 km by 11%. d Decrease 58 kg by 20%.
e Increase 32 m by 5%. f Decrease 67 cm by 27%.
g Increase £135 by 95%. h Decrease 364 kJ by 8%.
i Increase 32 kB by 6.5%. j Decrease £3250 by 1.8%.

3 a A shirt usually costs £35.
In a sale the price is reduced by 15%.
What is the sale price of the shirt?

b Last year Gina was paid £28 a week for her paper round.
At the start of this year, the newsagent increased Gina's wage by 12%.
What is Gina's new wage?

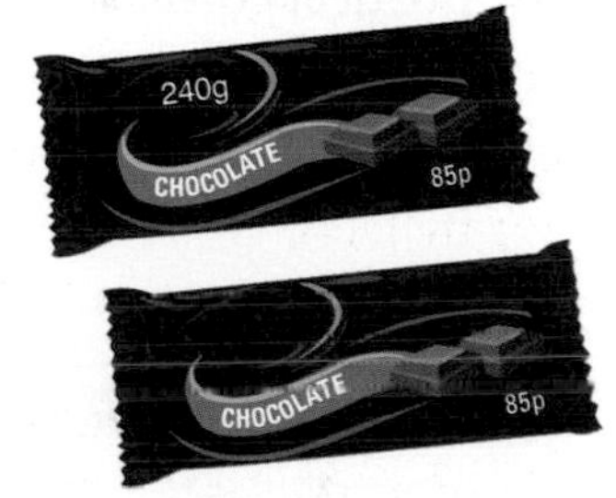

c A bar of chocolate usually weighs 240 g and costs 85 p.
The chocolate company decide to keep the price the same but reduce the weight of the chocolate bar by 20%. What is the new weight of the chocolate bar?

d In January a litre of petrol cost £1.15.
By March the price had increased by 35%.
What was the cost of a litre of petrol in March?

4 Match each of these statements with the correct mathematical calculation.

a Increase £40 by 30%. b 30% of £40.
c Decrease £40 by 30%. d Increase £40 by 3%.
e 3% of £40. f Decrease £40 by 3%.

0.03×40	1.03×40
0.3×40	1.3×40
0.97×40	0.7×40

investigation

a A computer game costs £20 in August.
In November it is increased in price by 10%.
In January the game is reduced in price by 10%.
Is the January sale price more, less or the same as the price in August?
Explain your answer.

b Investigate increasing and decreasing prices by other percentages.
Summarise what you have noticed and try to justify your answer.

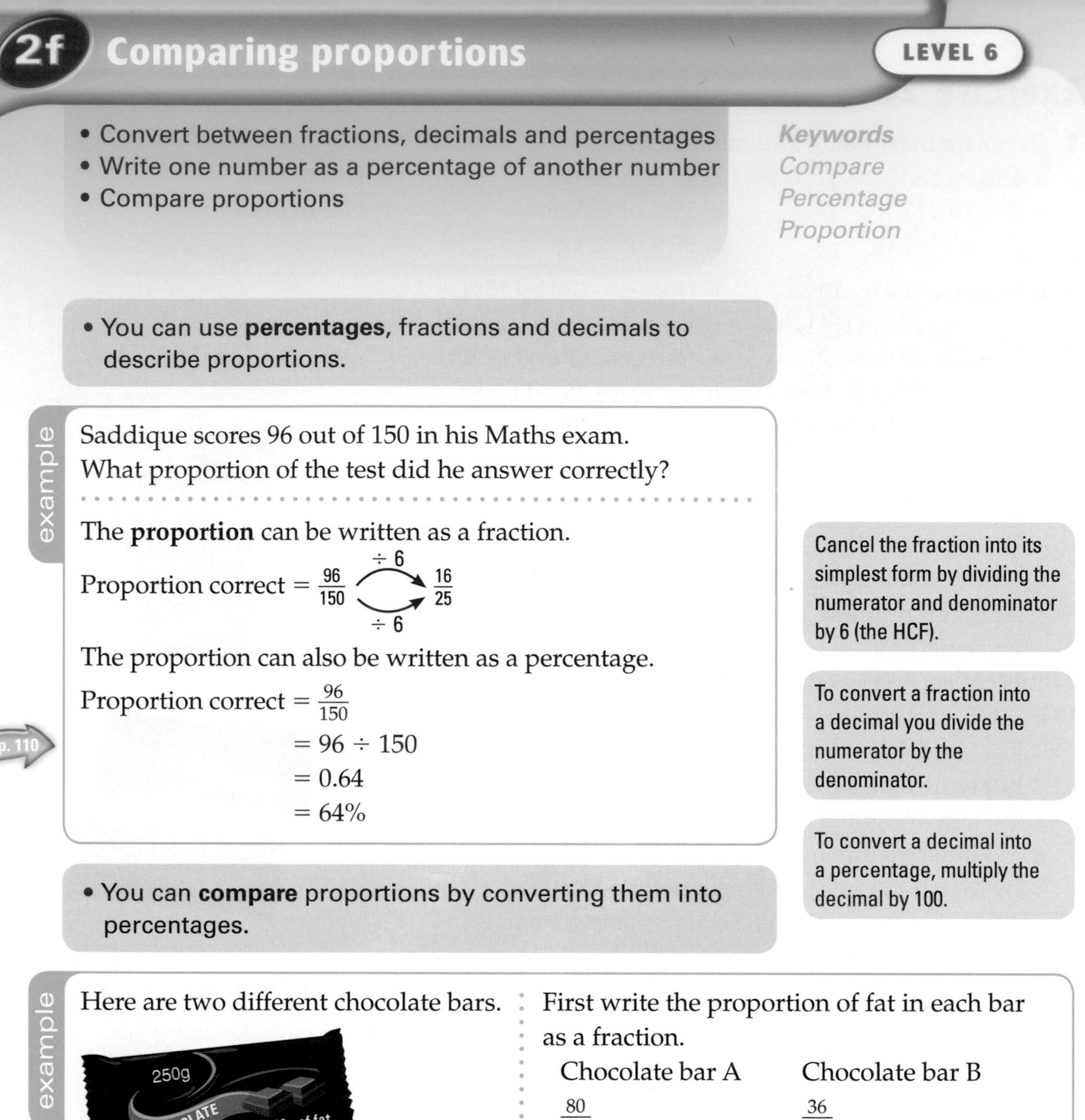

2f Comparing proportions

LEVEL 6

- Convert between fractions, decimals and percentages
- Write one number as a percentage of another number
- Compare proportions

Keywords
Compare
Percentage
Proportion

- You can use **percentages**, fractions and decimals to describe proportions.

example

Saddique scores 96 out of 150 in his Maths exam.
What proportion of the test did he answer correctly?

The **proportion** can be written as a fraction.

Proportion correct $= \frac{96}{150} \xrightarrow{\div 6} \frac{16}{25}$

The proportion can also be written as a percentage.

$$\begin{aligned}\text{Proportion correct} &= \frac{96}{150}\\ &= 96 \div 150\\ &= 0.64\\ &= 64\%\end{aligned}$$

p. 110

Cancel the fraction into its simplest form by dividing the numerator and denominator by 6 (the HCF).

To convert a fraction into a decimal you divide the numerator by the denominator.

To convert a decimal into a percentage, multiply the decimal by 100.

- You can **compare** proportions by converting them into percentages.

example

Here are two different chocolate bars.

Bar A

Bar B

Which bar contains the higher proportion of fat?

First write the proportion of fat in each bar as a fraction.

Chocolate bar A	Chocolate bar B
$\frac{80}{250}$	$\frac{36}{120}$

Then convert each fraction into a percentage.

Chocolate bar A	Chocolate bar B
$= 80 \div 250$	$= 36 \div 120$
$= 0.32$	$= 0.3$
$= 32\%$	$= 30\%$

Chocolate bar A contains the higher proportion of fat.

Exercise 2f

1 Convert these fractions into percentages using a calculator where appropriate. Round your answer to 2 decimal places.

a $\frac{17}{20}$ b $\frac{13}{25}$ c $\frac{28}{40}$ d $\frac{5}{7}$ e $\frac{38}{45}$

2 Copy and complete these sentences.

a 20 out of □ is the same as 40%. b □ out of □ is the same as 15%.

3 a Write the proportion of each rectangle that is yellow.

i

ii

iii

b Write each of your answers as a fraction in its simplest form and a percentage (rounded to 1 decimal place where appropriate).

c Which rectangle has the highest proportion of yellow?

4 For these questions express your answer as a percentage where appropriate. Round to 1 decimal place if necessary. Show your working.

a In John's class there are 16 boys and 14 girls.
In Geoff's class there are 13 boys and 12 girls.
Which class has the higher proportion of girls?

b Hanif scores 25 out of 80 in his History exam and 19 out of 60 in his English exam.
In which exam did Hanif do better?

c In a survey 117 out of 800 women said they were vegetarian.
In the same survey only 39 out of 700 men said they were vegetarian.

i What proportion of the women surveyed were vegetarian?

ii What proportion of the people surveyed were vegetarian?

investigation

This table shows the number of grams of fat in different snacks.

a Copy and complete the table.

b Which is the least healthy snack? Explain and justify your answer.

c Investigate other snacks to see what percentage of the snack is fat.

Type of food	Mass (grams)	Fat content (grams)	% fat
Crisps	35	11.6	
Olives	28	3.1	
Cereal bar	24	1.7	
Chocolate bar	62	14.9	
French fries	78	9	

2g Ratio

LEVEL 6

- Simplify a ratio
- Divide a quantity in a given ratio

Keywords
Ratio
Simplify

- You **simplify** a **ratio** by dividing all parts of the ratio by the same number.

example

Write these ratios in their simplest form.

a 15 : 12 **b** 18 cm : 60 mm

a

15 : 12
÷ 3 ↓ ↓ ÷ 3
5 : 4

b

18 cm : 60 mm
180 mm : 60 mm
÷ 10 ↓ ↓ ÷ 10
18 : 6
÷ 6 ↓ ↓ ÷ 6
3 : 1

Change both quantities into the same units.
18 cm is the same as 180 mm.

You can use ratios to divide quantities into unequal sized pieces. This is called dividing in a given ratio.

- You can divide a quantity in a given ratio using a unitary method. First find the value of one equal share of the quantity.

example

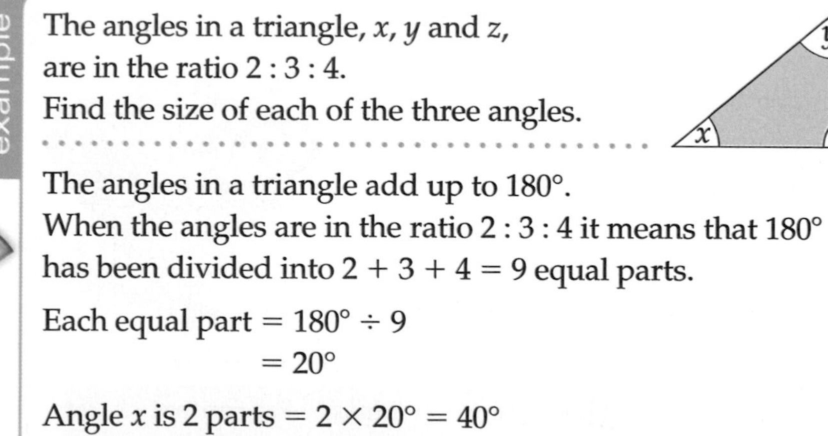

The angles in a triangle, x, y and z, are in the ratio 2 : 3 : 4.
Find the size of each of the three angles.

The angles in a triangle add up to 180°.
When the angles are in the ratio 2 : 3 : 4 it means that 180° has been divided into 2 + 3 + 4 = 9 equal parts.

p. 38

Each equal part = 180° ÷ 9
= 20°

Angle x is 2 parts = 2 × 20° = 40°
Angle y is 3 parts = 3 × 20° = 60°
Angle z is 4 parts = 4 × 20° = 80°

You can check your answer by adding up all the parts.
40° + 60° + 80° = 180° ✓

You could use the ratio to tell you what proportion each angle is of the total.
Angle $x = \frac{2}{9}$ of 180° = 40°
Angle $y = \frac{3}{9}$ of 180° = 60°
Angle $z = \frac{4}{9}$ of 180° = 80°

Exercise 2g

1 Write these ratios in their simplest form.

a 6 : 10 **b** 12 : 18 **c** 25 : 40

d 60 : 36 **e** 8 : 12 : 20 **f** 15 : 30 : 40

2 Write these ratios in their simplest form by first changing the quantities into the same units.

a £2 : £6 **b** £3 : 60p

c 3 cm : 24 mm **d** 125 cm : 4 m

e 3 kg : 750 g **f** 5 minutes : 50 seconds

3 Work out how many boys and girls there are in each of these classes.

a There are 33 students in total.
There are twice as many boys as girls.

b There are 29 students in total.
There are three more boys than girls.

c There are 36 students in total.
The ratio of boys to girls is 4 : 5.

4 Work out these, giving your answers to 2 decimal places where appropriate.

a Divide 40 apples in the ratio 3 : 5. **b** Divide £120 in the ratio 5 : 1.

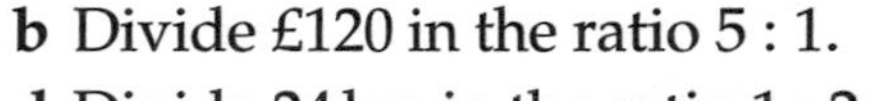

c Divide 36 kg in the ratio 2 : 7. **d** Divide 24 km in the ratio 1 : 2 : 3.

e Divide £72 in the ratio 7 : 3 : 2. **f** Divide £65 in the ratio 5 : 4.

5 Solve these problems.

a In a school the ratio of students to teachers is 15 : 1.
There are 992 students and teachers at the school.
How many teachers are there?

b A cake mixture contains flour, sugar and butter in the ratio 4 : 5 : 3.
How much butter is needed to make 900 g of cake mixture?

challenge

A square is 12 cm in length and has been divided into two smaller squares, shaded red, and two rectangles, shaded blue.

a Show that the ratio of red to blue is 13:5.

b How would you divide the square into squares and rectangles so that the ratio of red to blue was 5:3?

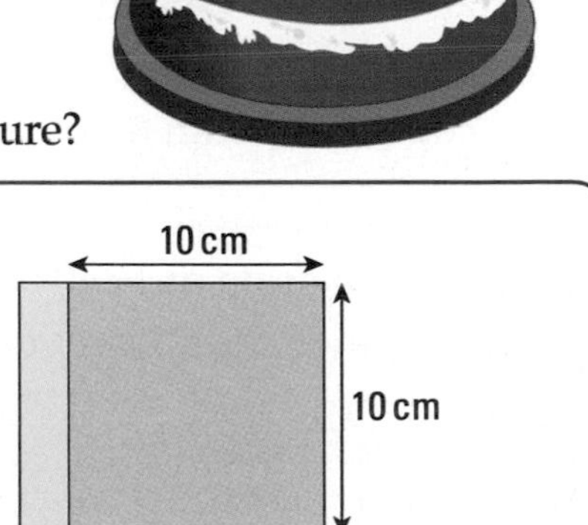

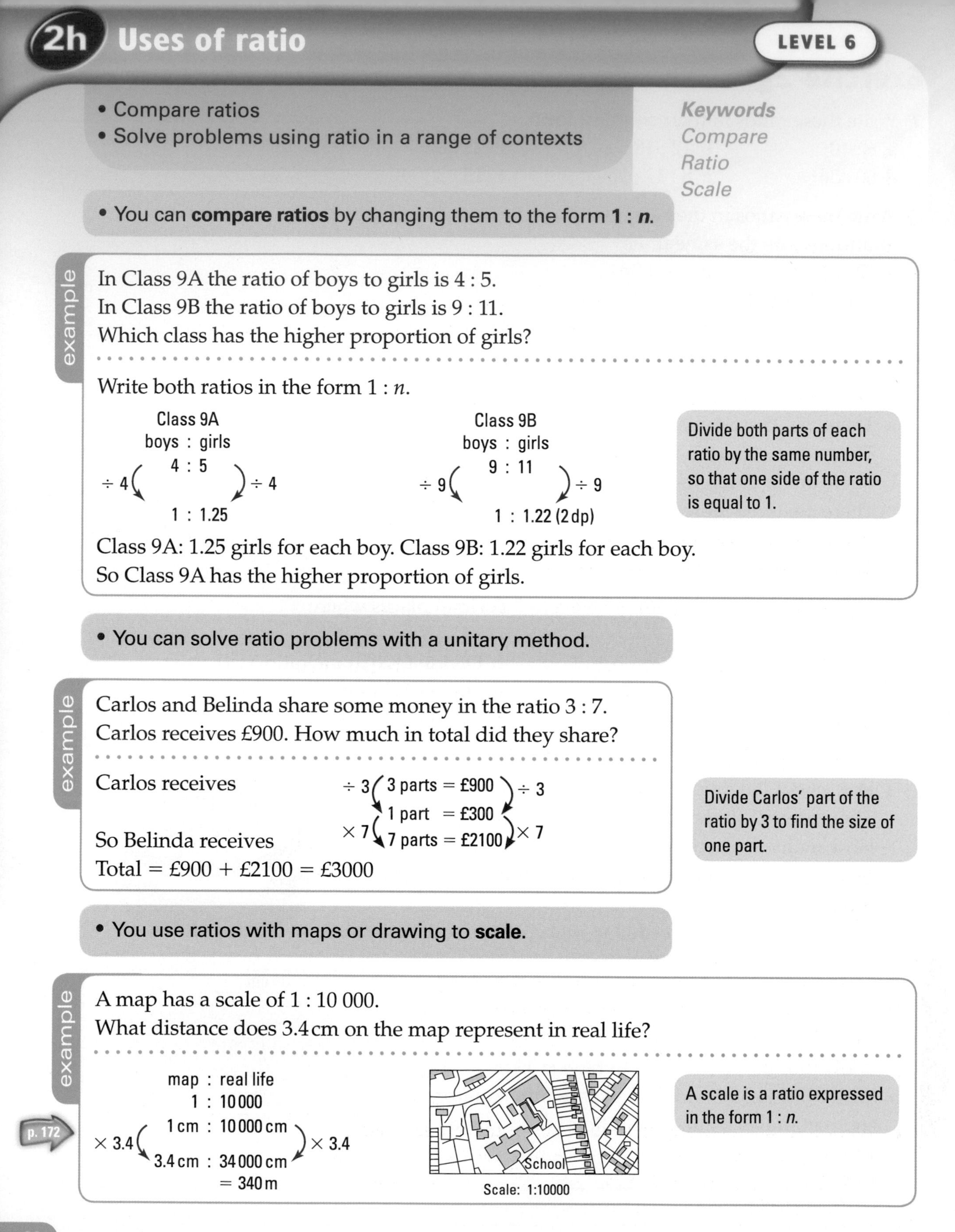

2h Uses of ratio

LEVEL 6

- Compare ratios
- Solve problems using ratio in a range of contexts

Keywords
Compare
Ratio
Scale

- You can **compare ratios** by changing them to the form **1 : *n***.

example

In Class 9A the ratio of boys to girls is 4 : 5.
In Class 9B the ratio of boys to girls is 9 : 11.
Which class has the higher proportion of girls?

Write both ratios in the form 1 : *n*.

Class 9A
boys : girls
4 : 5
÷ 4 ↓ ↓ ÷ 4
1 : 1.25

Class 9B
boys : girls
9 : 11
÷ 9 ↓ ↓ ÷ 9
1 : 1.22 (2 dp)

Divide both parts of each ratio by the same number, so that one side of the ratio is equal to 1.

Class 9A: 1.25 girls for each boy. Class 9B: 1.22 girls for each boy.
So Class 9A has the higher proportion of girls.

- You can solve ratio problems with a unitary method.

example

Carlos and Belinda share some money in the ratio 3 : 7.
Carlos receives £900. How much in total did they share?

Carlos receives ÷ 3 ↓ 3 parts = £900 ↓ ÷ 3
1 part = £300
So Belinda receives × 7 ↓ 7 parts = £2100 ↓ × 7
Total = £900 + £2100 = £3000

Divide Carlos' part of the ratio by 3 to find the size of one part.

- You use ratios with maps or drawing to **scale**.

example

A map has a scale of 1 : 10 000.
What distance does 3.4 cm on the map represent in real life?

map : real life
1 : 10 000
1 cm : 10 000 cm
× 3.4 ↓ ↓ × 3.4
3.4 cm : 34 000 cm
= 340 m

p. 172

Scale: 1:10000

A scale is a ratio expressed in the form 1 : *n*.

Exercise 2h

1 Write each of these ratios in the form 1 : *n*.

a 4 : 12 **b** 5 : 20 **c** 7 : 35 **d** 2 : 3

e 4 : 9 **f** 5 : 12 **g** 3 : 10 **h** 9 : 16

2 Solve each of these problems.

a At a sports club the ratio of boys to girls is 7 : 9.
There are 117 girls at the club.
How many children are there in the sports club?

b An alloy is made from iron, copper and aluminium in the ratio 4 : 5 : 1.
How much iron is needed to mix with 115 kg of copper?

3 a A map has a scale of 1 : 12 000.

i What distance does 7 cm on the map represent in real life?

ii What distance on the map represents a real-life measurement of 900 m?

b A model of a plane is built to a scale of 1 : 16.
The wingspan of the plane is 7.2 m.
What is the wingspan of the model?

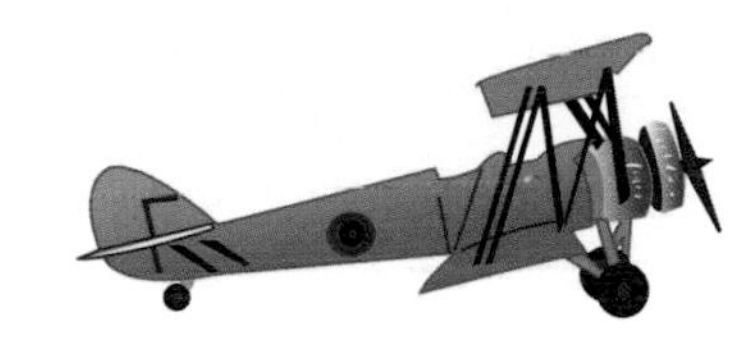

4 Simplify the ratios to the form 1 : *n* to answer these questions.

a The ratios of nylon to other materials in two T-shirts are 2 : 25 and 3 : 40. Which T-shirt has the greater proportion of nylon?

b The ratio of teachers to students in Oxford School is 3 : 41.
The ratio at Melville Comprehensive is 2 : 29.
Which school has the higher proportion of teachers?

5 Josiah is making rectangular tiles.
The ratio of length : width must always be 5 : 3.

a He makes a tile 15 cm long.
How wide must the tile be?

b He makes a tile 4.5 cm wide.
How long must the tile be?

c He makes a miniature tile in the same ratio, with a length of 2.5 cm. How wide must the tile be?

investigation

Aftab guessed the masses of some objects.
He wrote the ratio of actual weight : guessed weight in the form 1 : *n*. He called this his accuracy ratio.
For the bottle of pop his accuracy ratio was 1 : 0.86 (2 dp).

Object	Actual weight	Guess
Bottle of pop	350 g	300 g
Can of pop	240 g	200 g
Loaf of bread	750 g	800 g
Cake	500 g	600 g

a Work out the accuracy ratio for each of the other objects.

b Which guess was the most accurate? Explain your answer.

c Choose some objects, guess their mass and calculate your own accuracy ratios.

2i Ratio and proportion problems

LEVEL 7

- Solve problems involving ratio and proportion
- Use a unitary method to solve problems involving percentage change
- Write the change in a quantity as a percentage

Keywords
Percentage change
Proportion
Ratio

- You can write each part of a ratio as a proportion of the whole.

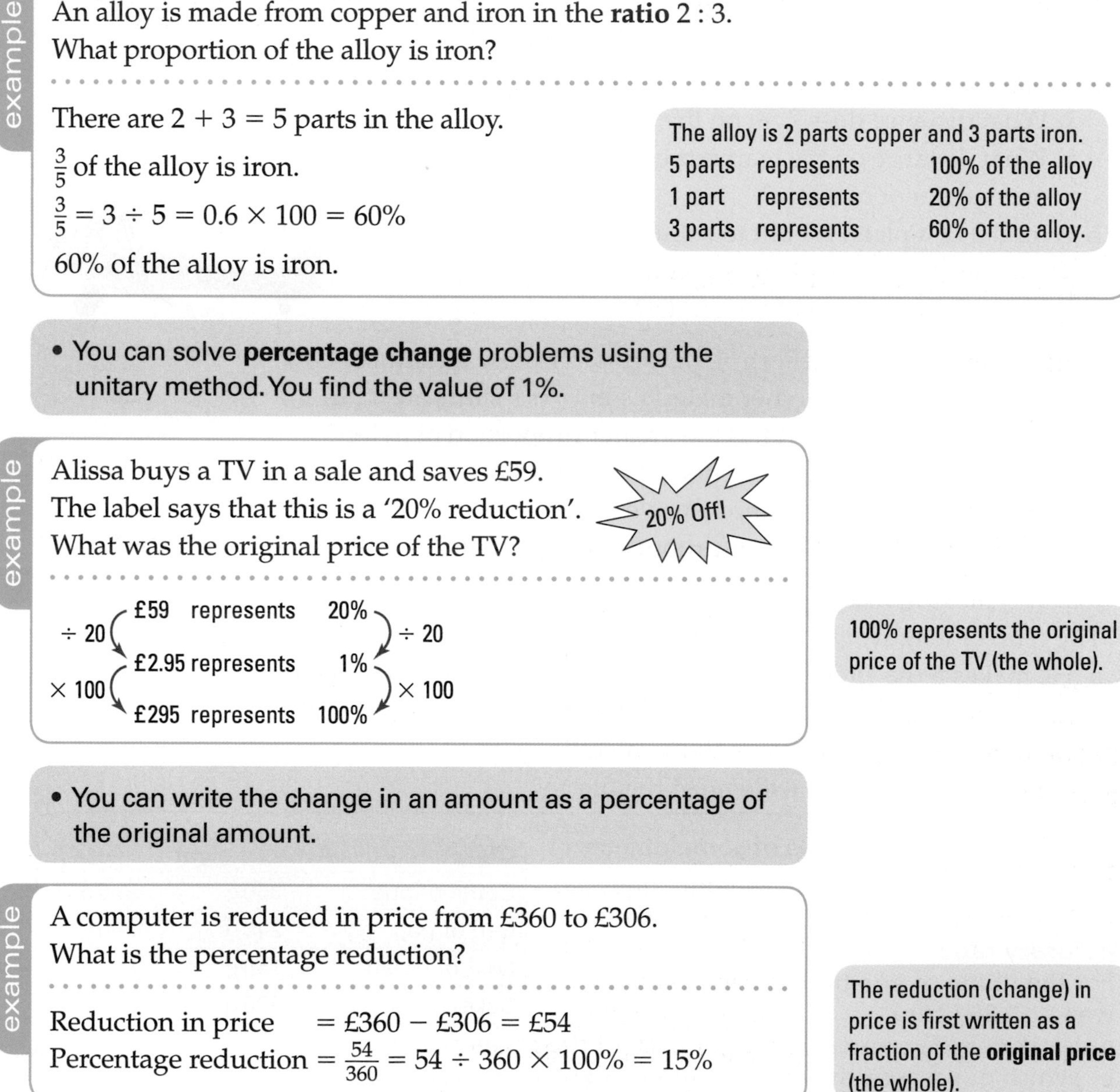

example

An alloy is made from copper and iron in the **ratio** 2 : 3.
What proportion of the alloy is iron?

There are $2 + 3 = 5$ parts in the alloy.
$\frac{3}{5}$ of the alloy is iron.
$\frac{3}{5} = 3 \div 5 = 0.6 \times 100 = 60\%$
60% of the alloy is iron.

The alloy is 2 parts copper and 3 parts iron.

5 parts	represents	100% of the alloy
1 part	represents	20% of the alloy
3 parts	represents	60% of the alloy.

- You can solve **percentage change** problems using the unitary method. You find the value of 1%.

example

Alissa buys a TV in a sale and saves £59.
The label says that this is a '20% reduction'.
What was the original price of the TV?

÷ 20	£59 represents	20%	÷ 20
	£2.95 represents	1%	
× 100	£295 represents	100%	× 100

100% represents the original price of the TV (the whole).

- You can write the change in an amount as a percentage of the original amount.

example

A computer is reduced in price from £360 to £306.
What is the percentage reduction?

Reduction in price $= £360 - £306 = £54$
Percentage reduction $= \frac{54}{360} = 54 \div 360 \times 100\% = 15\%$

The reduction (change) in price is first written as a fraction of the **original price** (the whole).

Exercise 2i

Grade D-C

1 In a bag there are 12 lemon and 18 lime sweets.
  a Write the ratio of lemon sweets : lime sweets in its simplest form.
  b What proportion of the bag is lemon sweets?

2 Different metal alloys are made from iron and zinc in these ratios.
  a 2 : 3 **b** 1 : 3 **c** 3 : 7 **d** 5 : 3
  e 7 : 13 **f** 7 : 9 **g** 3 : 12 **h** 11 : 14
  What proportion of each alloy is iron?

3 In each of these examples calculate the whole (100%).
  a 25% of a quantity is £30. **b** 10% of a quantity is £8.
  c 5% of a quantity is £12. **d** 20% of a quantity is £4.50.

Did you know?

Some foods are made according to very simple ratios - a traditional recipe for short crust pastry uses a ratio of 2 parts flour to 1 part fat.

4 **a** Gina bought a DVD in a sale and saved £4.
  The label said that it was a 20% reduction.
  What was the original price of the DVD?
  b Javid bought a packet of biscuits.
  The label said that the packet had 15% extra free.
  Javid worked out that he got three extra biscuits free in the packet.
  How many biscuits were there in the packet altogether?

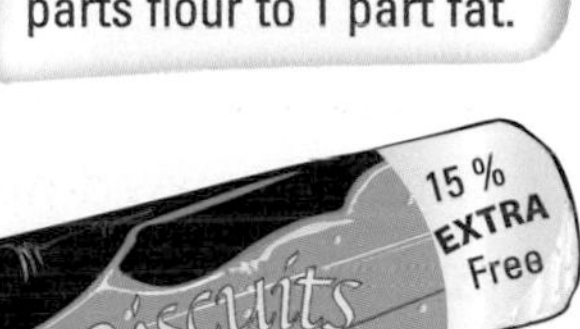

5 Calculate the percentage change in price for each of these items.

Item	Original price	New price
Jacket	£50	£35
Suit	£240	£192
Tie	£40	£42
Trousers	£45	£39.60

6 **a** A music centre costs £300.
  In a sale the price is reduced to £255.
  What is the percentage reduction?
  b In one year, the cost of a litre of petrol rises from 80p to £1.10.
  What is the percentage increase in the cost of a litre of petrol?

challenge

Solve each of these problems involving ratio and proportion.
  a Pastry is made with fat and flour in the ratio 3 : 5.
  How many grams of fat are needed to mix with 300 g of flour?
  b A 370 g packet of coffee costs £2.22.
  How much does 100 g of coffee cost?
  c A full box contains identical chocolates with a total mass 495 g.
  12 of the chocolates are eaten.
  The mass of the chocolates is now 315 g.
  How many chocolates were in the box originally?
  d An alloy is made from copper and iron in the ratio 2 : 5.
  How much copper needs to be mixed with 65 kg of iron?

2 Consolidation

2a

1 Work out these. Give your answer as a fraction in its simplest form.

a $\frac{2}{7} + \frac{5}{14}$ **b** $\frac{1}{2} + \frac{1}{8}$ **c** $\frac{4}{9} - \frac{1}{3}$ **d** $\frac{5}{6} + \frac{3}{8}$

e $\frac{2}{15} + \frac{2}{5}$ **f** $\frac{7}{12} - \frac{1}{3}$ **g** $\frac{4}{21} + \frac{9}{14}$ **h** $\frac{11}{12} - \frac{3}{4}$

2 Work out these. Give your answer as a fraction in its simplest form and as a mixed number where appropriate.

a $\frac{7}{12} + \frac{11}{18}$ **b** $\frac{2}{15} + \frac{7}{20}$ **c** $\frac{13}{15} - \frac{7}{10}$ **d** $\frac{1}{12} + \frac{5}{16}$

e $\frac{4}{21} + \frac{4}{15}$ **f** $\frac{13}{16} - \frac{3}{4}$ **g** $\frac{19}{30} + \frac{5}{18}$ **h** $\frac{17}{40} - \frac{3}{16}$

2b

3 Work out these. Give your answer as a fraction in its simplest form and as a mixed number where appropriate.

a $\frac{3}{5}$ of 15 cm **b** $\frac{3}{8}$ of 13 kg **c** $\frac{2}{3}$ of £51 **d** $\frac{5}{12}$ of 40 secs

e $\frac{3}{10}$ of \$70 **f** $\frac{7}{12}$ of 15 m **g** $\frac{3}{5}$ of 240 ml **h** $\frac{3}{4}$ of 50 km

4 Work out these. Use cancellation to simplify your answer where appropriate.

a $\frac{3}{4} \times \frac{8}{9}$ **b** $\frac{2}{3} \times \frac{6}{7}$ **c** $\frac{5}{8} \times \frac{7}{10}$ **d** $\frac{2}{7} \times \frac{7}{12}$

e $\frac{3}{8} \times \frac{12}{21}$ **f** $\frac{9}{10} \times \frac{5}{6}$ **g** $\frac{3}{4} \times \frac{6}{7}$ **h** $\frac{8}{15} \times \frac{25}{32}$

2c

5 Work out these. Give your answer as a mixed number in its simplest form.

a $3 \div \frac{2}{3}$ **b** $4 \div \frac{3}{5}$ **c** $8 \div \frac{3}{5}$ **d** $9 \div \frac{6}{7}$

e $4 \div \frac{8}{9}$ **f** $5 \div \frac{10}{11}$ **g** $12 \div \frac{3}{5}$ **h** $6 \div \frac{4}{11}$

6 Calculate these.

a $\frac{2}{5} \div \frac{3}{4}$ **b** $\frac{3}{4} \div \frac{5}{7}$ **c** $\frac{4}{9} \div \frac{2}{5}$ **d** $\frac{1}{6} \div \frac{1}{5}$

e $\frac{5}{8} \div \frac{3}{4}$ **f** $\frac{7}{9} \div \frac{5}{6}$ **g** $\frac{7}{12} \div \frac{3}{4}$ **h** $\frac{8}{15} \div \frac{16}{21}$

2d

7 Use direct proportion to solve these problems.

a 3 litres of lemonade cost £2.13.
What is the cost of 5 litres of lemonade?

b There are 21 sweets in a packet.
The mass of the packet is 336 g.
What is the mass of a packet of 30 sweets?

c 12 inches is approximately 30 cm.
i How many centimetres are equal to 20 inches?
ii How many inches are equal to 100 cm?

2e

8 **a** A mobile phone normally costs £75. In a sale the price is reduced by 20%.
What is the sale price of the mobile?

b Last year Archie earned £240 a week.
At the start of this year, the manager increased Archie's wage by 18%.
What is Archie's new wage?

2f

9 Write the number of goals scored as a proportion of the number of shots taken for each of these strikers.

a Andrews	12 goals	48 shots
b Roland	15 goals	40 shots
c Tonaldo	22 goals	55 shots

Who is the best striker? Explain your answer.

10 At the pony club there are 23 girls and 7 boys.
At the dance club there are 14 girls and 5 boys.
Which club has the higher proportion of boys?
Write your answer as a percentage (rounded to 1 decimal place where appropriate).

2g

11 Write these ratios in their simplest form.
First change the quantities into the same units.
a £5 : 350 p **b** 4 kg : 2500 g **c** 12 cm : 50 mm **d** 250 ml : 30 cl

12 Work out these, giving your answers to 2 decimal places where appropriate.
a Divide 60 pears in the ratio 7 : 5. **b** Divide £300 in the ratio 2 : 3.

2h

13 At a school the ratio of boys to girls is 4 : 5.
There are 572 boys at the school. How many children are there at the school?

14 A model of a yacht is built to a scale of 1 : 24.
The length of the yacht is 15.6 m.
What is the length of the model yacht?

2i

15 **a** John bought a CD in a sale and saved £5.20.
The label said that it was a 40% reduction.
What was the original price of the CD?

b A mobile phone costs £240. In a sale the price is reduced to £204.
What is the percentage reduction?

2 Summary

Assessment criteria

- Use equivalent fractions, decimals and percentages **Level 6**
- Divide a quantity into two or more parts in a given ratio **Level 6**
- Add, subtract, multiply and divide fractions **Level 7**

Level 6

1 Alicia and Pete together buy one ticket in a lottery.
The ticket costs £5.
Alicia pays £2 and Pete pays £3 for the ticket.
They win £150 and decide to divide the money in the ratio 2 : 3.
How much money does each person receive?

Instant take 5
Quick Pick free play £5 See back for details.
5 5 5
5 5 5
Win Up To £5000

Francesca's answer ✔

2 + 3 = 5 parts
Each part = £150 ÷ 5 = £30
Alicia receives 2 × £30 = £60
Pete receives 3 × £30 = £90

Fran makes sure Alicia has 2 parts and Pete has 3 parts.

She checks that the answers add to £150
£60 + £90 = £150

Kelly's answer ✔

2 + 3 = 5 parts
Alicia receives $\frac{2}{5}$ of £30 = £60
Pete receives $\frac{3}{5}$ of £30 = £90

Kelly checks that the answers add to £150
£60 + £90 = £150

Level 6

2 How many eighths are there in one quarter?
Now work out $\frac{3}{4} \div \frac{1}{8}$

Key Stage 3 2005 5–7 Paper 1

3 Geometry

Geometrical reasoning and construction

Origami is the ancient art of paper folding.

You can make many 2-D and 3-D shapes starting with a square sheet of paper.

Some can be very complex mathematical models.

What's the point? Origami uses the symmetrical and geometrical properties of shapes to create intricate designs.

Check in

Level 5

1 Calculate the size of the angles marked with letters.

a 46°, 71°, a

b

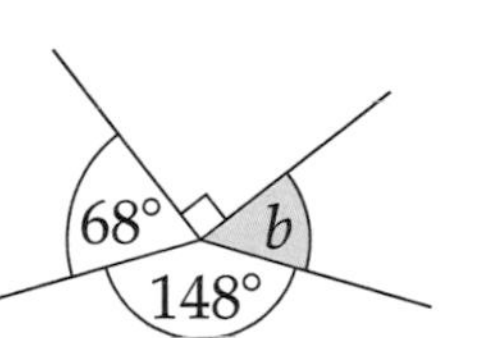

c

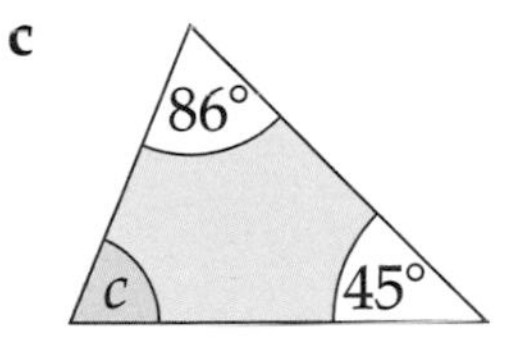

2 Match these quadrilaterals with their mathematical names.

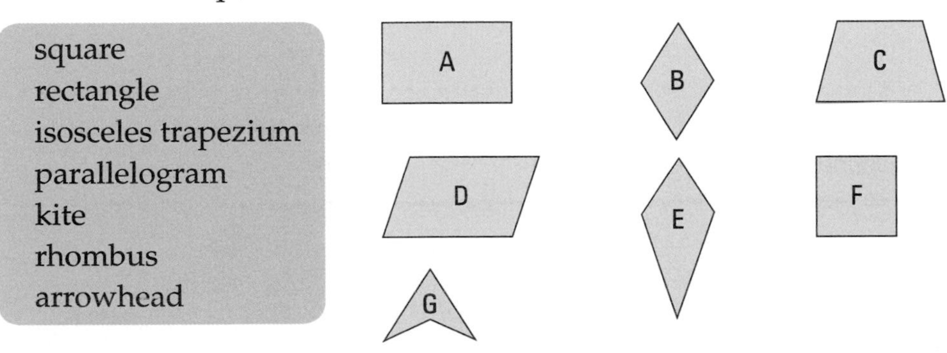

square
rectangle
isosceles trapezium
parallelogram
kite
rhombus
arrowhead

3a Angle properties of a triangle

LEVEL 6

- Know facts about angles on parallel and intersecting lines
- Know facts about angles in a triangle

Keywords
Alternate *Interior*
Corresponding *Intersect*
Exterior *Parallel*
Vertically opposite

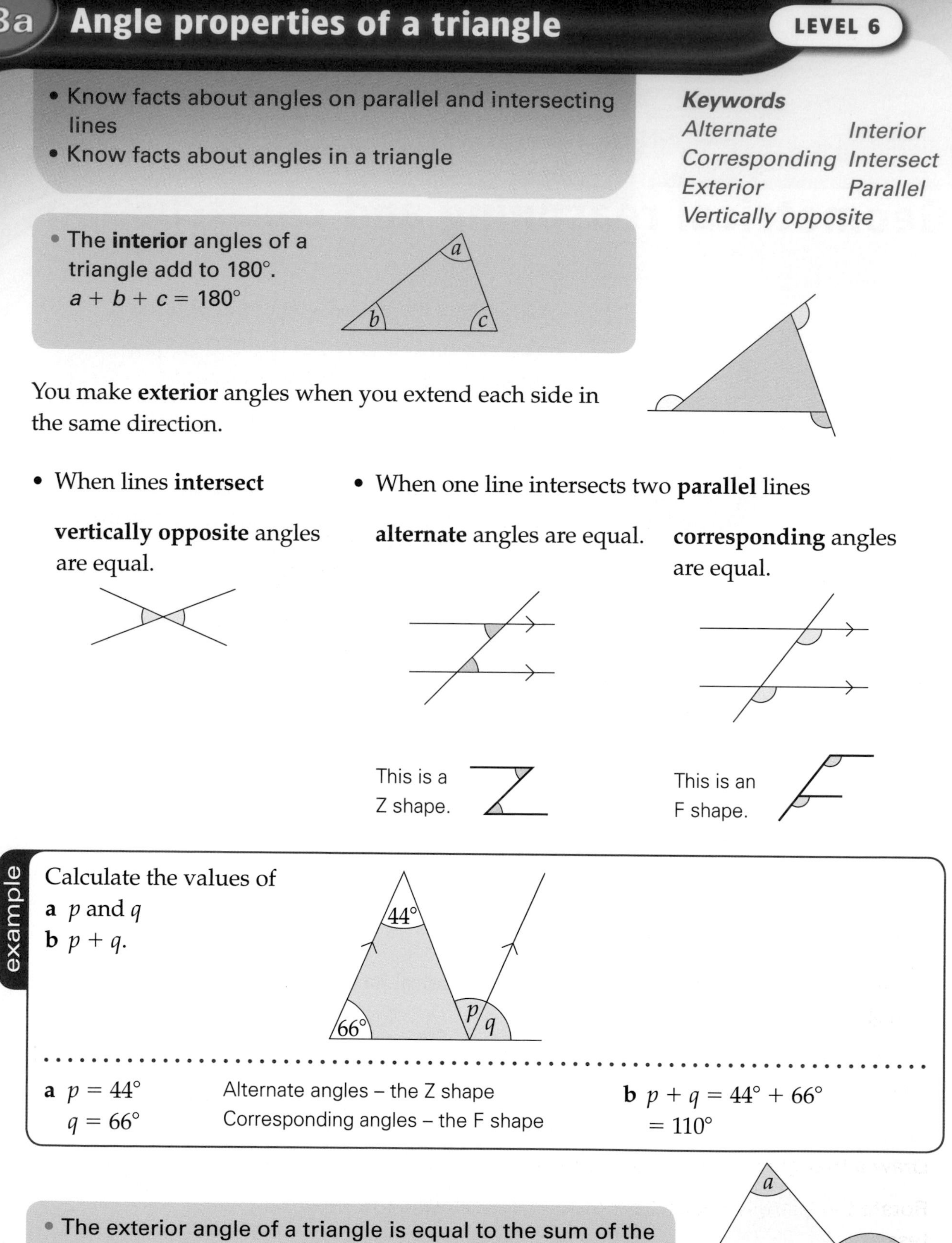

- The **interior** angles of a triangle add to 180°.
  $a + b + c = 180°$

You make **exterior** angles when you extend each side in the same direction.

- When lines **intersect**

  vertically opposite angles are equal.

- When one line intersects two **parallel** lines

  alternate angles are equal.

  This is a Z shape.

  corresponding angles are equal.

  This is an F shape.

example

Calculate the values of

a p and q

b $p + q$.

a $p = 44°$ Alternate angles – the Z shape

$q = 66°$ Corresponding angles – the F shape

b $p + q = 44° + 66°$

$= 110°$

- The exterior angle of a triangle is equal to the sum of the two opposite interior angles.

Grade D

Exercise 3a

1 Calculate the third angle in each triangle.
State the type of triangle in each case.

a 43°, 47° **b** 32°, 116° **c** 60°, 60°
d 37°, 108° **e** 45°, 45° **f** 18°, 144°

Choose from right-angled, isosceles, scalene or equilateral.

2 Calculate the angles marked with letters.

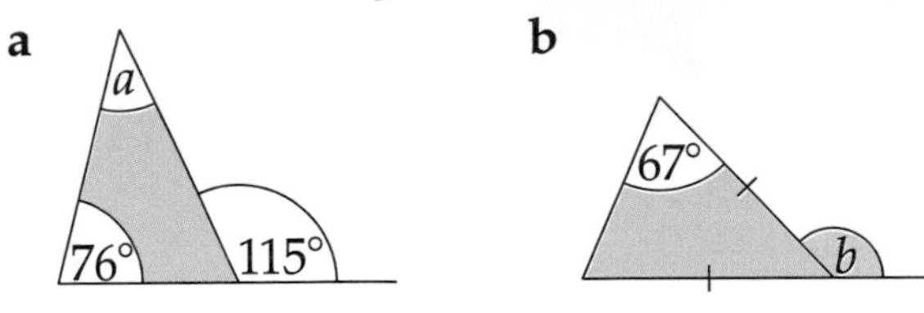

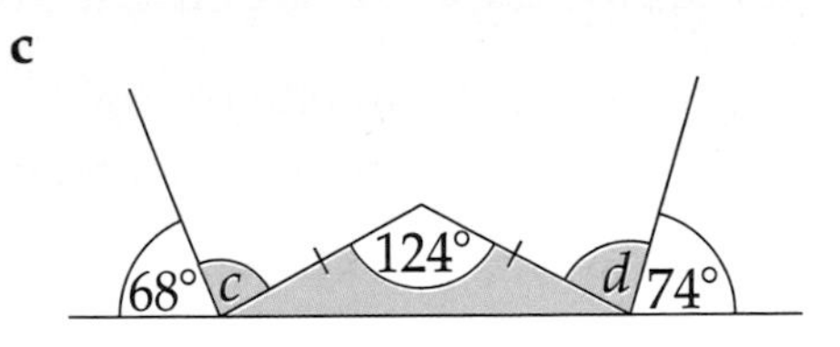

3 Calculate the angles marked with letters.
Give a reason for your answers.

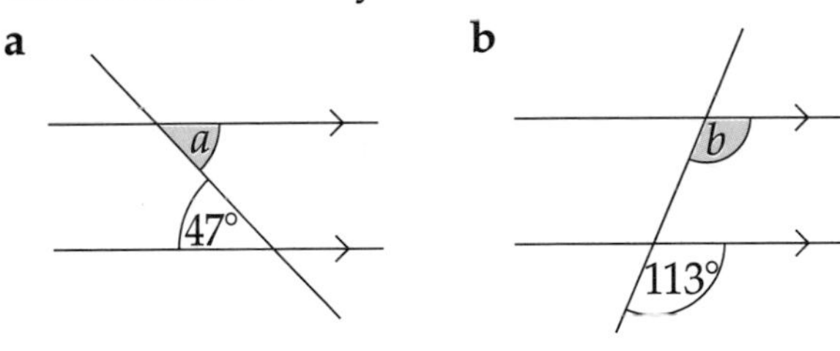

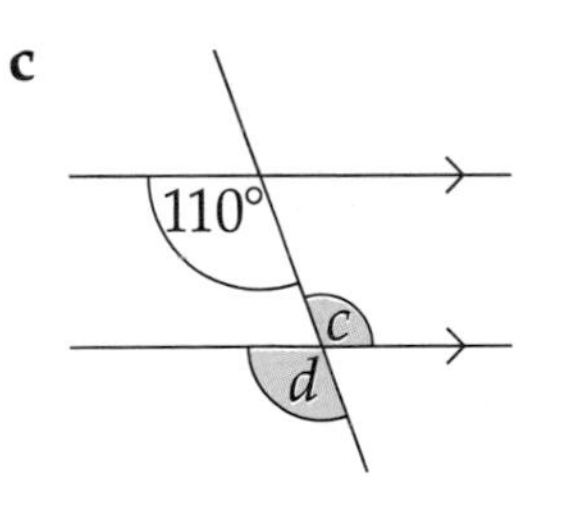

4 Calculate the angles marked with letters.

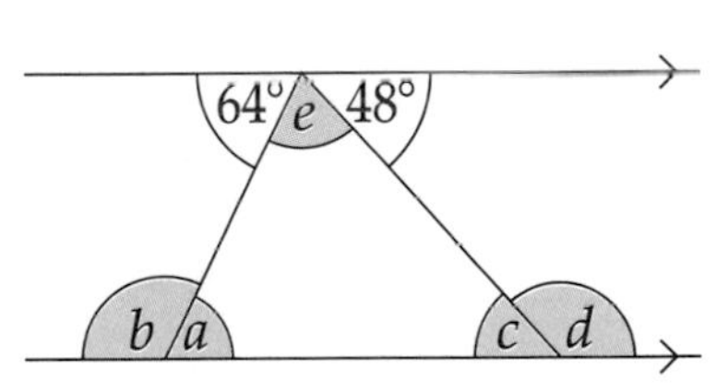

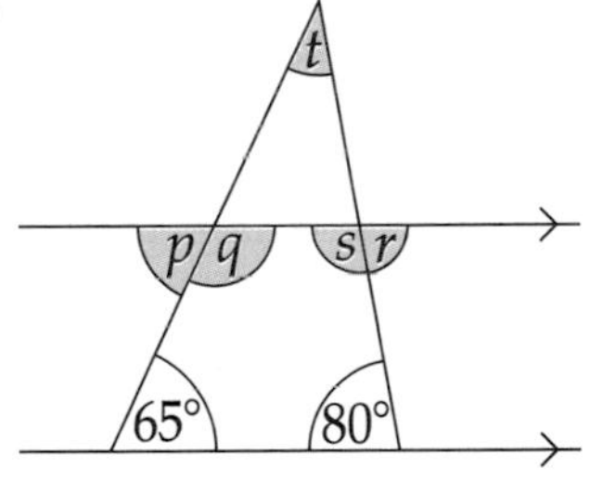

5 Find p and q in terms of a and b.

You already know that $p + q + c = 180°$ as angles on a straight line add up to 180°.
You now know $a + b + c = 180°$ which proves that the angle sum of a triangle is 180°.

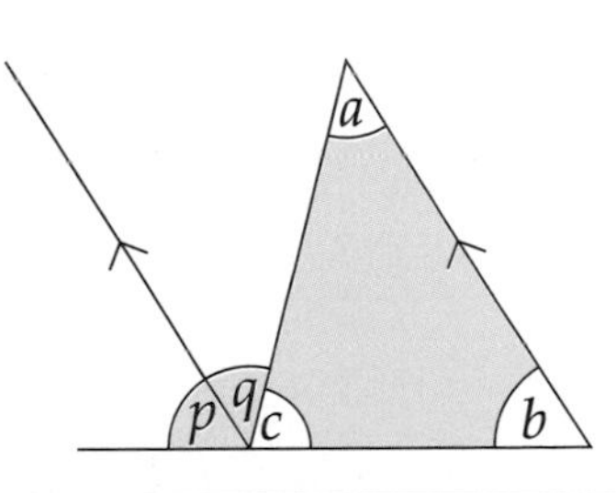

activity

Draw a triangle and colour the angles.

Rotate the triangle about the midpoint of each side to create a tessellation. Show examples of alternate and corresponding angles on your tessellation.

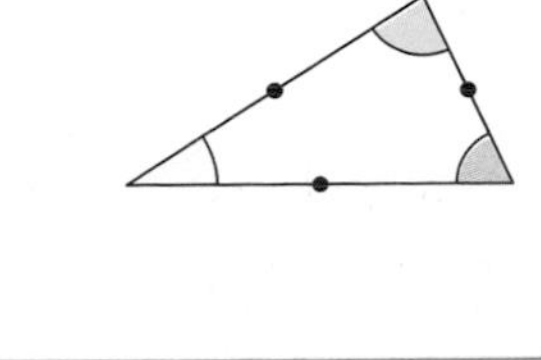

p. 44

3b Angle properties of a quadrilateral

LEVEL 6

- Know angle facts and types of quadrilaterals
- Understand a proof about the angle sum of a quadrilateral
- Identify symmetrical properties of quadrilaterals

Keywords
Interior
Reflection symmetry
Rotation symmetry
Quadrilateral

You can divide a **quadrilateral** into two triangles.

$a + b + c = 180°$ in one triangle
$d + e + f = 180°$ in the other triangle

So $a + b + c + d + e + f = 360°$

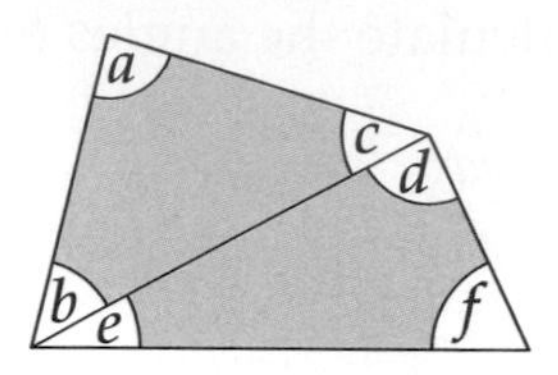

- The **interior** angles of a quadrilateral add up to 360°.
  $p + q + r + s = 360°$

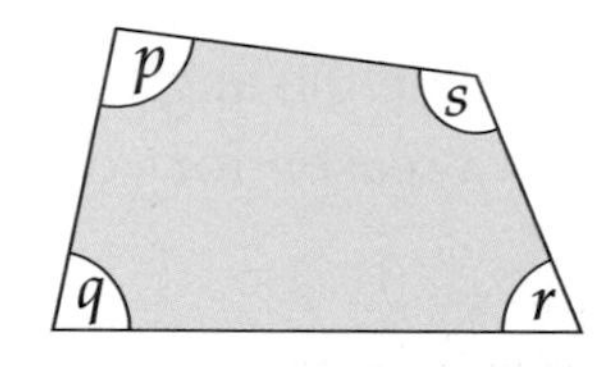

example

Calculate the size of angle a.

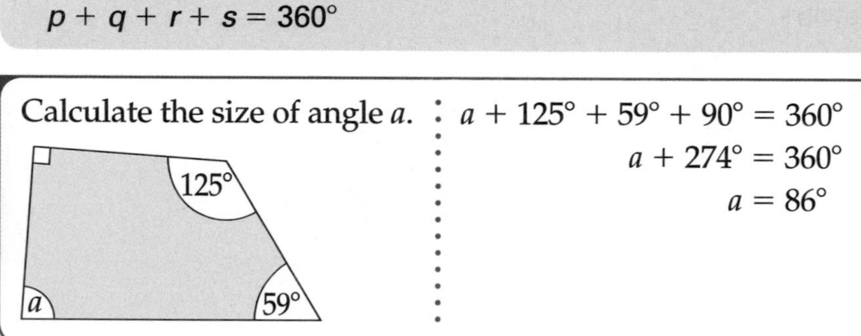

$a + 125° + 59° + 90° = 360°$
$a + 274° = 360°$
$a = 86°$

- A shape has **reflection symmetry** if it divides into two identical halves each of which is the mirror image of the other.

- A shape has **rotation symmetry** if it rotates onto itself more than once in a complete turn.

The **order** is the number of times it rotates onto itself in a full turn.

Square

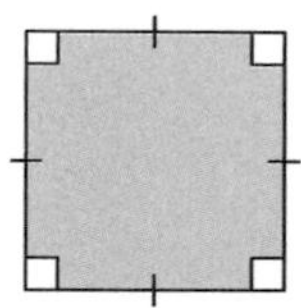

Rectangle

Rhombus

Parallelogram

Trapezium

Isosceles trapezium

Kite

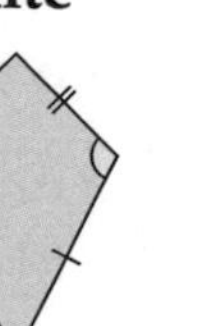

Arrowhead

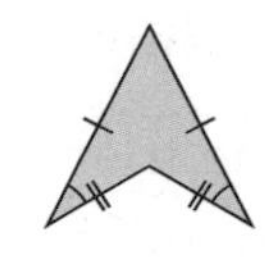

Grade D

Exercise 3b

Remember:
> means sides are parallel.
I means they are equal.

1 Calculate the angles marked with letters.
State the type of quadrilateral in each case.

a

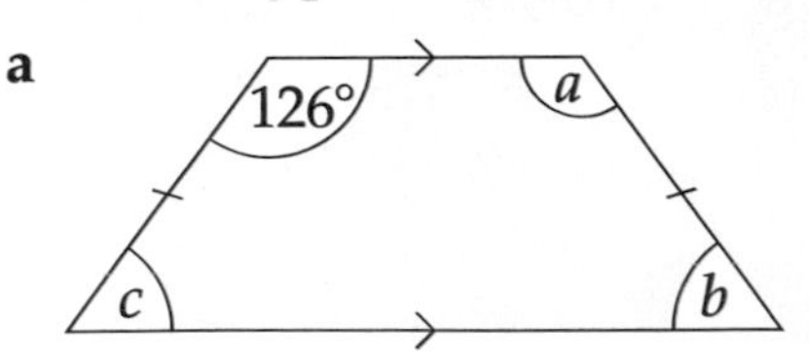

b

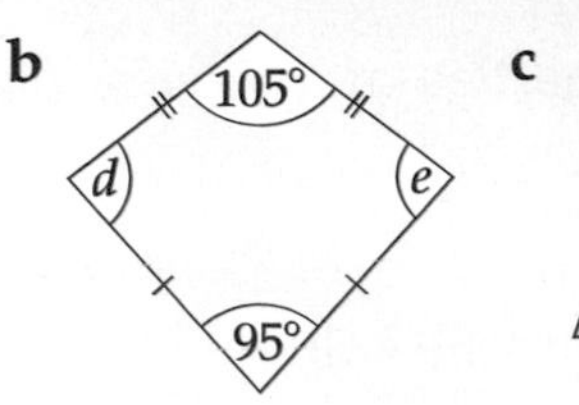

c 111°, f, h, g

2 Copy and complete this table using the eight different quadrilaterals on the opposite page.
The square is done for you.

A shape with order 1 has no rotation symmetry.

You can put several shapes into the same box.

		Number of lines of symmetry				
		0	1	2	3	4
Order of rotation symmetry	1					
	2					
	3					
	4					square

p. 38

3 Use parallel line angle properties to help you find the angles marked with letters.

a

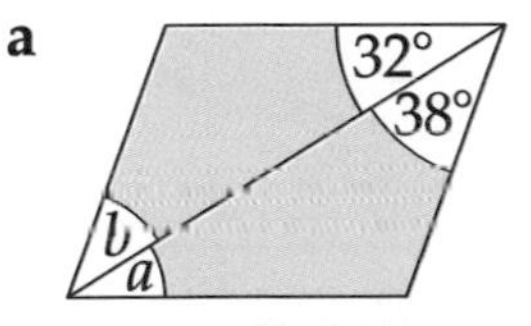

A parallelogram

b

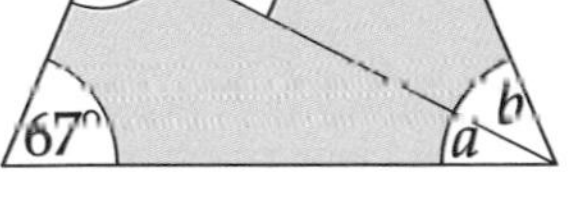

An isosceles trapezium

p. 46

4 Here are two congruent triangles.
The sides of equal length are stuck together to form a quadrilateral.
Draw three different possible shapes and describe the type of quadrilateral in each case.

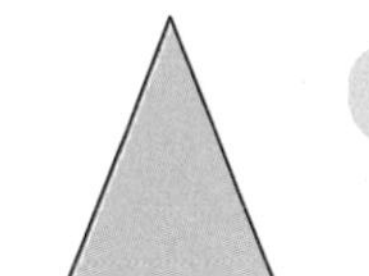

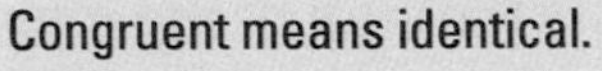

5 A parallelogram has rotation symmetry of order 2.
Explain why this shows the opposite angles of a parallelogram are equal.

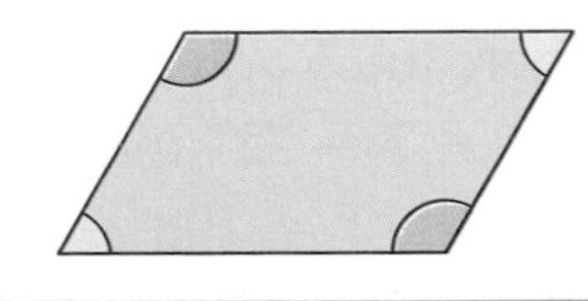

activity

Fold a square piece of paper to form this quadrilateral.
State the mathematical name and calculate the interior angles of the quadrilateral.

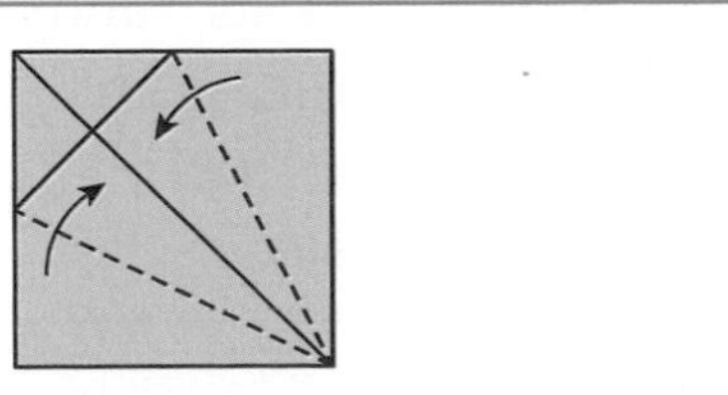

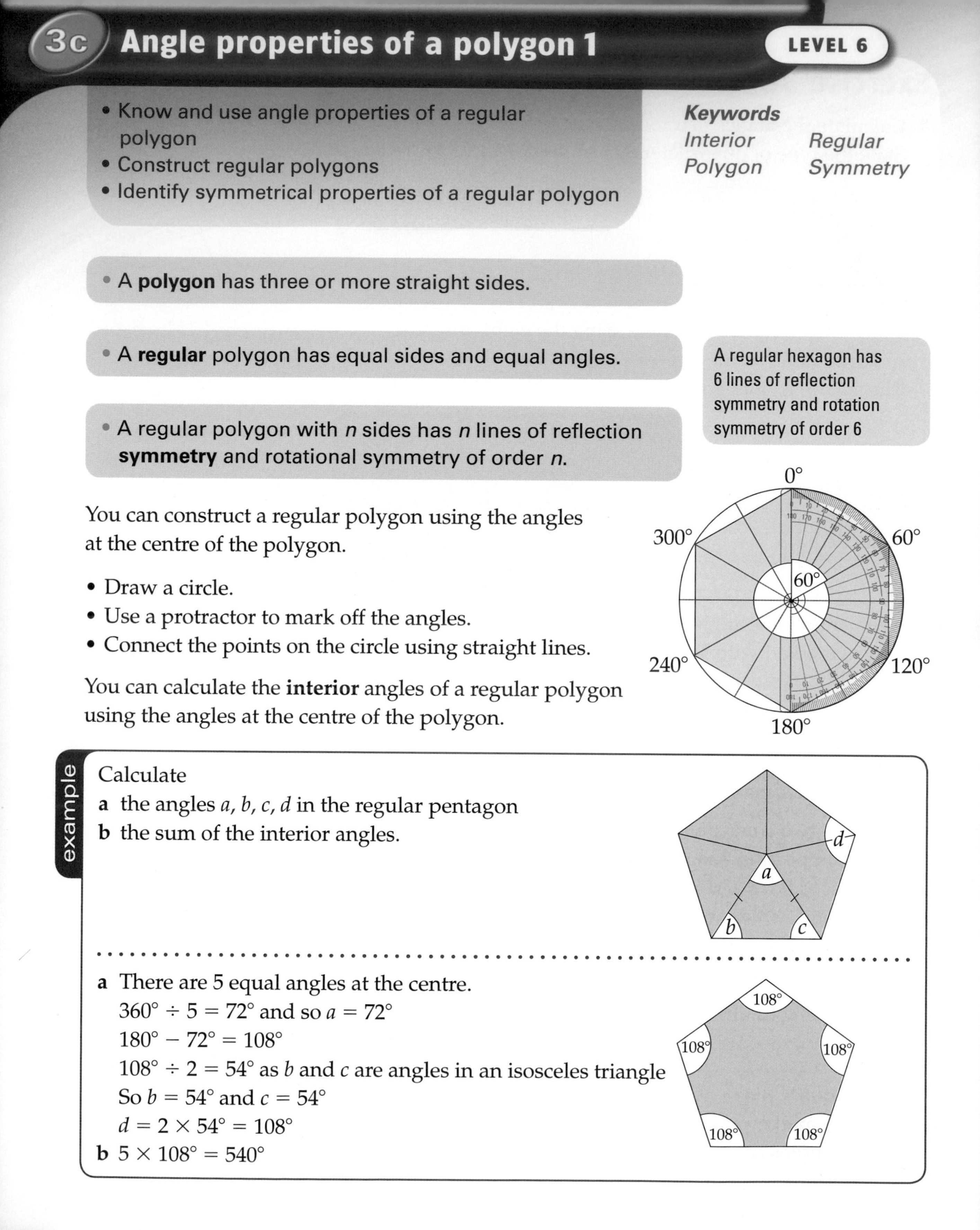

3c Angle properties of a polygon 1

LEVEL 6

- Know and use angle properties of a regular polygon
- Construct regular polygons
- Identify symmetrical properties of a regular polygon

Keywords
Interior *Regular*
Polygon *Symmetry*

- A **polygon** has three or more straight sides.

- A **regular** polygon has equal sides and equal angles.

- A regular polygon with n sides has n lines of reflection **symmetry** and rotational symmetry of order n.

A regular hexagon has 6 lines of reflection symmetry and rotation symmetry of order 6

You can construct a regular polygon using the angles at the centre of the polygon.

- Draw a circle.
- Use a protractor to mark off the angles.
- Connect the points on the circle using straight lines.

You can calculate the **interior** angles of a regular polygon using the angles at the centre of the polygon.

example

Calculate

a the angles a, b, c, d in the regular pentagon

b the sum of the interior angles.

a There are 5 equal angles at the centre.

$360° \div 5 = 72°$ and so $a = 72°$

$180° - 72° = 108°$

$108° \div 2 = 54°$ as b and c are angles in an isosceles triangle

So $b = 54°$ and $c = 54°$

$d = 2 \times 54° = 108°$

b $5 \times 108° = 540°$

LEVEL 6

Grade D

Exercise 3c

1 **a** Draw the lines of reflection symmetry on a copy of these regular polygons.

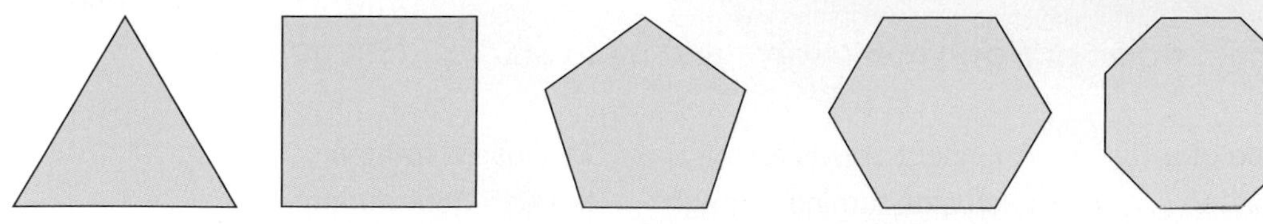

b Give the order of rotation symmetry for each polygon.

2 A regular hexagon is made from 6 equilateral triangles.

Calculate **a** the interior angle of an equilateral triangle

b the interior angle of a regular hexagon

c the sum of all the interior angles of a regular hexagon.

3 Calculate the angles a, b, c, d in each regular polygon

a

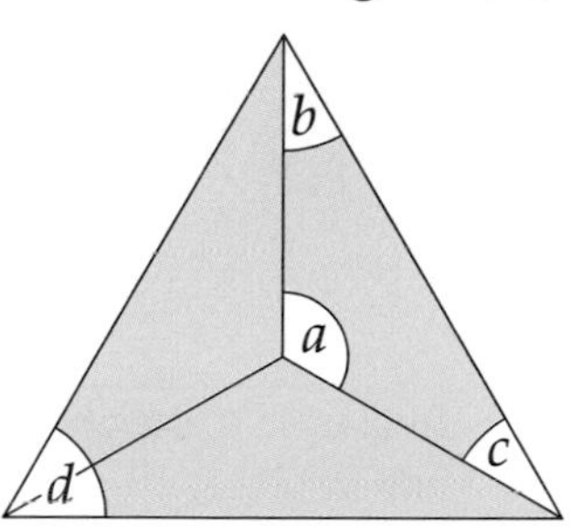

b

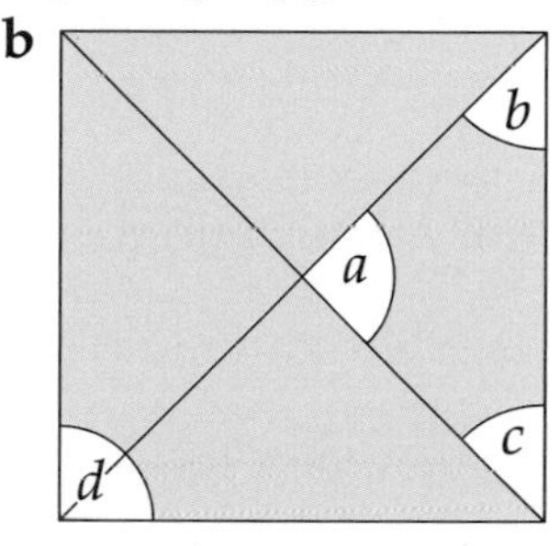

4 This is a regular decagon.

Calculate **a** the angle at the centre, a

b the angle marked b in the isosceles triangle

c the interior angle of a regular decagon.

d the sum of all the interior angles of a regular decagon.

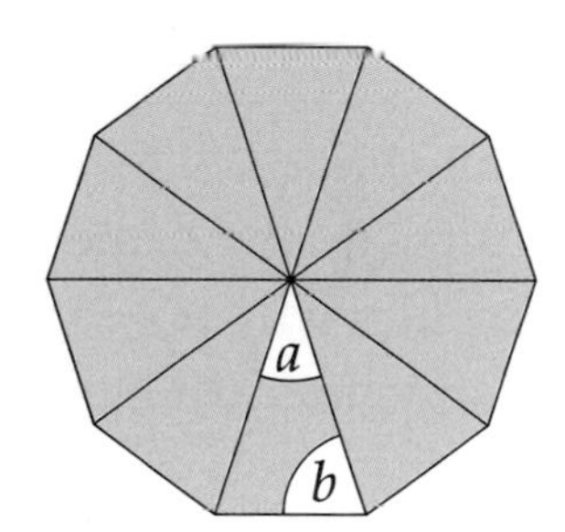

activity

a Construct an inscribed regular pentagon.

b Draw diagonals to form a smaller pentagon.

c Show that this smaller pentagon is regular.

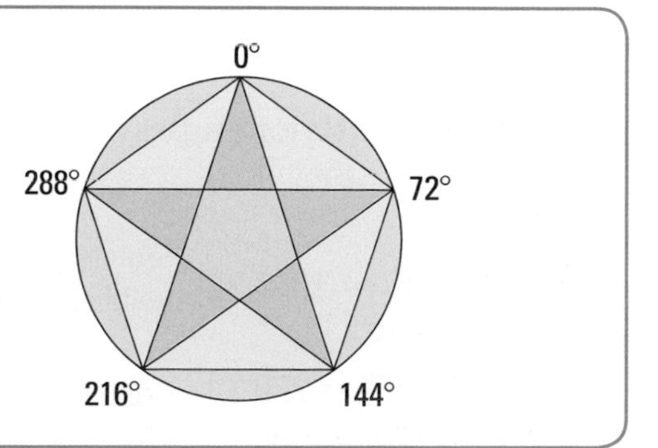

Angle properties of a polygon 2

LEVEL 6

- Know and use angle properties of a regular polygon

Keywords
Exterior
Interior
Polygon
Tessellation
Vertex

- The **exterior** angles of a **polygon** always add up to 360°.

Extend each side of a polygon in the same direction to draw the exterior angles.

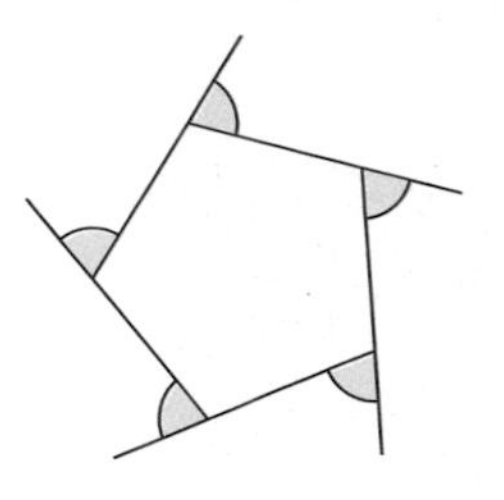

An insect crawls along each side turning through each exterior angle.

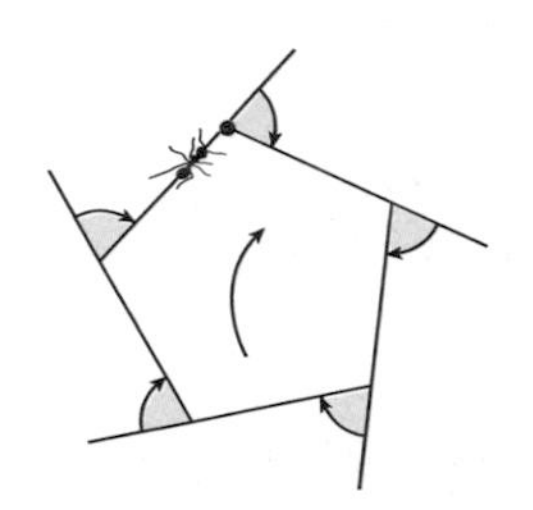

The insect rotates through 360° during the journey.

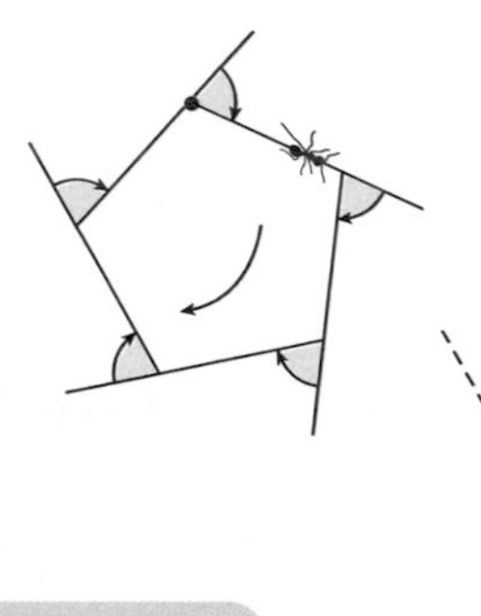

ext int

- The exterior and the **interior** angles add to 180° at each **vertex** (corner).

- A **tessellation** is a tiling pattern with no gaps.

Angles on a straight line add to 180°.

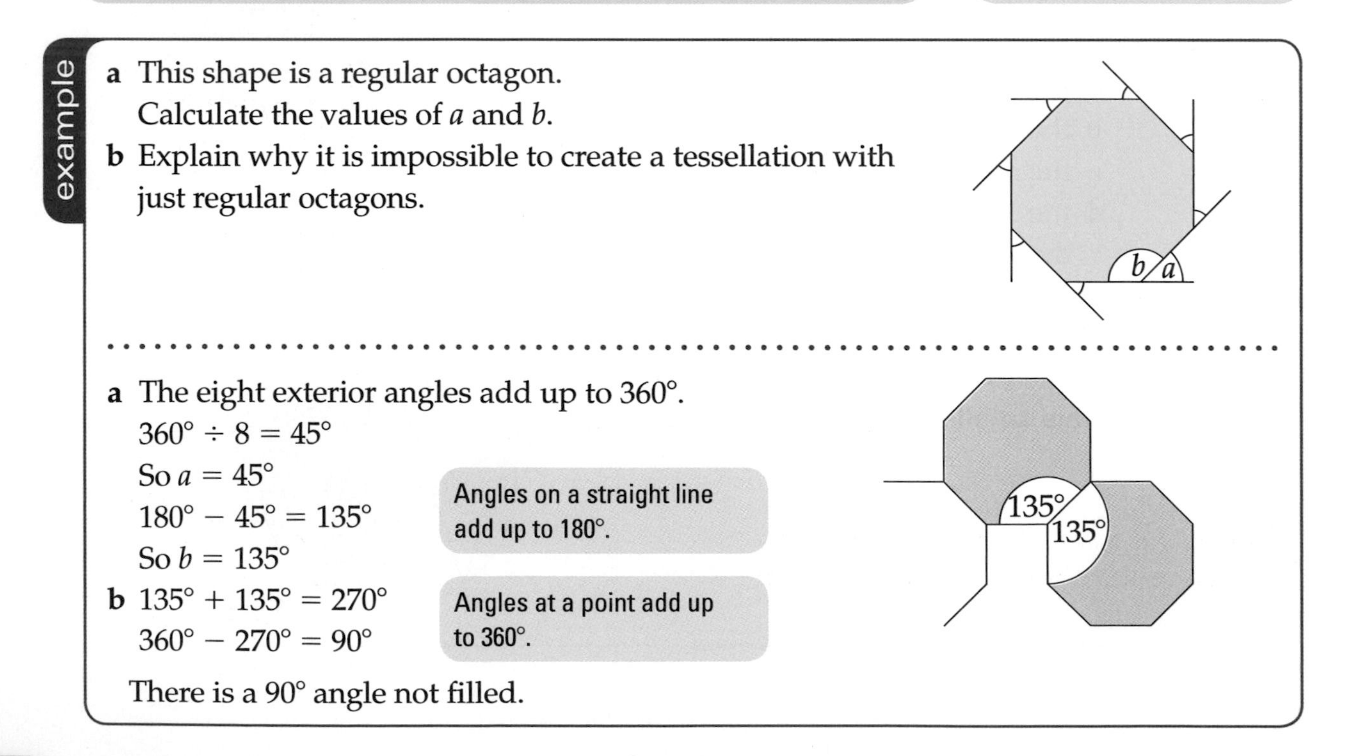

example

a This shape is a regular octagon.
Calculate the values of a and b.

b Explain why it is impossible to create a tessellation with just regular octagons.

a The eight exterior angles add up to 360°.
$360° \div 8 = 45°$
So $a = 45°$
$180° - 45° = 135°$
So $b = 135°$

Angles on a straight line add up to 180°.

b $135° + 135° = 270°$
$360° - 270° = 90°$

Angles at a point add up to 360°.

There is a 90° angle not filled.

Exercise 3d

1 Copy these regular polygons.
Draw a set of exterior angles on each of your shapes.
Work out the value of one exterior angle for each shape.

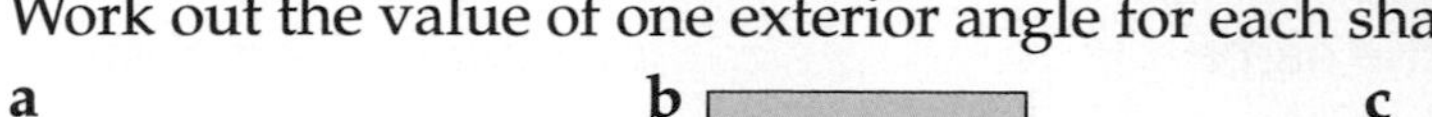

a

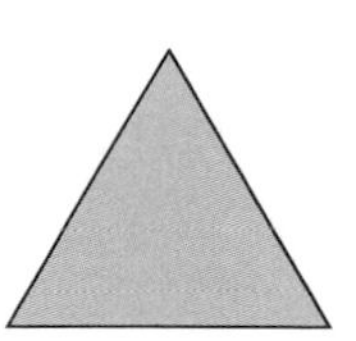

b

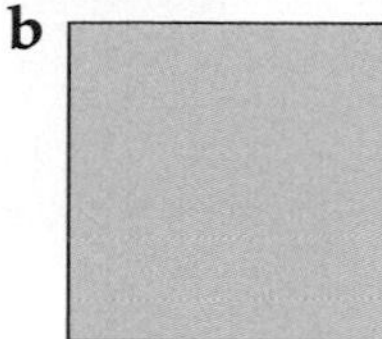

c **d**

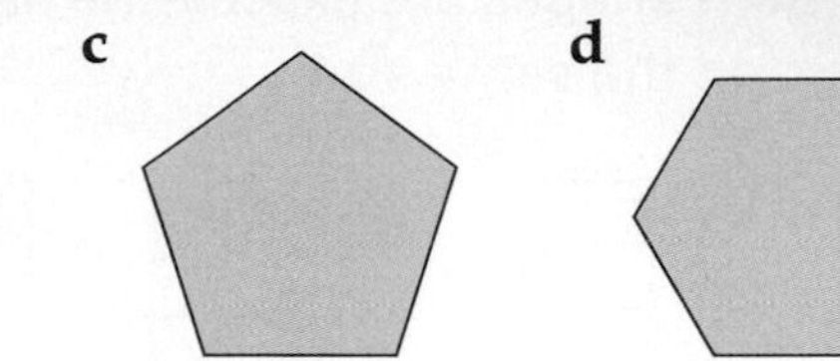

2 Copy and complete this table for regular polygons with 3 sides to 10 sides.
Use your answers to question **1** to help you.

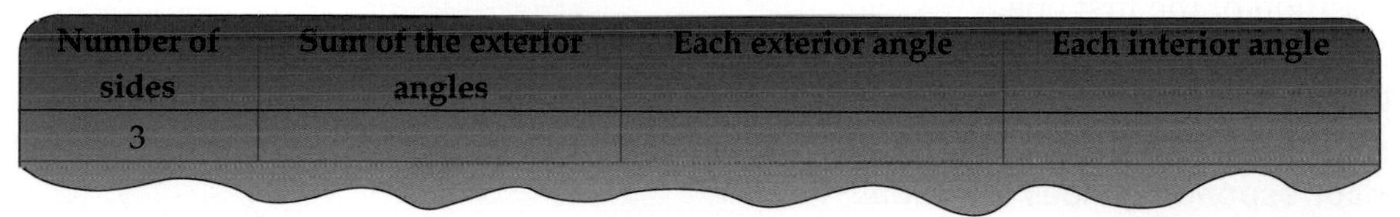

Number of sides	Sum of the exterior angles	Each exterior angle	Each interior angle
3			

3 There are only three regular polygons that tessellate.
Explain why it is possible to tessellate
a a regular hexagon
b a square
c an equilateral triangle.

4 Two diagonals of a regular pentagon are drawn to form three isosceles triangles.
Calculate the size of angles a to i.

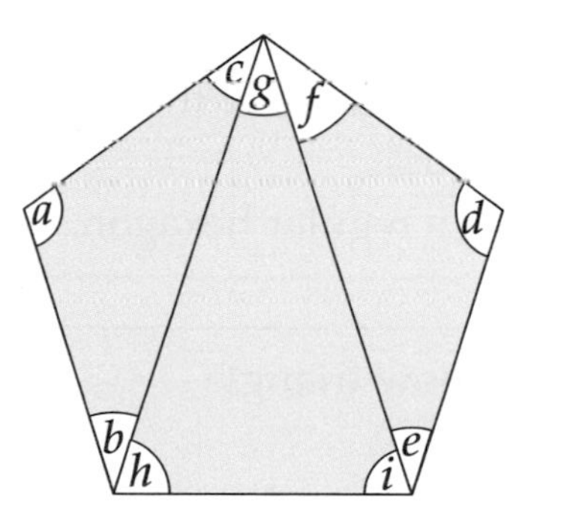

5 The exterior angle of a regular polygon is 24°.
How many sides does it have?

24°
24°

Did you know?

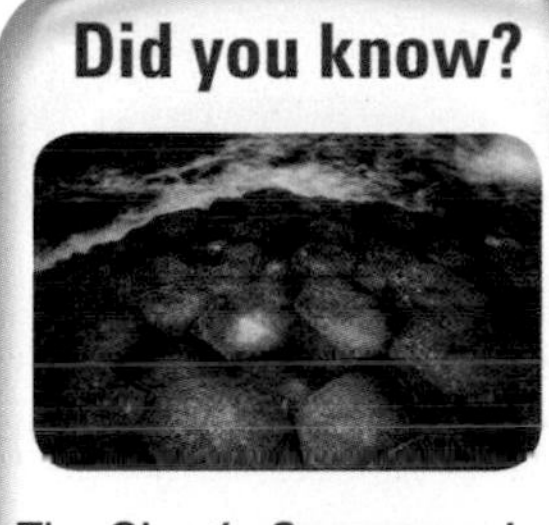

The Giant's Causeway in Ireland contains about 40 000 interlocking columns of volcanic basalt. Many are hexagonal and form a tessellating pattern.

challenge

Explain why the angle at the centre of any regular polygon is always the same as its exterior angle.

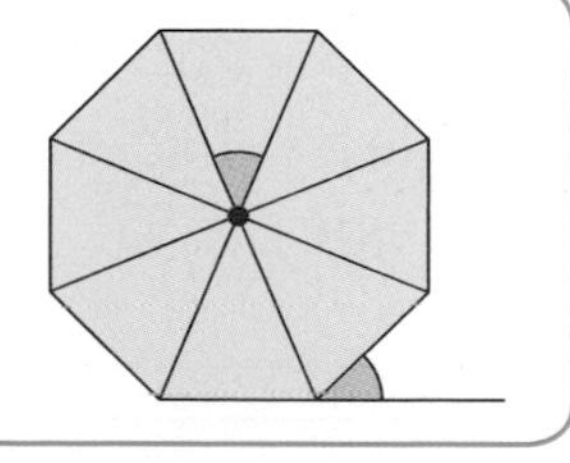

3e Congruent shapes

LEVEL 6

- Recognise congruent shapes

Keywords
Congruent
Corresponding angles
Corresponding sides

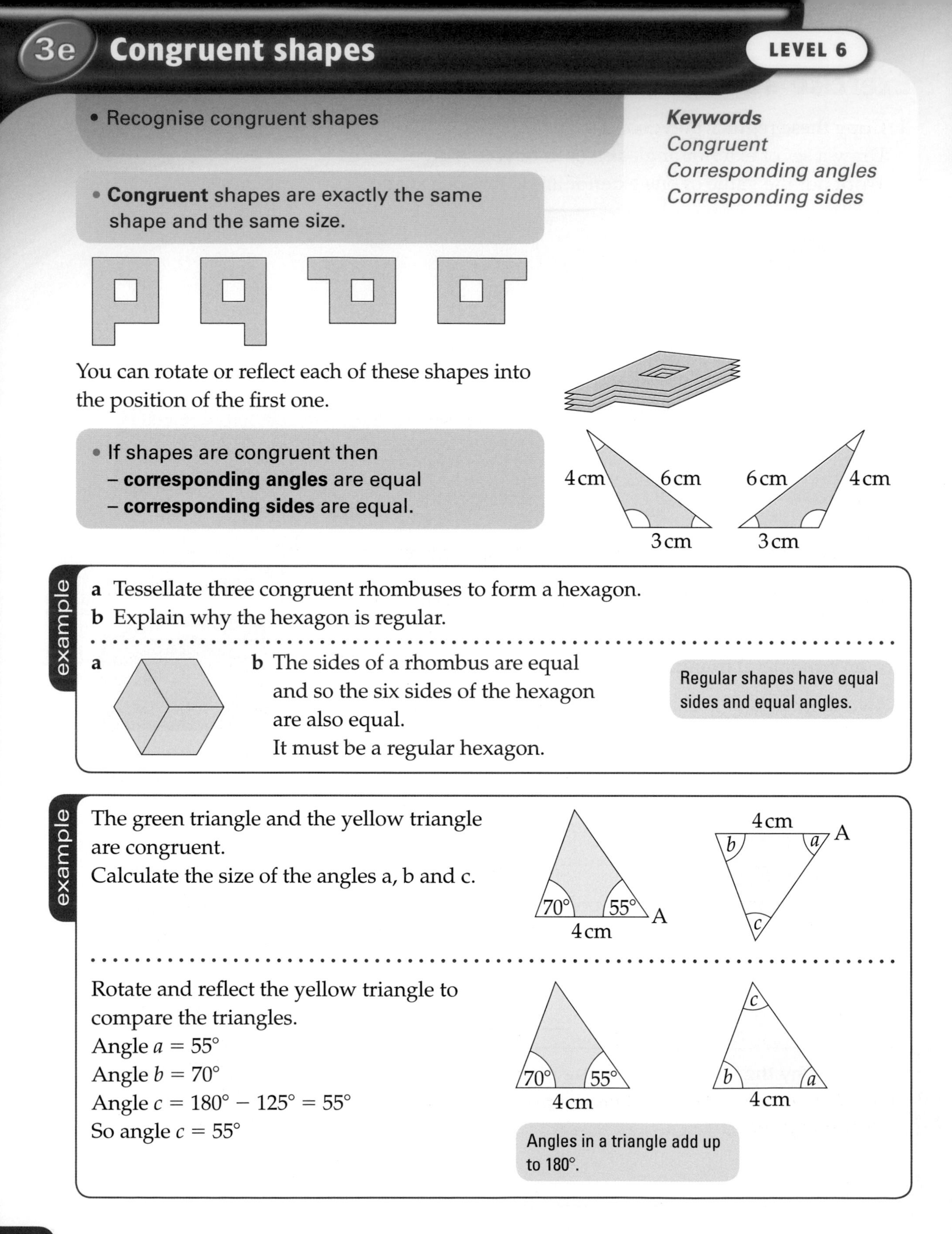

- **Congruent** shapes are exactly the same shape and the same size.

You can rotate or reflect each of these shapes into the position of the first one.

- If shapes are congruent then
  - **corresponding angles** are equal
  - **corresponding sides** are equal.

example

a Tessellate three congruent rhombuses to form a hexagon.
b Explain why the hexagon is regular.

a

b The sides of a rhombus are equal and so the six sides of the hexagon are also equal.
It must be a regular hexagon.

Regular shapes have equal sides and equal angles.

example

The green triangle and the yellow triangle are congruent.
Calculate the size of the angles a, b and c.

Rotate and reflect the yellow triangle to compare the triangles.
Angle $a = 55°$
Angle $b = 70°$
Angle $c = 180° - 125° = 55°$
So angle $c = 55°$

Angles in a triangle add up to 180°.

Exercise 3e

1 These isosceles triangles are congruent.

  a Find the size of angles p, q and r.

  b Find the length of sides AC and BC.

8 cm 8 cm 55°

A B p q r C

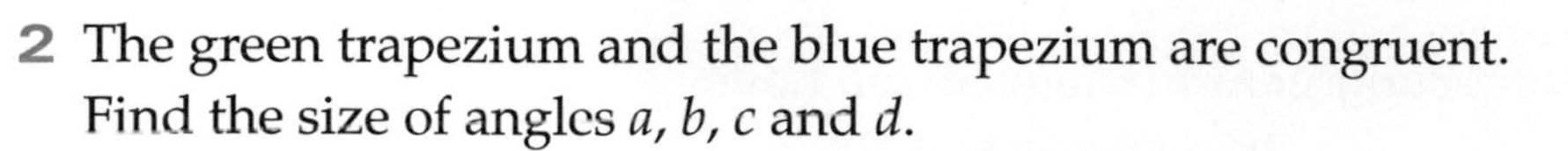

2 The green trapezium and the blue trapezium are congruent.
Find the size of angles a, b, c and d.

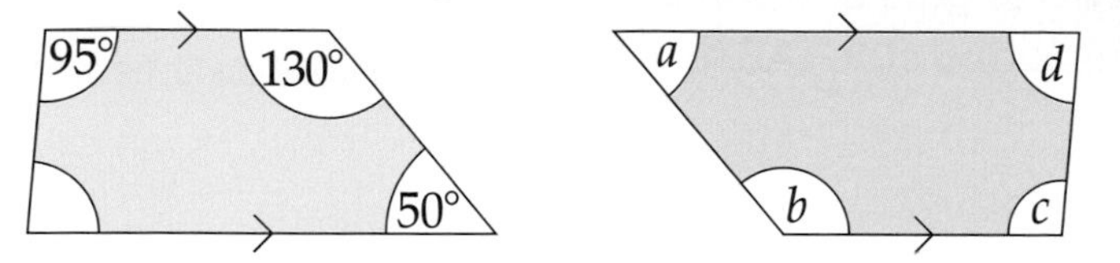

3 ABCD is an isosceles trapezium.
Which triangle is congruent to

  a AXD

  b ABD

  c ACD?

A B X D C

4 a Calculate the size of the lettered angle in each triangle.

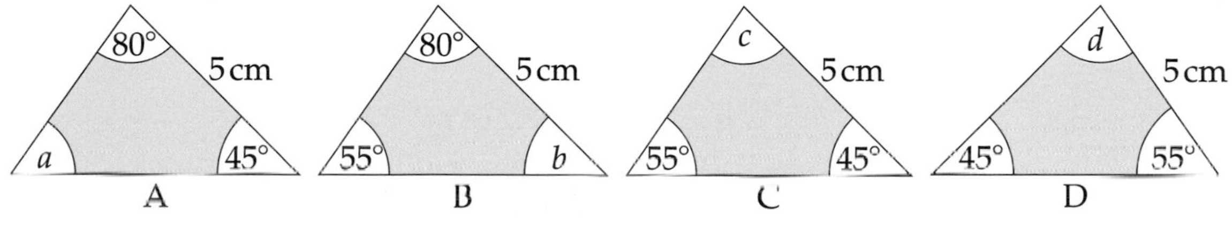

  b Which triangles are congruent to triangle A?

5 One diagonal of a parallelogram is drawn to form two congruent triangles, ABC and CDA.
Copy the diagram and mark the equal angles and the equal sides in the congruent triangles.
Explain how you know which angles and which sides are equal.

A B D C

challenge

This decagon is drawn on isometric paper.

  a Find one way to divide the decagon into four congruent pieces.

  b Find 10 different ways to divide the decagon into two congruent pieces.

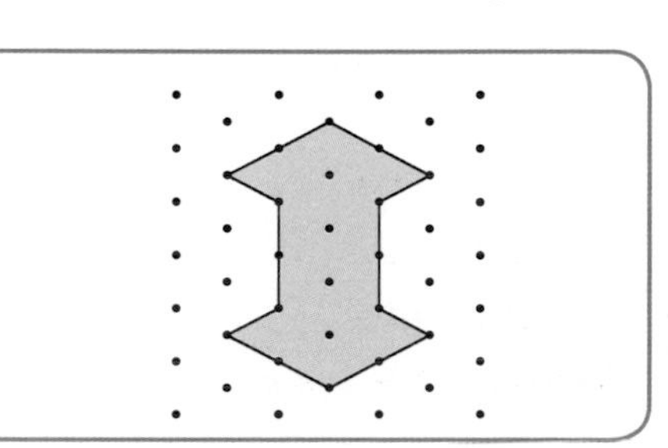

3f Constructing a triangle 1

LEVEL 6

- Use a ruler and protractor to construct triangles and quadrilaterals

Keywords
Congruent
Construct
Protractor

You can **construct** a triangle using a ruler and **protractor**.

- You will always construct **congruent** triangles if you have two sides and the included angle (SAS) or two angles and the included side (ASA).

Included means 'in between'.

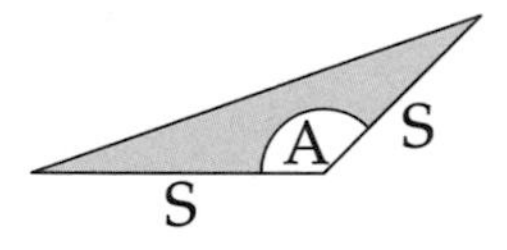

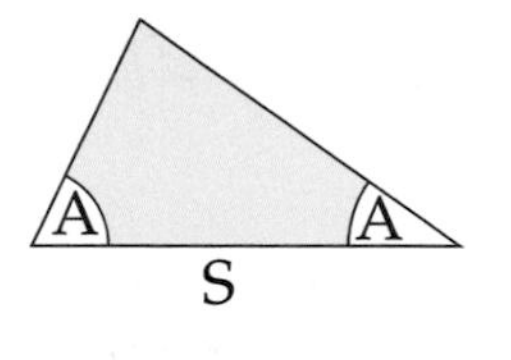

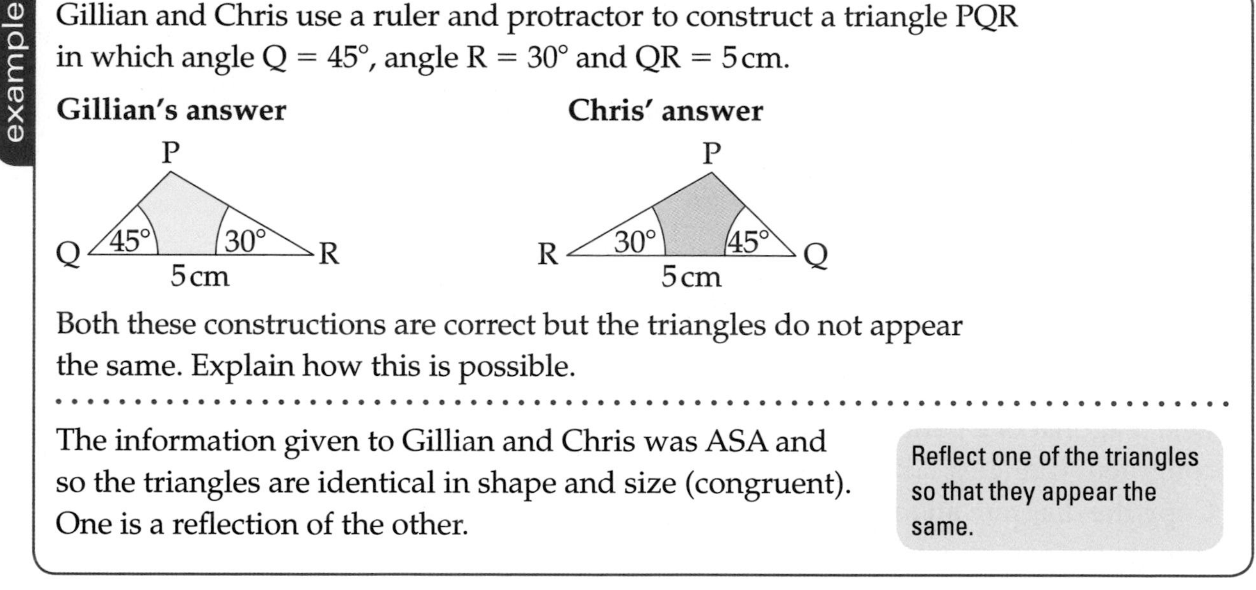

example

Gillian and Chris use a ruler and protractor to construct a triangle PQR in which angle Q = 45°, angle R = 30° and QR = 5 cm.

Gillian's answer

Chris' answer

Both these constructions are correct but the triangles do not appear the same. Explain how this is possible.

The information given to Gillian and Chris was ASA and so the triangles are identical in shape and size (congruent). One is a reflection of the other.

Reflect one of the triangles so that they appear the same.

Gillian's construction

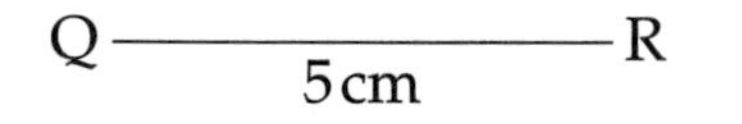

Draw a base line of 5 cm with a rule.

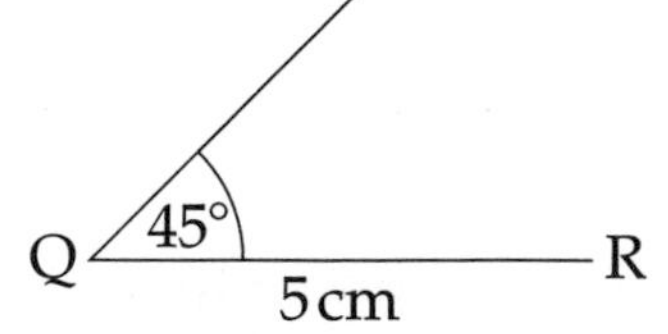

Draw an angle of 45° at Q with a protractor.

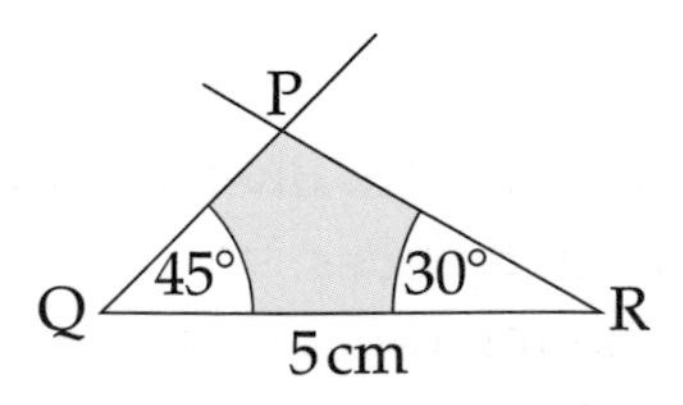

Draw an angle of 30° at R and join the lines at P.

Exercise 3f

1 Using a ruler and protractor, construct each triangle.
Give the mathematical name of each triangle.

a

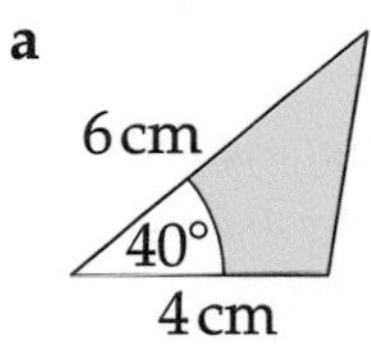

b

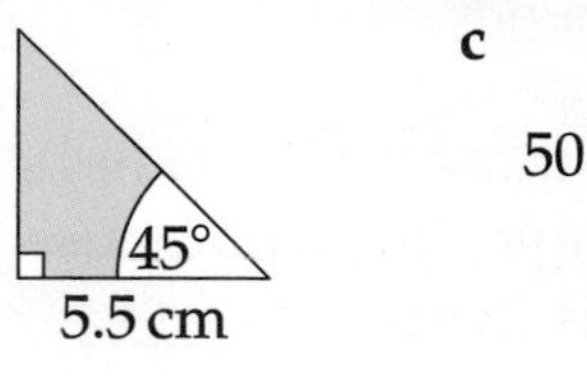

c

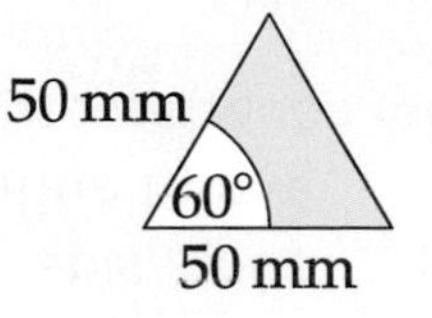

2 Draw a sketch and then construct these triangles.
Measure and calculate the perimeter of each triangle.

a AB = 6.5 cm, angle A = 40°, angle B = 45°
b QR = 6 cm, PR = 5 cm, angle R = 50°
c XY = 5 cm, angle X = 35°, angle Y = 55°

3 Construct these quadrilaterals using a ruler and protractor.
Give the mathematical name of the quadrilateral and measure the length of the unknown diagonal.

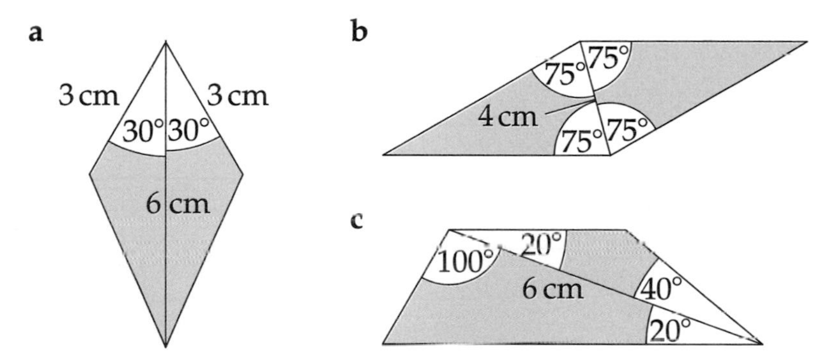

Did you know?

This impossible triangle is a famous optical illusion first published in 1958 by Roger Penrose.

Construct each triangle in turn.

4 The diagonal of a square lawn measures 8 metres.

a Construct a scale drawing of the lawn using a scale of 1 centimetre represents 1 metre.

p. 172

b What is the perimeter of the lawn?

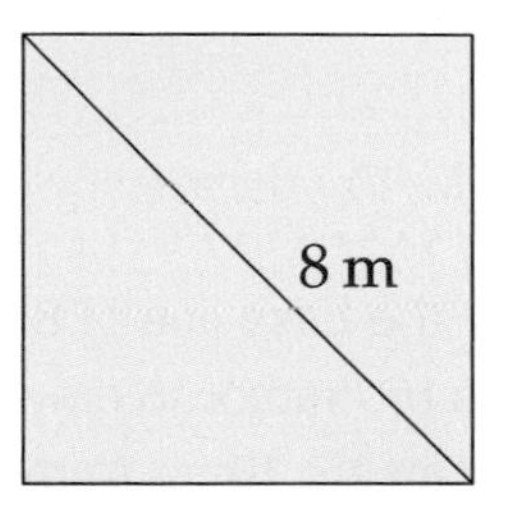

activity

a Use four of these congruent right-angled triangles to accurately construct these shapes.

i a square
ii a rectangle
iii a right-angled triangle
iv an isosceles trapezium
v a different isosceles trapezium.

b Measure the perimeter of each shape.

4 cm
2 cm

3g Constructing a triangle 2

LEVEL 6

- Use a ruler, protractor and compasses to construct triangles and quadrilaterals.

Keywords
Compasses Construct
Congruent Hypotenuse

- You will always **construct** congruent triangles if you have three sides (SSS) or a right angle, the **hypotenuse** and a side (RHS).

The hypotenuse is the longest side in a right-angled triangle.

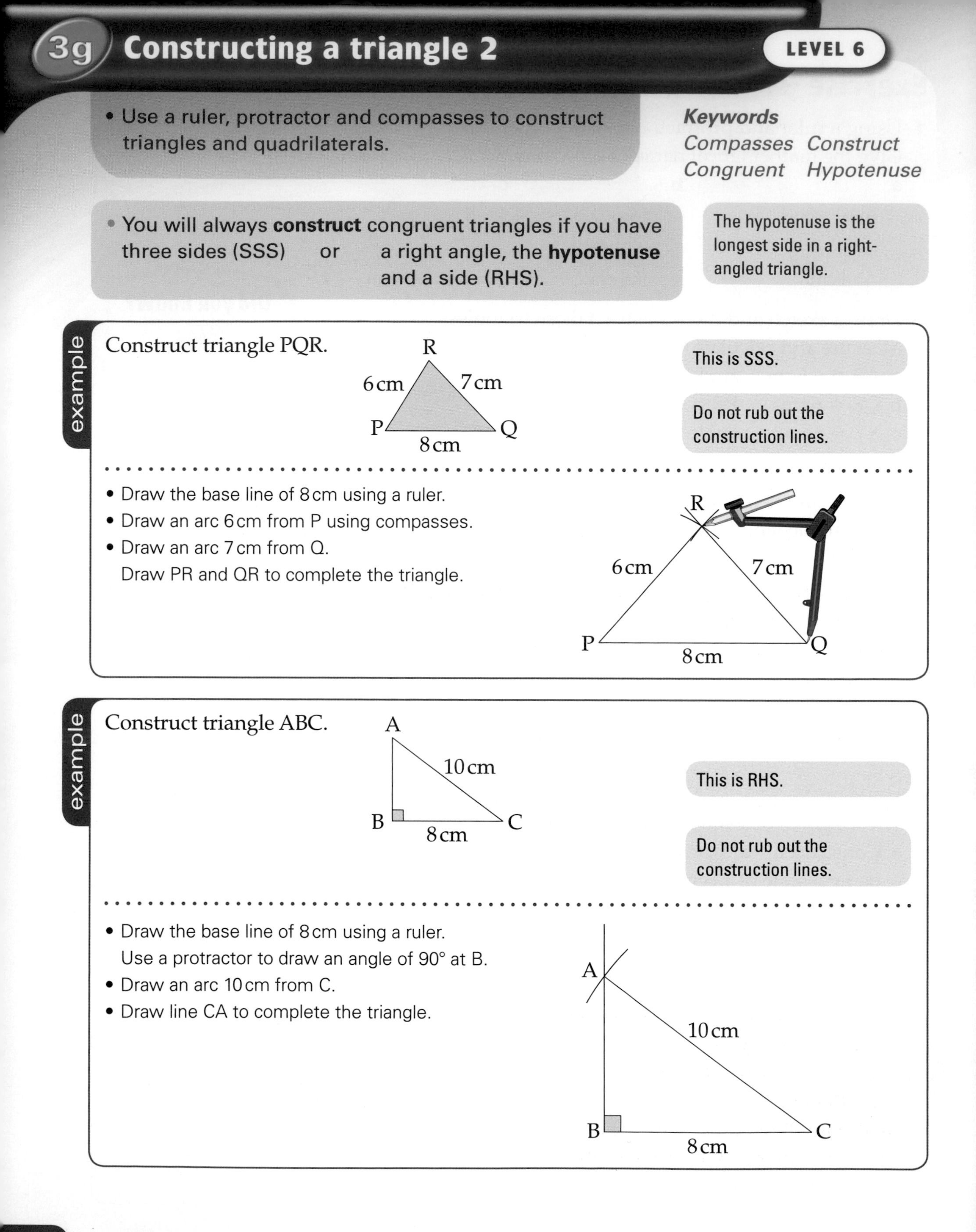

Exercise 3g

1 Construct these isosceles triangles.
Measure each angle in the triangles.

a

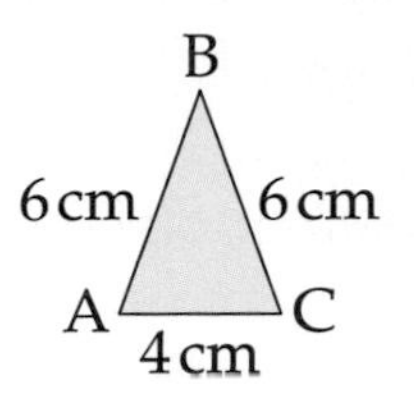

b

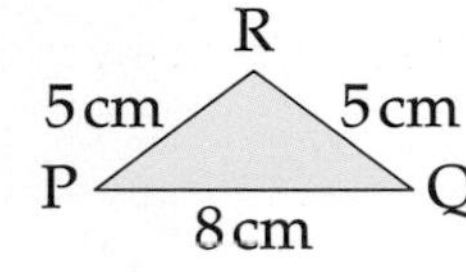

c

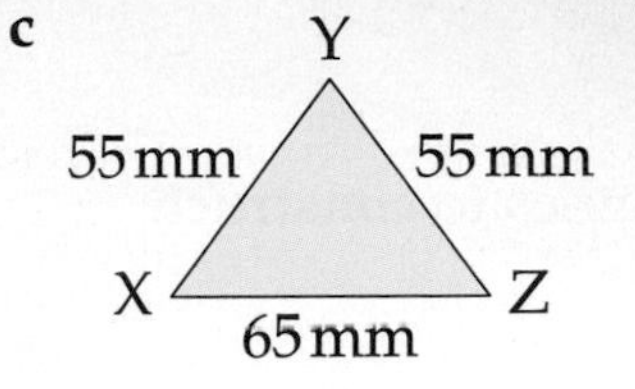

2 Construct these right-angled triangles.
Measure the perimeter of each triangle.

a

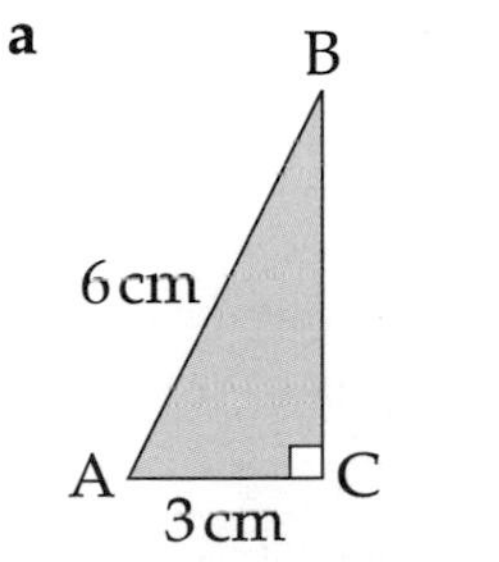

b

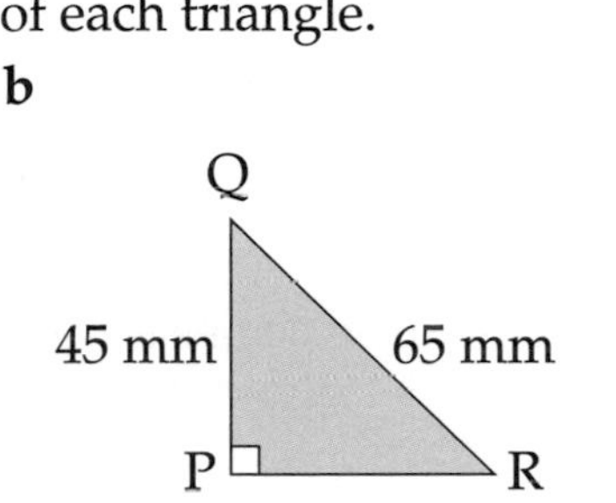

c

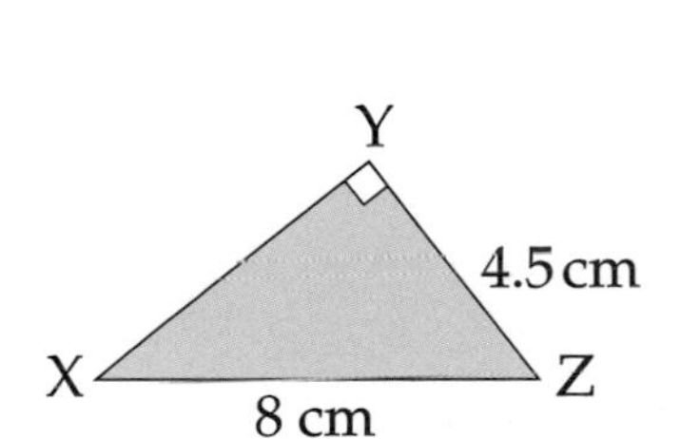

3 Two equilateral triangles of side 4 cm are joined together to form a rhombus.

a Using ruler and compasses, construct the rhombus.

b Measure the long diagonal.

c Use a protractor and ruler to check that the diagonals of a rhombus are perpendicular and bisect each other.

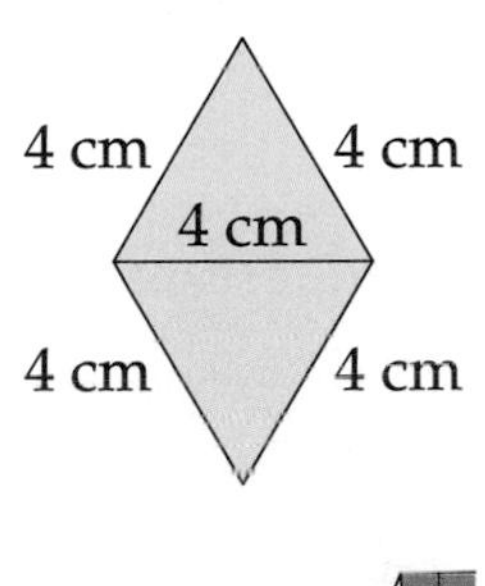

p. 172

4 A 5-metre ladder is put against a wall.
The foot of the ladder is 2 metres from the wall.

a Construct a scale drawing of the ladder using a scale of 1 centimetre represents 1 metre.

b Measure the angle between the ladder and the ground.

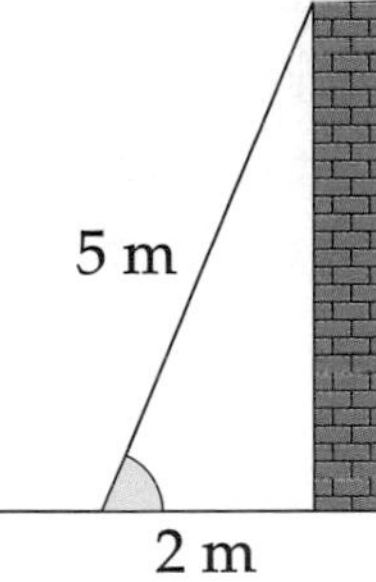

activity

Construct a triangle with sides of length 3 cm, 3.5 cm and 4 cm.
Construct congruent triangles to form a tessellation.
Use three different colours to show the angles that are equal in the tessellation.

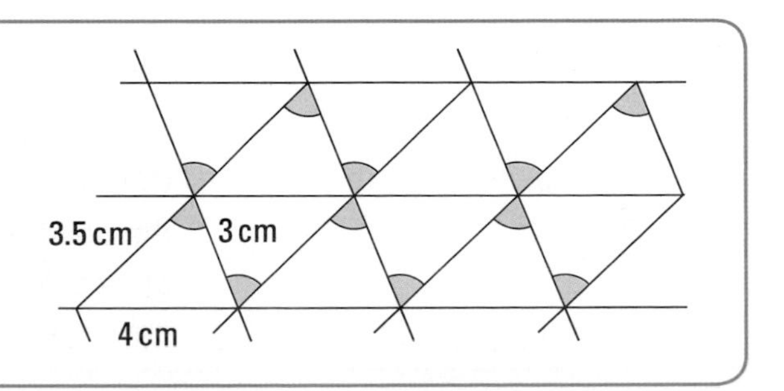

3h Loci and constructions

LEVEL 6/7

- Use a ruler and compasses to do constructions
- Find the locus of a point that moves according to a simple rule

Keywords
Angle bisector
Construct
Equidistant
Locus
Perpendicular bisector

You use compasses to **construct**:

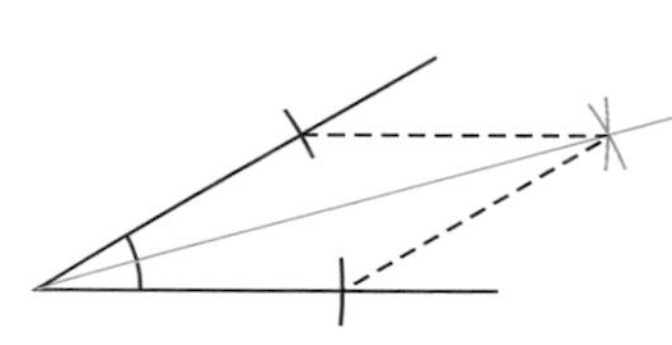

an **angle bisector**

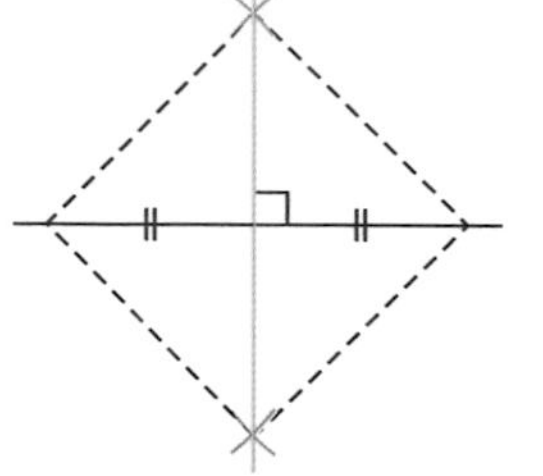

a **perpendicular bisector** of a line

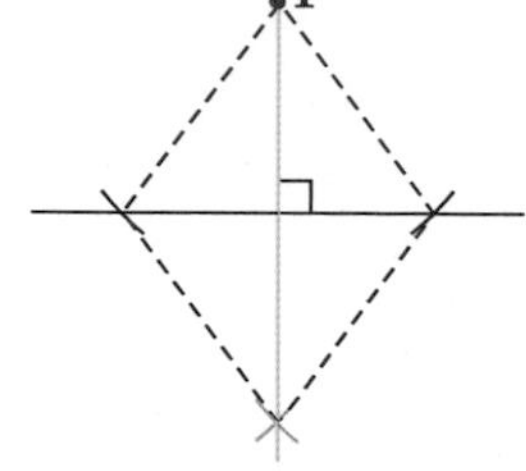

a perpendicular from a point P to a line

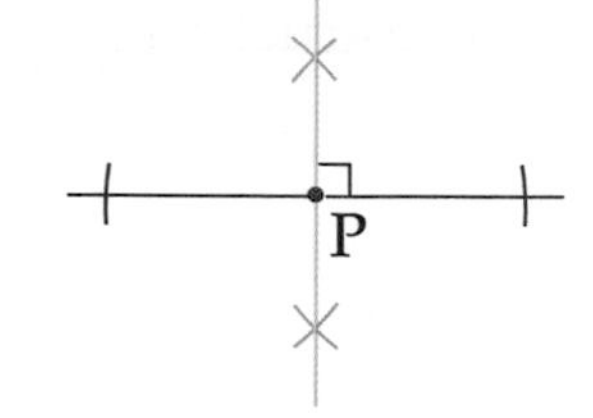

a perpendicular from a point P on a line.

- The **locus** of an object is its path.

- A point that moves according to a rule forms a locus.

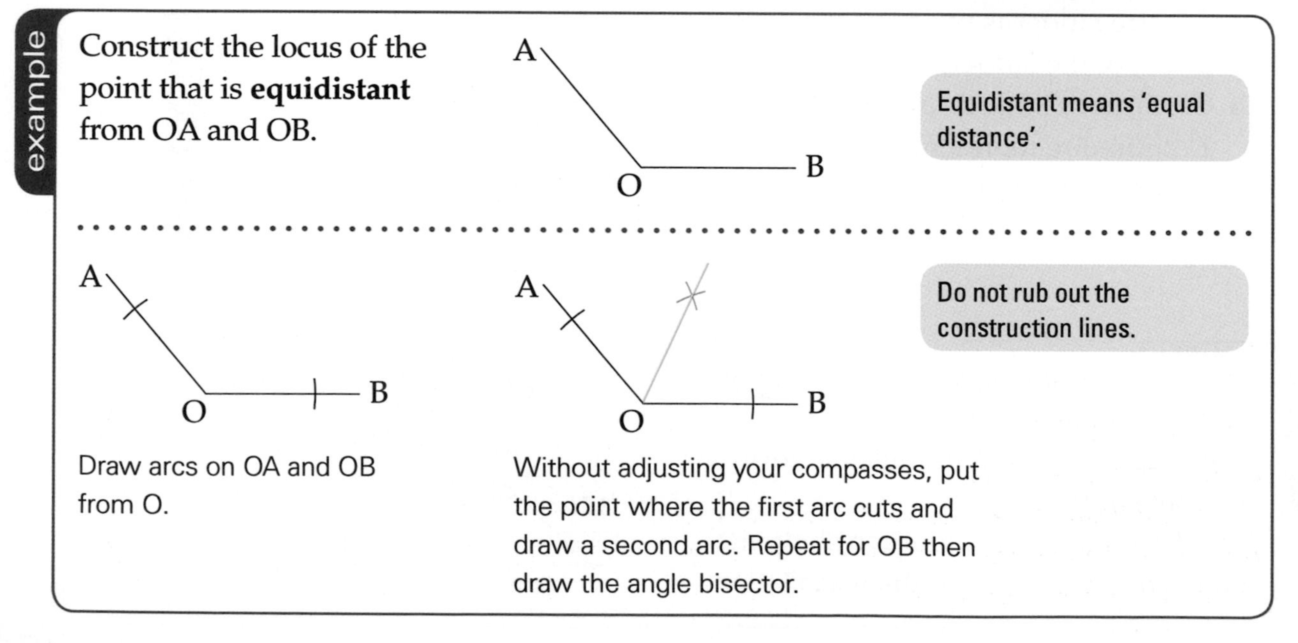

example

Construct the locus of the point that is **equidistant** from OA and OB.

Equidistant means 'equal distance'.

Draw arcs on OA and OB from O.

Without adjusting your compasses, put the point where the first arc cuts and draw a second arc. Repeat for OB then draw the angle bisector.

Do not rub out the construction lines.

LEVEL 6/7

Grade C

Exercise 3h

1 Draw a line AB of length 5 cm.
Construct the locus of a point that is equidistant from the points A and B.

2 Draw the locus of a point that is equidistant from two parallel lines 4 cm apart.

3 Construct the locus of a point that is 30 mm from a fixed point O.

Think about what shape this will make.

4 Use compasses to construct angles of

a 60° b 30°
c 120° d 90°.

An equilateral triangle has interior angles of 60°.

5 a Copy the diagram.
Construct the perpendicular
i from point P to line AB
ii from point Q on line AB.

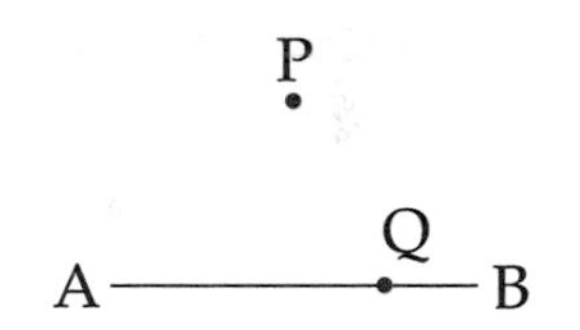

b Write a property of the two perpendicular lines you have constructed.

6 a An equilateral triangle is rolled along a straight line.
Describe the locus of the point P.

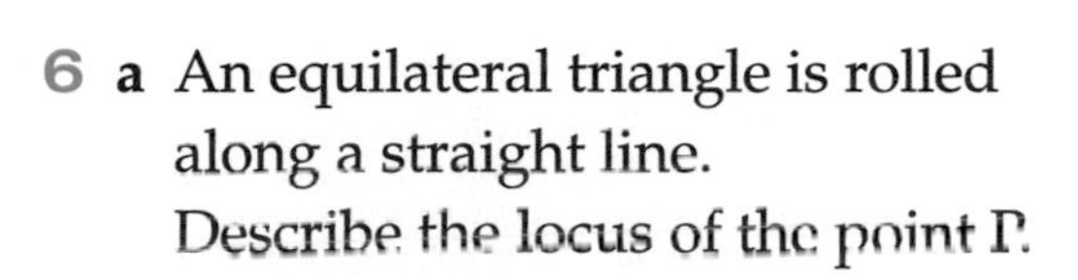

b A square is rolled along a straight line.
Describe the locus of the point Q.

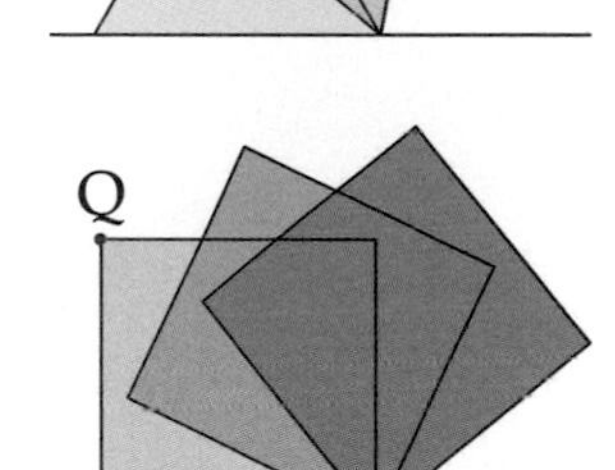

challenge

a Draw two circles with the same radius.
b Draw a line AC joining their centres.
c Draw the line BD.
d BD intersects AC at X.
Are triangles ABX and CBX congruent?
e Use this information to show that BD is the perpendicular bisector of AC.

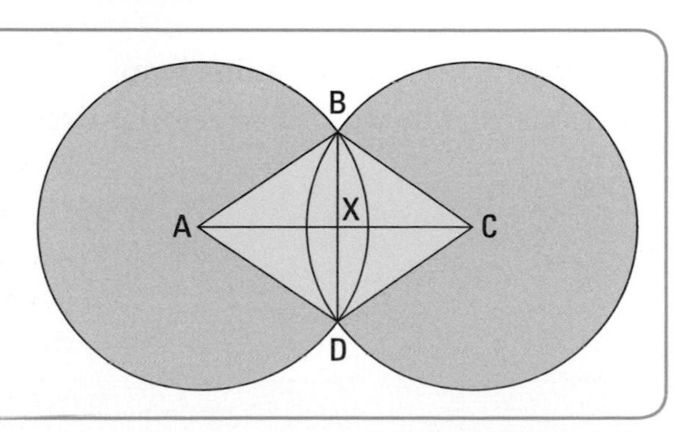

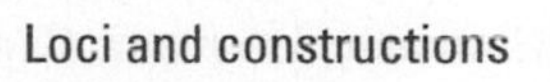

3 Consolidation

3a

1 Calculate the value of the unknown angles.

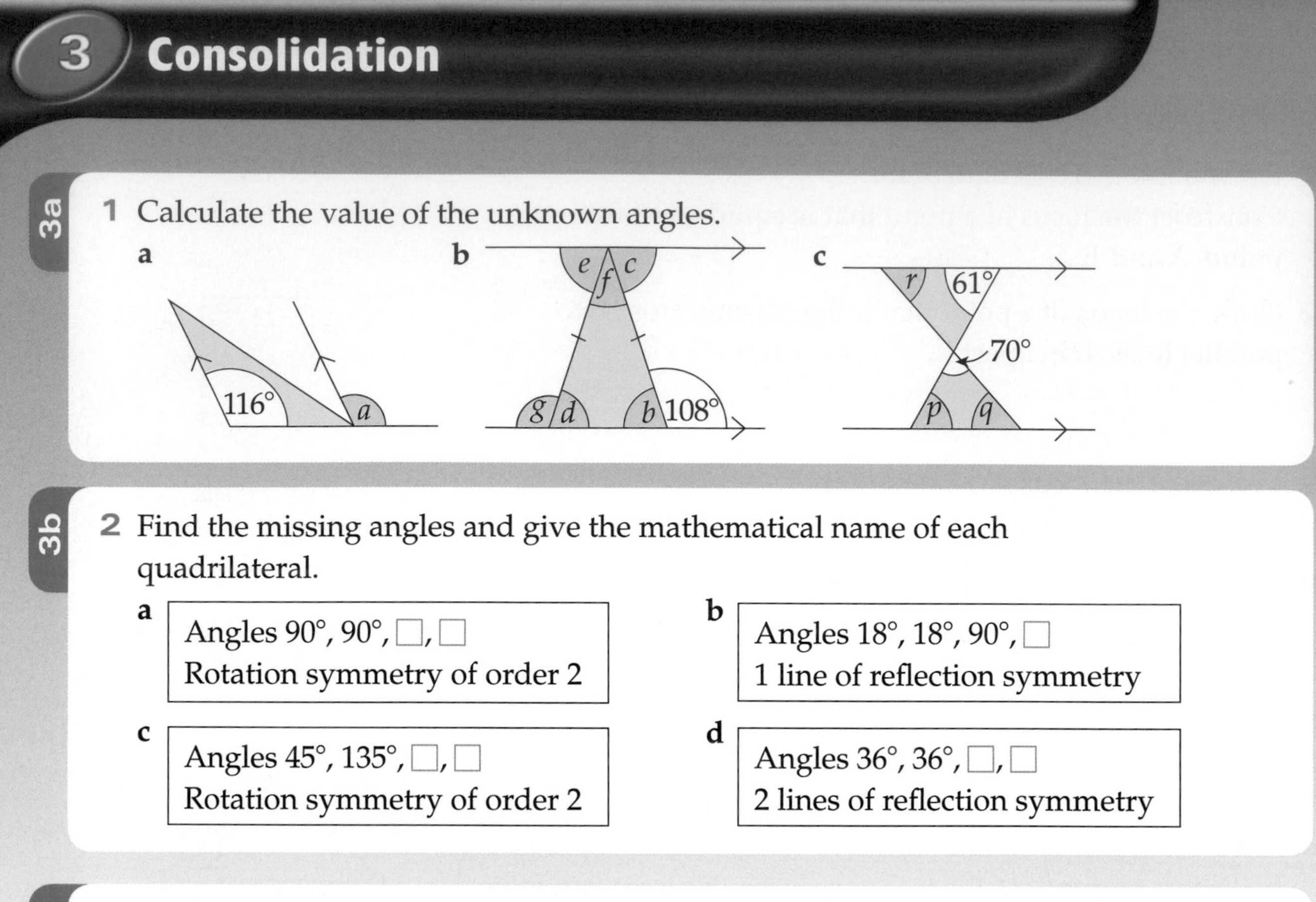

3b

2 Find the missing angles and give the mathematical name of each quadrilateral.

a Angles 90°, 90°, □, □
Rotation symmetry of order 2

b Angles 18°, 18°, 90°, □
1 line of reflection symmetry

c Angles 45°, 135°, □, □
Rotation symmetry of order 2

d Angles 36°, 36°, □, □
2 lines of reflection symmetry

3c

3 The diagram shows a regular nonagon.

a Calculate the values of a, b and c.

b Hence find the interior angle of a regular nonagon.

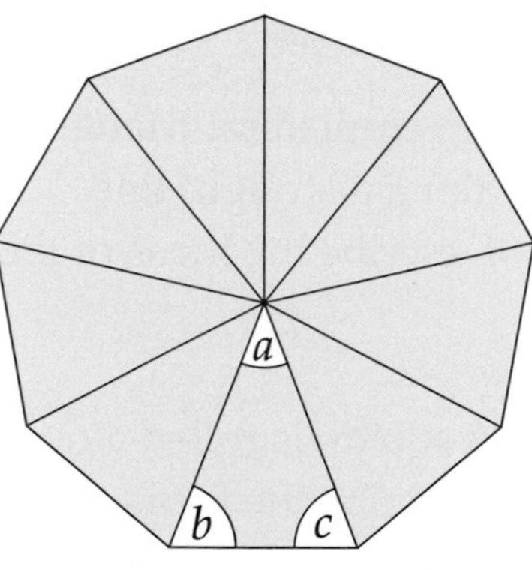

3d

4 An inscribed polygon is the largest polygon that fits inside a circle.

a Draw a circle with radius 5 cm

b Construct the inscribed regular decagon.

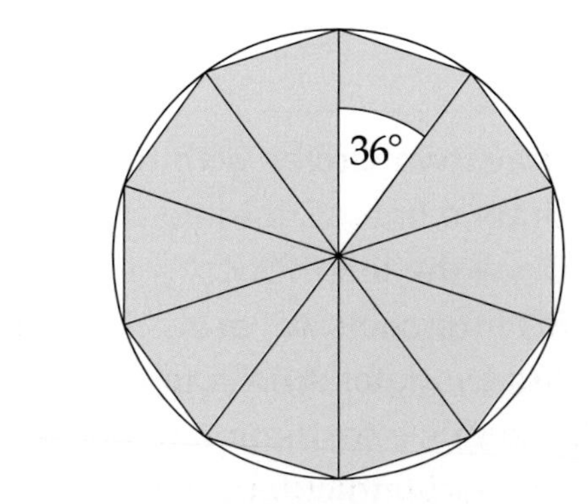

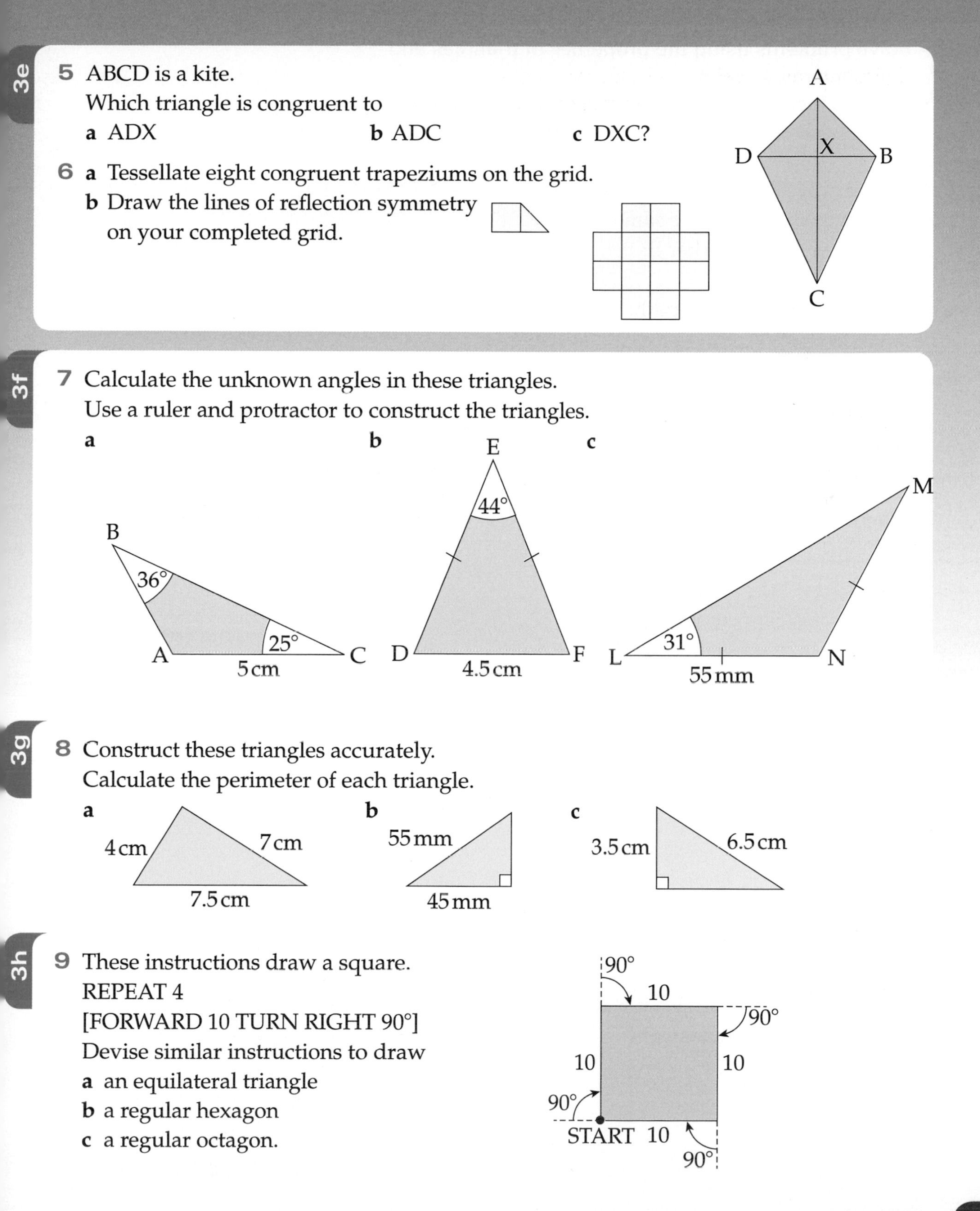

5 ABCD is a kite.
Which triangle is congruent to

a ADX **b** ADC **c** DXC?

6 **a** Tessellate eight congruent trapeziums on the grid.
b Draw the lines of reflection symmetry on your completed grid.

7 Calculate the unknown angles in these triangles.
Use a ruler and protractor to construct the triangles.

a **b** **c**

8 Construct these triangles accurately.
Calculate the perimeter of each triangle.

a **b** **c**

9 These instructions draw a square.
REPEAT 4
[FORWARD 10 TURN RIGHT 90°]
Devise similar instructions to draw

a an equilateral triangle
b a regular hexagon
c a regular octagon.

3 Summary

Assessment criteria

- Solve problems using the properties of triangles and quadrilaterals **Level 6**
- Find the locus of a point that moves according to a given rule **Level 7**

Level 6

1 Tony can only ski in a straight line.
He wants to ski exactly the same distance from marker A and marker B.

Marker A ×   × Marker B

Construct the locus of his path.

Ashvik's answer ✔

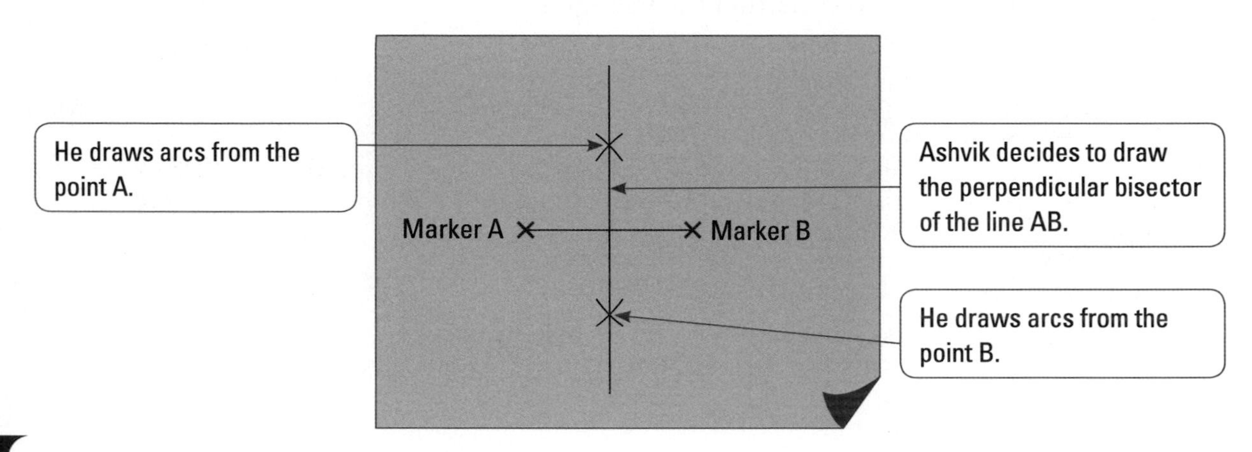

Level 6

2 Look at triangle ABC.
ABD is an isosceles triangle where AB = AD.

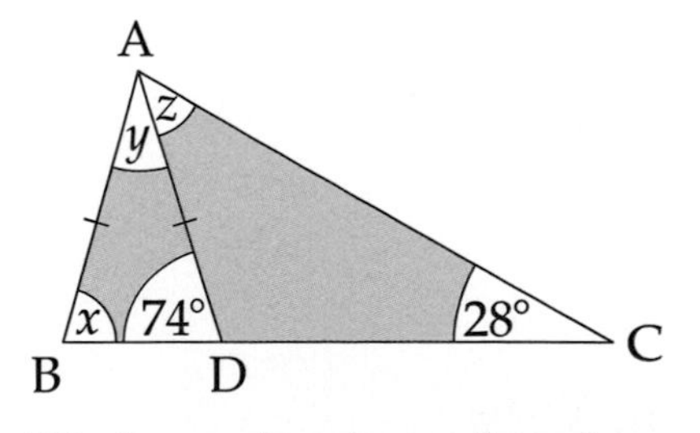

Not drawn accurately

Work out the sizes of angles x, y and z
Give reasons for your answers.

Key Stage 3 2008 5–7 Paper 2

4 Algebra

Equations

Structural engineers use equations to design buildings. Every force, angle and length must be calculated so that the structure is sturdy. Skyscrapers, for example, must be designed to withstand wind and earthquakes, be able to support their own weight, protect those inside from fire and still be economical to build.

What's the point? Some of the most famous skyscrapers in the world, such as the Burj Al Arab in Dubai, the Empire State Building in New York or the Space Needle in Seattle, wouldn't exist without the use of equations to design them.

Check in

Level 4

1 Copy and complete these.

a $3 + 3 + 3 + 3 + 3$ is written as $5 \times \square$.

b $3 \times 3 \times 3 \times 3 \times 3$ is written as $3^{\square}$.

2 Copy and complete these.

a $\square \times \square \times \square = 27$ **b** $\square^2 = 9$

Use the same number in all three boxes in part **a**.

Level 5

3 Use inverse operations to find the numbers that go in the boxes.

a $\square + 4 = 12$ **b** $\square - 4 = 12$

c $4 \times \square = 12$ **d** $\square \div 4 = 12$

4 Simplify these by collecting like terms.

a $3x + 2y + 4x + 5y + x$

b $9x + 3y - x + 6y - 2x$

5 **a** Work out $3(6 - 5) + 2(8 - 3)$.

b Simplify $2(3x + 5) + 5(x + 3)$.

Algebraic language

- Recognise and use the difference between a formula, a function, an equation and an identity.

Keywords
Equation Function
Expression Identity
Formula Substitute

- You can find the value of a **formula** by **substituting** a number for each letter in the formula

The cost £P of a train journey depends on the number of adults a and the number of children c in the group.

$P = 12a + 7c$

For three adults and four children,

$P = 12 \times 3 + 7 \times 4$

$= 36 + 28 = £64$

Substitute 3 for a and 4 for c.

- A **function** is like a formula but usually shows how two quantities relate to each other.

If $y = 3x - 1$, when $x = 2$, $y = 3 \times 2 - 1 = 6 - 1 = 5$,
when $x = 3$, $y = 3 \times 3 - 1 = 9 - 1 = 8, \ldots$

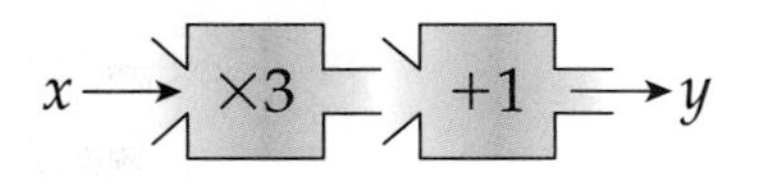

- An **equation** is a balance of two **expressions** that are equal for one particular value of the letter.

To find the value of x on this balance, write an equation for the boxes and weights on each side.

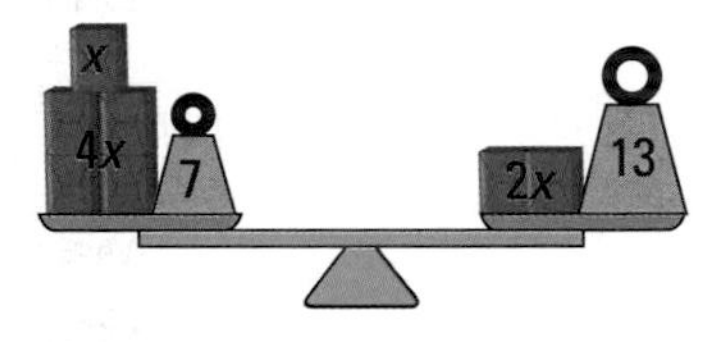

	$4x + x + 7 = 2x + 13$
Simplify the left-hand side.	$5x + 7 = 2x + 13$
Subtract $2x$ from both sides.	$3x + 7 = 13$
Subtract 7 from both sides.	$3x = 6$
Divide both sides by 3.	$x = 2$

- **Identities** have two expressions that are equal to each other no matter what the value of x.

example

Show that $3(x + 2) + 4x - 1 \equiv 2(2x - 3) + 3x + 11$ is an identity.

= means 'is equal to' and ≡ means 'is identical to'.

Simplify the left-hand side. $3(x + 2) + 4x - 1 \equiv 3x + 6 + 4x - 1$
$\equiv 7x + 5$

Simplify the right-hand side. $2(2x - 3) + 3x + 11 \equiv 4x - 6 + 3x + 11$
$\equiv 7x + 5$

Both expressions are equal to $7x + 5$, so it is an identity.

LEVEL 6

Grade D

Exercise 4a

1 Decide if each of these is a formula, a function, an equation or an identity.

a A rectangle has length l and a width w.
Its perimeter P is given by $P = 2l + 2w$.

b The instructions 'double and add 5' can be written as
$y = 2x + 5$, where x is the input and y is the output.

c If I cycle for c hours and walk for w hours, then I cover a distance, d miles, where $d = 8c + 2w$.

d Each box weighs x kg.
If three boxes balance two boxes and 5 kg, then $3x = 2x + 5$.

e The expression $4x + 2x + 3x + 6$ and the expression $9x + 8 - 2$ are related by $4x + 2x + 3x + 6 \equiv 9x + 8 - 2$.

l

w

x x x

x x 5

2 Use question **1** to work out these.

a Using part **a**, find P when $l = 5$ and $w = 2$.

b Using part **b**, find the output, y, when $x = 2\frac{1}{2}$.

c Using part **c**, find d when $c = 2$ and $w = 3$.

d Using part **d**, find the value of x.

e Explain why it is correct to use the symbol $\equiv$ in part **e**.

3 Match the words in the box with the descriptions **a** to **d**.

Equation	Formula
Function	Identity

a A taxi fare £F for m miles is $F = 2 + 4m$.

b You can find the solution to $2x + 4 = 10$.

c You can simplify $3x + 4 + 5x - 1$.

d The graph of $y = 2x + 3$ contains the point (5, 13).

4 Would you use a formula, a function, an equation or an identity to find,

a The time to cook a turkey when you know its mass

b The points on the straight line $y = 3x - 1$ where $x = 2$ and $x = 5$

c A simpler way of writing $4x + 2x + 5 - 3x + 6$

d The value of x when $3x + 1 = x + 9$?

5 a Substitute $z = 5$ into $P = 2(z^2 + 1)$ to find P.

b Solve the equation $3x + 4 = 2x + 10$

c Use this function machine to find y when $x = 4$

x → ×3 → Subtract from 50 → y

d Simplify $4(2x - 3) + 2(3 - x)$

challenge

Invent three formulae, three equations, three functions and three identities of your own.
Say which are which.

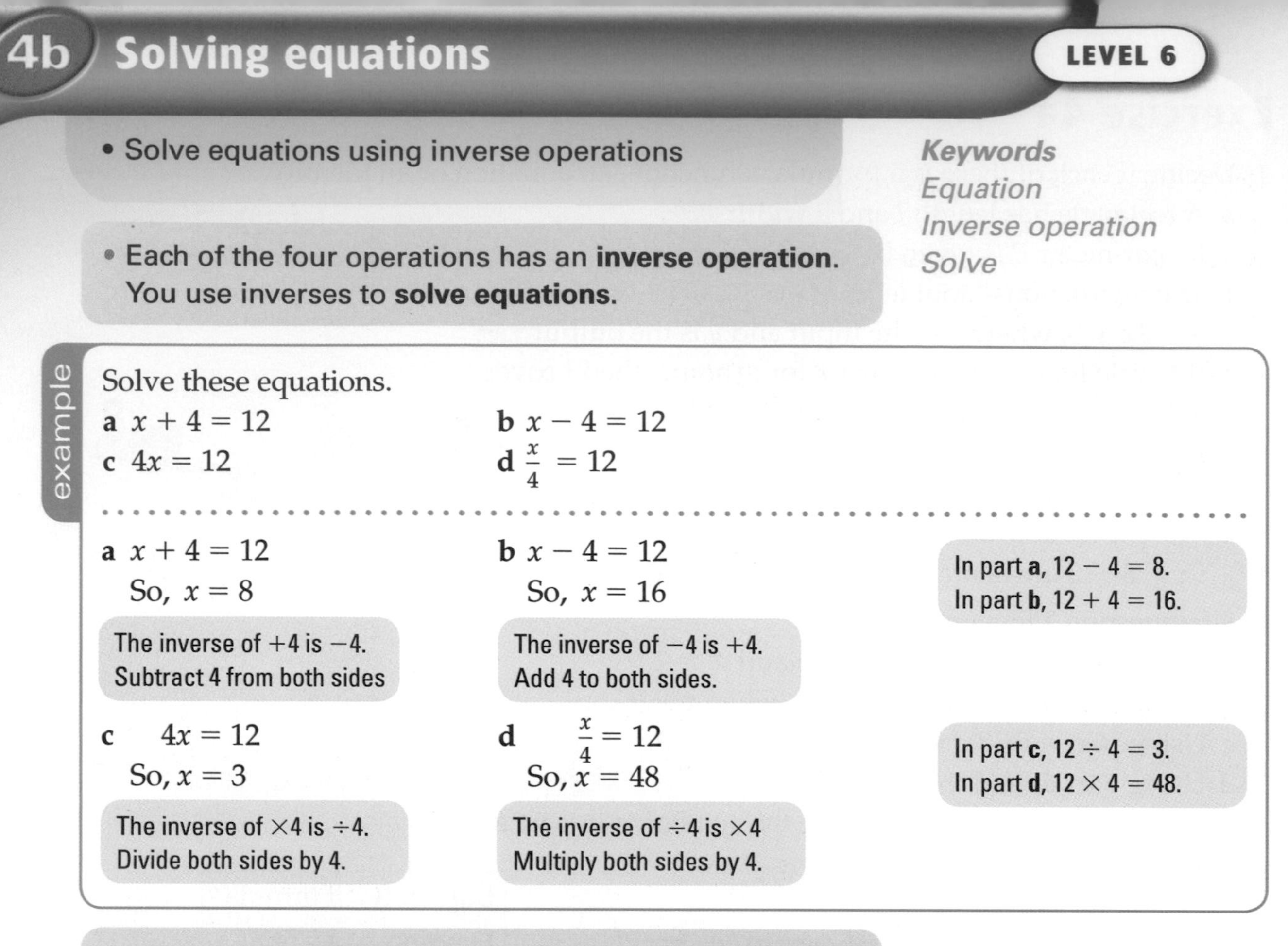

4b Solving equations

LEVEL 6

- Solve equations using inverse operations

Keywords
Equation
Inverse operation
Solve

- Each of the four operations has an **inverse operation**. You use inverses to **solve equations.**

example

Solve these equations.

a $x + 4 = 12$ **b** $x - 4 = 12$

c $4x = 12$ **d** $\frac{x}{4} = 12$

a $x + 4 = 12$

So, $x = 8$

The inverse of +4 is −4.
Subtract 4 from both sides

b $x - 4 = 12$

So, $x = 16$

The inverse of −4 is +4.
Add 4 to both sides.

In part **a**, $12 - 4 = 8$.
In part **b**, $12 + 4 = 16$.

c $4x = 12$

So, $x = 3$

The inverse of ×4 is ÷4.
Divide both sides by 4.

d $\frac{x}{4} = 12$

So, $x = 48$

The inverse of ÷4 is ×4
Multiply both sides by 4.

In part **c**, $12 \div 4 = 3$.
In part **d**, $12 \times 4 = 48$.

- To solve some equations you use more than one inverse operation.

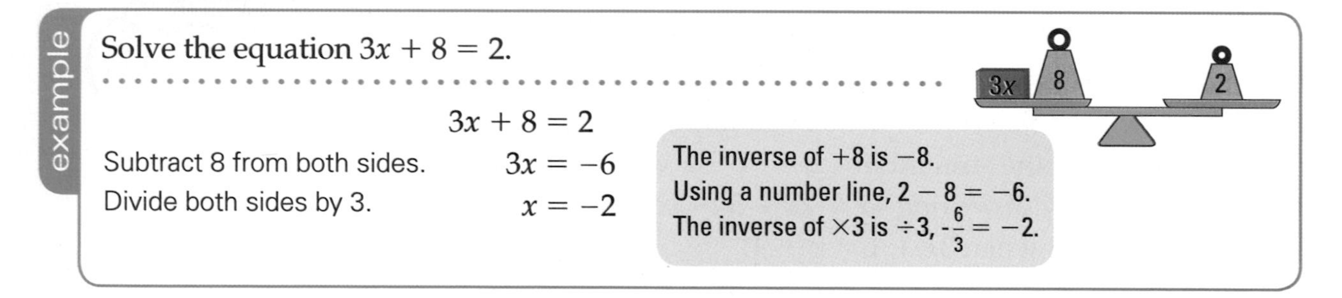

example

Solve the equation $3x + 8 = 2$.

$$3x + 8 = 2$$

Subtract 8 from both sides. $3x = -6$

Divide both sides by 3. $x = -2$

The inverse of +8 is −8.
Using a number line, $2 - 8 = -6$.
The inverse of ×3 is ÷3, $-\frac{6}{3} = -2$.

- An equation can have unknowns on the right-hand side.

example

Solve the equation $23 = 5x - 7$.

Re-write the equation. $5x - 7 = 23$

Add 7 to both sides. $5x = 30$

Divide both sides by 5. $x = 6$

The inverse of −7 is +7;
$23 + 7 = 30$.
The inverse of ×5 is ÷5;
$\frac{30}{5} = 6$.

Exercise 4b

1 Solve these equations using inverse operations.

a $x + 4 = 9$ **b** $x - 4 = 9$ **c** $x + 3 = 4$

d $2x = 10$ **e** $\frac{x}{2} = 10$ **f** $3x = 15$

g $\frac{x}{3} = 2$ **h** $x - 7 = 1$ **i** $x + 4 = 1$

2 Find the value of x in each of these balances.

a

b

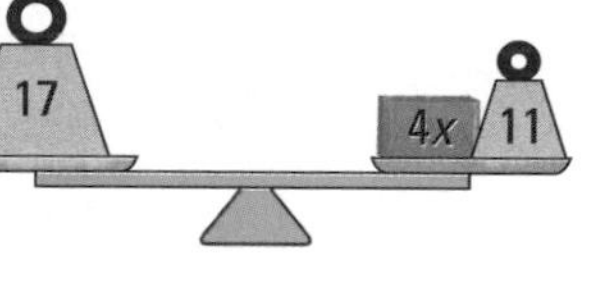

3 Solve these equations. Each solution takes two steps.

a $2x + 1 = 15$ **b** $2x - 1 = 15$ **c** $3x + 6 = 21$

d $3x - 6 = 21$ **e** $4x + 5 = 17$ **f** $6x + 7 = 7$

g $2x + 5 = 8$ **h** $2x - 1 = 10$ **i** $6 = 4x - 3$

j $40 = 7x + 5$ **k** $2 = 4x + 8$ **l** $1 = 6x + 4$

4 Solve these equations. Some solutions are negative.

a $5x - 2 = 33$ **b** $2x + 6 = 2$ **c** $4x + 10 = 2$

d $3x - 9 = 0$ **e** $16 = 3x + 1$ **f** $13 = 2x + 15$

g $12 = 2x + 11$ **h** $3 = 4x + 9$ **i** $2x - 1 = -5$

j $3x - 2 = -5$ **k** $2x + 7 = -1$ **l** $4x + 3 = -6$

5 Solve these equations. You need to use a mixture of methods.

a $6x + 5 = 5$ **b** $2x - 16 = 1$ **c** $4x - 3 = 7$

d $\frac{x}{2} + 3 = 8$ **e** $\frac{x + 3}{2} = 8$ **f** $\frac{x}{4} - 1 = 2$

g $\frac{x - 1}{4} = 2$ **h** $10 = 3x + 2$ **i** $5 = 9 + 2x$

j $5x - 1 = -11$ **k** $4 = 12 + 2x$ **l** $3 - x = 2$

6 Jon has 5 boxes with x mints in each. Sara has 3 of these boxes and 12 loose mints. Find the value of x if they have equal numbers of mints.

Did you know?

The Ahmes (Rhind) papyrus shows how Egyptian students learnt to solve linear equations, such as $x + \frac{1}{7}x = 19$, almost 4000 years ago!

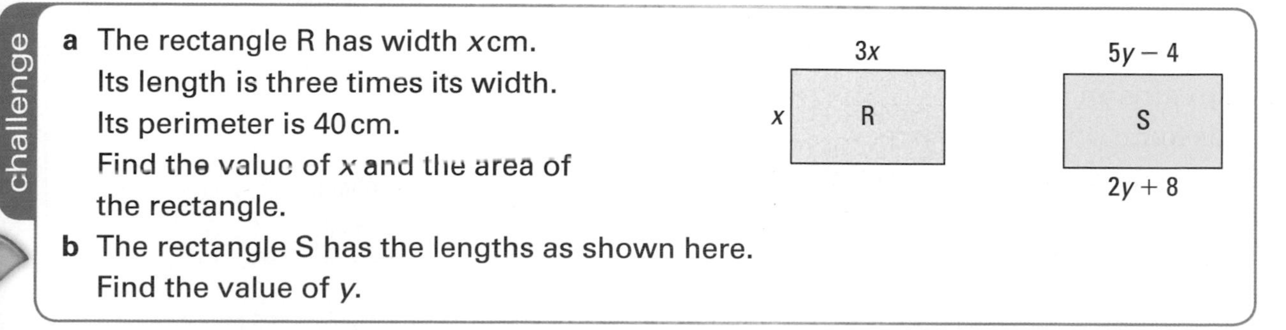

challenge

a The rectangle R has width x cm.
Its length is three times its width.
Its perimeter is 40 cm.
Find the value of x and the area of the rectangle.

b The rectangle S has the lengths as shown here.
Find the value of y.

4c Equations with brackets

LEVEL 6

- Solve equations which have brackets
- Solve equations using directed numbers

Keywords
Brackets
Expand
Like terms

- Equations can use **brackets**.

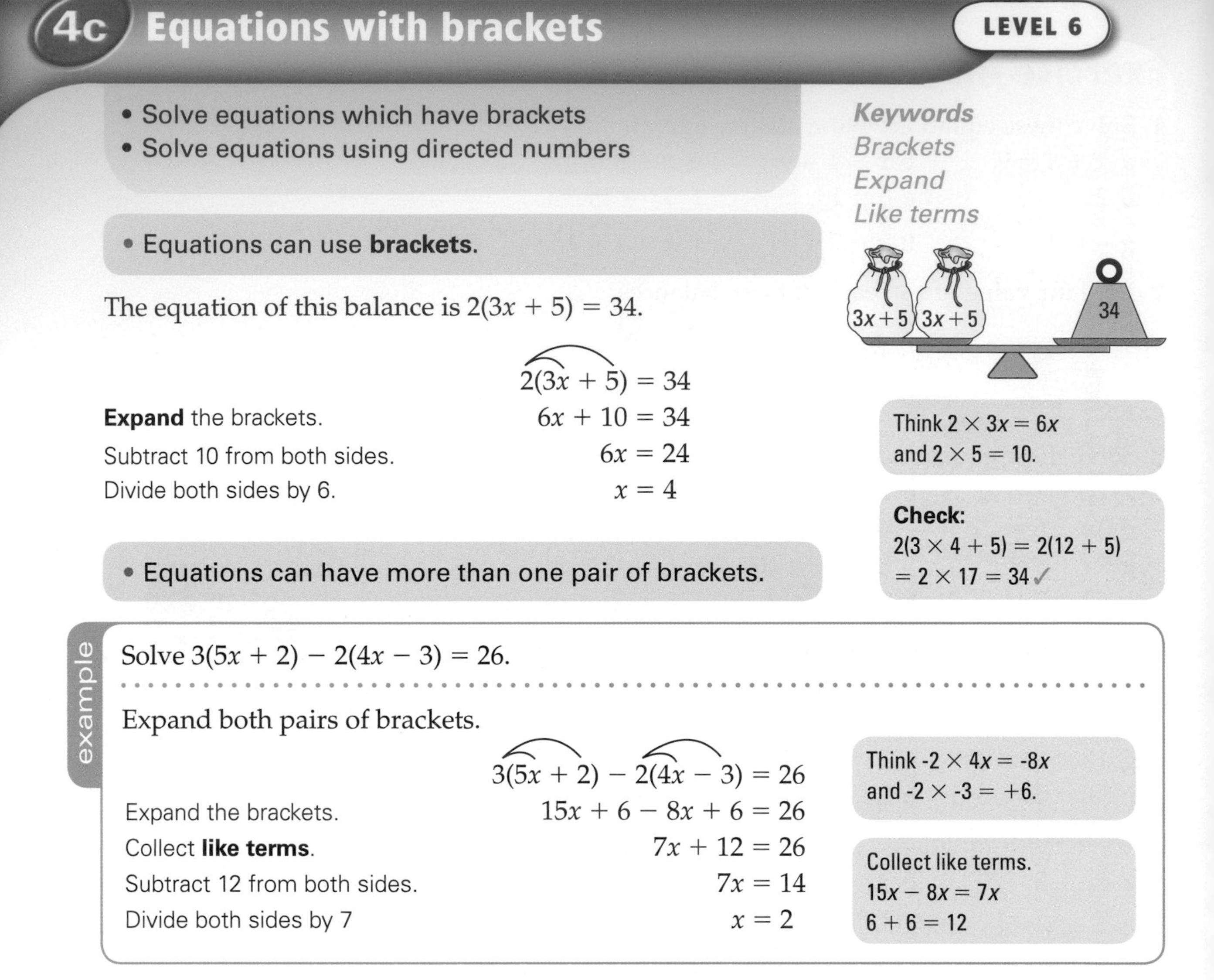

The equation of this balance is $2(3x + 5) = 34$.

	$2(3x + 5) = 34$
Expand the brackets.	$6x + 10 = 34$
Subtract 10 from both sides.	$6x = 24$
Divide both sides by 6.	$x = 4$

Think $2 \times 3x = 6x$ and $2 \times 5 = 10$.

Check:
$2(3 \times 4 + 5) = 2(12 + 5)$
$= 2 \times 17 = 34$ ✓

- Equations can have more than one pair of brackets.

example

Solve $3(5x + 2) - 2(4x - 3) = 26$.

Expand both pairs of brackets.

	$3(5x + 2) - 2(4x - 3) = 26$
Expand the brackets.	$15x + 6 - 8x + 6 = 26$
Collect **like terms**.	$7x + 12 = 26$
Subtract 12 from both sides.	$7x = 14$
Divide both sides by 7	$x = 2$

Think $-2 \times 4x = -8x$ and $-2 \times -3 = +6$.

Collect like terms.
$15x - 8x = 7x$
$6 + 6 = 12$

- You can solve problems using equations and brackets.

example

John has £x. He earns £3.
His mum doubles his money.
He then spends £x and has £20 left.
How much did he have to start with?

He earns an extra £3.	$x + 3$
His mum doubles his money.	$2(x + 3)$
He then spends £x and has £20 left.	$2(x + 3) - x = 20$
Expand the brackets.	$2x + 6 - x = 20$
Collect like terms.	$x + 6 = 20$
Subtract 6 from both sides.	$x = 14$

He had £14 to start with.

Check:
$14 + 3 = 17$
$2 \times 17 = 34$
$34 - 14 = 20$
There is £20 left. ✓

LEVEL 6

Grade D

Exercise 4c

1 Find the value of x in each balance.

a

b

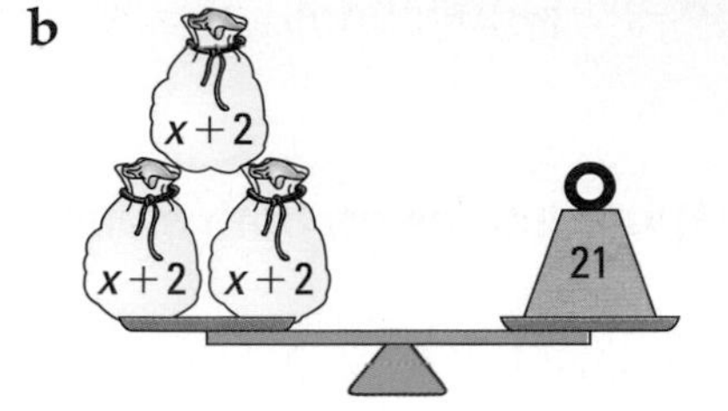

2 Solve these equations.

a $2(3x + 2) = 16$ **b** $4(2x + 3) = 28$ **c** $3(2x - 3) = 15$

d $5(x - 2) = 30$ **e** $2(6x - 7) = 10$ **f** $\frac{1}{2}(4x + 6) = 13$

g $20 = 4(2x + 3)$ **h** $12 = 3(5x - 6)$ **i** $7 = \frac{1}{4}(8x - 12)$

3 Solve these equations. You will need to collect like terms.

a $4(2x + 1) + 3(3x + 2) = 44$ **b** $2(5x + 2) + 5(x + 2) = 29$

c $3(4x + 3) + 4(2x - 2) = 1$ **d** $6(2 + x) + 2(1 - 2x) = 20$

e $5(2x - 3) + 4(5 - 2x) = 9$ **f** $4(3 - 2x) + 9x - 15 = 0$

g $(8x - 6) + 7 - 2x = 12$ **h** $(9x + 12) - 2(x + 3) = 6$

4 Solve these equations. Some answers are negative.

a $2(2x - 4) = 4$ **b** $2(2x + 4) = 4$

c $3(3x - 5) = 12$ **d** $4(3x + 6) = 12$

e $5(2x + 3) - 8x = 11$ **f** $2(7 + 5x) - 6x = 2$

g $5x + 3(2x - 9) = 17$ **h** $9x + 4(2 - 2x) = 5$

i $4(1 - x) + 7x = 4$

5 Solve these equations. Remember how to multiply positive and negative numbers.

a $3(3x + 2) + 4(2x + 2) = 48$ **b** $4(2x + 3) + 3(2x - 3) = 17$

c $5(2x - 1) + 2(3x + 4) = 51$ **d** $4(3x - 5) + 3(2 - 3x) = 1$

e $3(5x + 2) - 2(3x - 2) = 19$ **f** $6(3x - 2) - 2(2x - 5) = 26$

g $8(3 - 2x) + 20x - 9 = 31$ **h** $5x - 2 - 3(6 - 2x) = 2$

i $2(2x - 5) - 3(4 + 6x) = 6$ **j** $\frac{1}{2}(4 - 6x) - 2(\frac{1}{2}x - 4) = 26$

challenge

Mayah has £x and she spends £5.
She trebles how much she has left with a gift from her grandma.
She then spends another £5 and has £13 left.
Write an equation and find the value of x.
How much did her grandma give her?

4d More equations

LEVEL 6

- Solve equations which have unknowns on both sides
- Solve equations involving fractions

Keywords
Fractional
LHS (left-hand side)
RHS (right-hand side)
Unknown

- Equations can have **unknowns** on both sides.

The equation for this balance is $8x + 2 = 3x + 12$.

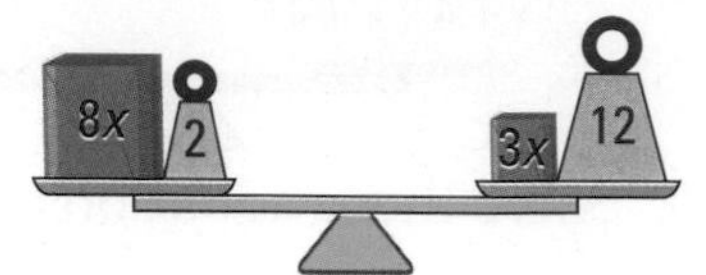

Subtract $3x$ from both sides.	$5x + 2 = 12$
Subtract 2 from both sides.	$5x = 10$
Divide both sides by 5.	$x = 2$

Check:
LHS $= 8 \times 2 + 2$
$= 16 + 2 = 18$
RHS $= 3 \times 2 + 12$
$= 6 + 12 = 18$ ✓

- Equations can have **fractional** answers.

- Equations can involve fractions of expressions.

example

Solve these equations.

a $7x - 2 = 4x + 5$

b $\frac{1}{3}(7x - 1) = 2x + 3$

a $7x - 2 = 4x + 5$

Subtract $4x$ from both sides.	$3x - 2 = 5$
Add 2 to both sides.	$3x = 7$
Divide both sides by 3.	$x = 2\frac{1}{3}$

b $\frac{1}{3}(7x - 1) = 2x + 3$

Multiply both sides by 3.	$7x - 1 = 6x + 9$
Subtract $6x$ from both sides.	$x - 1 = 9$
Add 1 to both sides.	$x = 10$

- You can solve problems using equations and fractions.

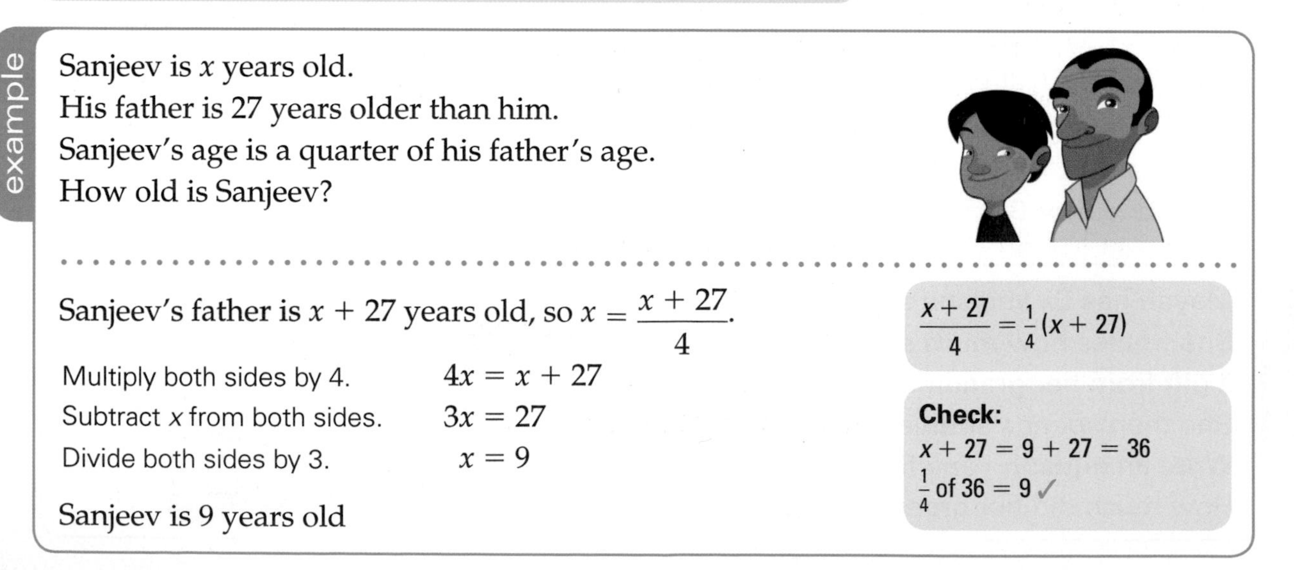

example

Sanjeev is x years old.
His father is 27 years older than him.
Sanjeev's age is a quarter of his father's age.
How old is Sanjeev?

Sanjeev's father is $x + 27$ years old, so $x = \frac{x + 27}{4}$.

Multiply both sides by 4.	$4x = x + 27$
Subtract x from both sides.	$3x = 27$
Divide both sides by 3.	$x = 9$

Sanjeev is 9 years old

$\frac{x + 27}{4} = \frac{1}{4}(x + 27)$

Check:
$x + 27 = 9 + 27 = 36$
$\frac{1}{4}$ of $36 = 9$ ✓

LEVEL 6

Grade D–C

Exercise 4d

1 Solve these equations.

a $7x + 3 = 4x + 18$ **b** $6x + 2 = 4x + 9$ **c** $8x - 2 = 6x + 1$

d $4x - 6 = x + 1$ **e** $9x - 8 = 5x + 4$ **f** $7x - 6 = 5x - 2$

g $9x - 8 = 5x - 3$ **h** $5x - 1 = 3x + 6$ **i** $3(2x + 5) = 2x + 20$

j $8x - 7 = 2(3x - 1)$ **k** $9x = 2(4 + 3x)$ **l** $7(2x - 3) = 5(1 + 2x)$

2 Solve these equations. Take care with negative signs.

a $8x + 4 = 34 + 2x$ **b** $8x + 4 = 34 - 2x$ **c** $5x + 6 = 18 + x$

d $5x + 6 = 18 - x$ **e** $3x - 2 = 8 - x$ **f** $7 + 3x = 12 - x$

g $9 + x = 3(3 - x)$ **h** $x + 2 = 2(4 - x)$ **i** $2x + 5 = 10 - 3x$

j $3 + x = 8 - x$ **k** $1 - x = 11 - 4x$ **l** $7 - 2x = 3(1 - 2x)$

3 Solve these equations.

a $\frac{6x + 1}{2} = 2x + 3$ **b** $\frac{7x - 2}{2} = 3x + 4$ **c** $\frac{5x + 4}{3} = x + 2$

d $\frac{8x - 1}{3} = 2x + 1$ **e** $3x - 2 = \frac{10x + 1}{4}$ **f** $4x + 1 = \frac{8x + 23}{5}$

g $3 + x = \frac{15 - x}{2}$ **h** $5 + 2x = \frac{29 - x}{3}$ **i** $5 + 2x = \frac{1}{3}(29 - x)$

j $4 - x = \frac{1}{2}(10 - 3x)$ **k** $\frac{1}{4}(7x - 1) = x + 2$ **l** $\frac{1}{3}(2 - x) = 3 - 2x$

4 Use a range of methods to solve this mixture of equations.

a $8x + 3 = 6x + 17$ **b** $8x - 3 = 6x + 17$ **c** $8x + 3 = 17 - 6x$

d $5x - 2 = 9 + 3x$ **e** $3x - 1 = 4 - x$ **f** $9x - 6 = 2(3x + 2)$

g $\frac{11x - 3}{2} = 4x + 3$ **h** $\frac{1}{2}(9x - 3) = 5x - 4$ **i** $\frac{7x - 2}{3} = 4x - 6$

5 a Harry is x years old. His mother is 26 years older than him. Harry's age is a third of his mother's age. How old is Harry?

b Jo has £30 and buys two shirts at £x each. Sue has £40 and buys shoes for £$3x$. They have the same amount left over. Find the cost of the shoes.

puzzle

The number in a square is the sum of the two numbers in the circles on either side of the square.
Find expressions in terms of x for the values inside circles B and C.

Write an equation in x and solve it to find the value of x.

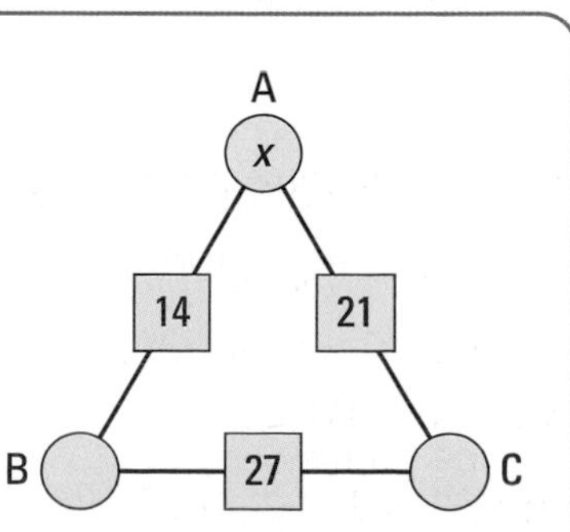

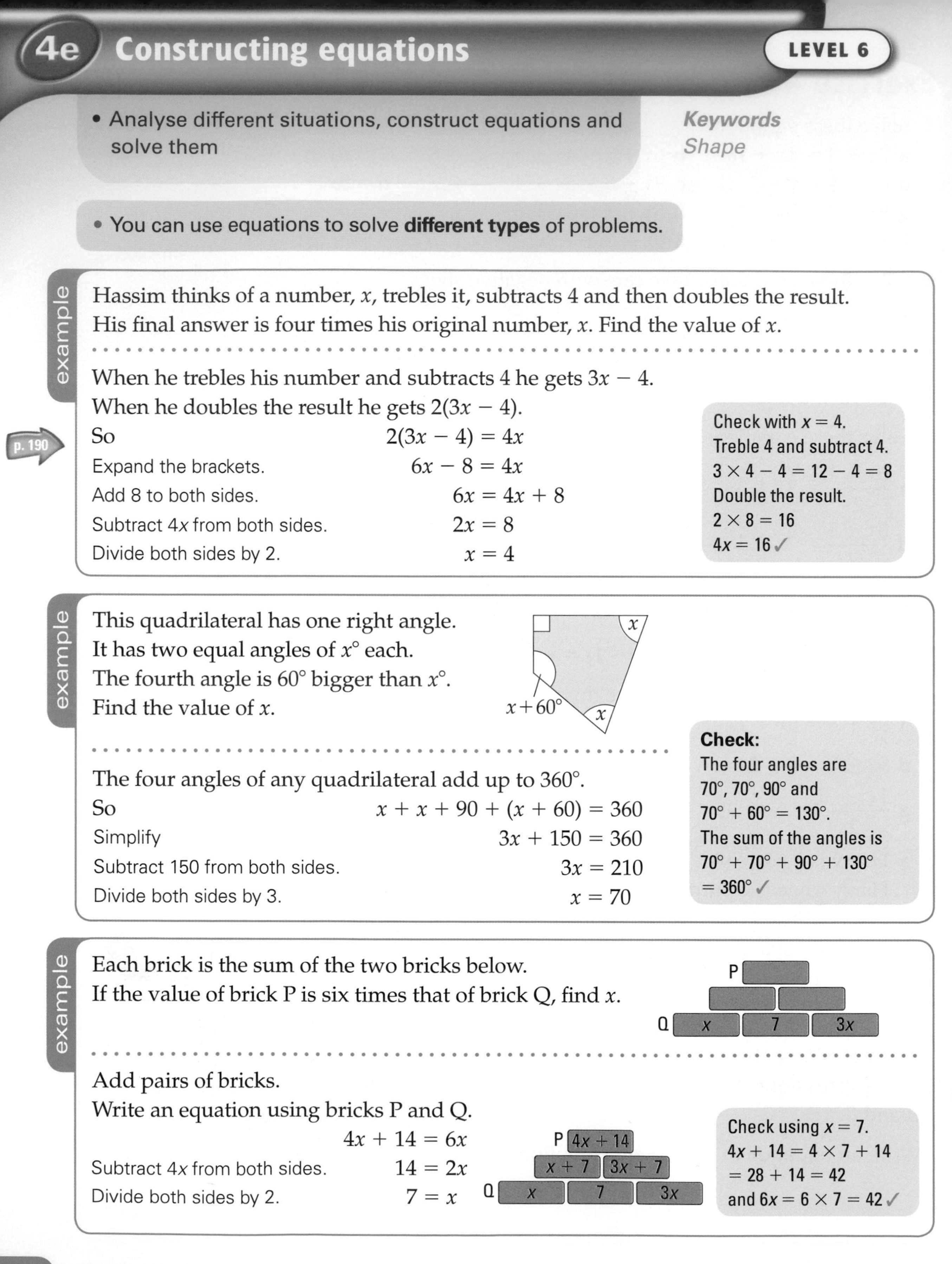

4e Constructing equations

LEVEL 6

- Analyse different situations, construct equations and solve them

Keywords
Shape

- You can use equations to solve **different types** of problems.

example

Hassim thinks of a number, x, trebles it, subtracts 4 and then doubles the result. His final answer is four times his original number, x. Find the value of x.

When he trebles his number and subtracts 4 he gets $3x - 4$.
When he doubles the result he gets $2(3x - 4)$.

p. 190

So $\quad 2(3x - 4) = 4x$
Expand the brackets. $\quad 6x - 8 = 4x$
Add 8 to both sides. $\quad 6x = 4x + 8$
Subtract $4x$ from both sides. $\quad 2x = 8$
Divide both sides by 2. $\quad x = 4$

Check with $x = 4$.
Treble 4 and subtract 4.
$3 \times 4 - 4 = 12 - 4 = 8$
Double the result.
$2 \times 8 = 16$
$4x = 16$ ✓

example

This quadrilateral has one right angle.
It has two equal angles of $x°$ each.
The fourth angle is 60° bigger than $x°$.
Find the value of x.

The four angles of any quadrilateral add up to 360°.

So $\quad x + x + 90 + (x + 60) = 360$
Simplify $\quad 3x + 150 = 360$
Subtract 150 from both sides. $\quad 3x = 210$
Divide both sides by 3. $\quad x = 70$

Check:
The four angles are 70°, 70°, 90° and 70° + 60° = 130°.
The sum of the angles is 70° + 70° + 90° + 130° = 360° ✓

example

Each brick is the sum of the two bricks below.
If the value of brick P is six times that of brick Q, find x.

Add pairs of bricks.
Write an equation using bricks P and Q.

$\quad 4x + 14 = 6x$
Subtract $4x$ from both sides. $\quad 14 = 2x$
Divide both sides by 2. $\quad 7 = x$

Check using $x = 7$.
$4x + 14 = 4 \times 7 + 14$
$= 28 + 14 = 42$
and $6x = 6 \times 7 = 42$ ✓

Exercise 4e

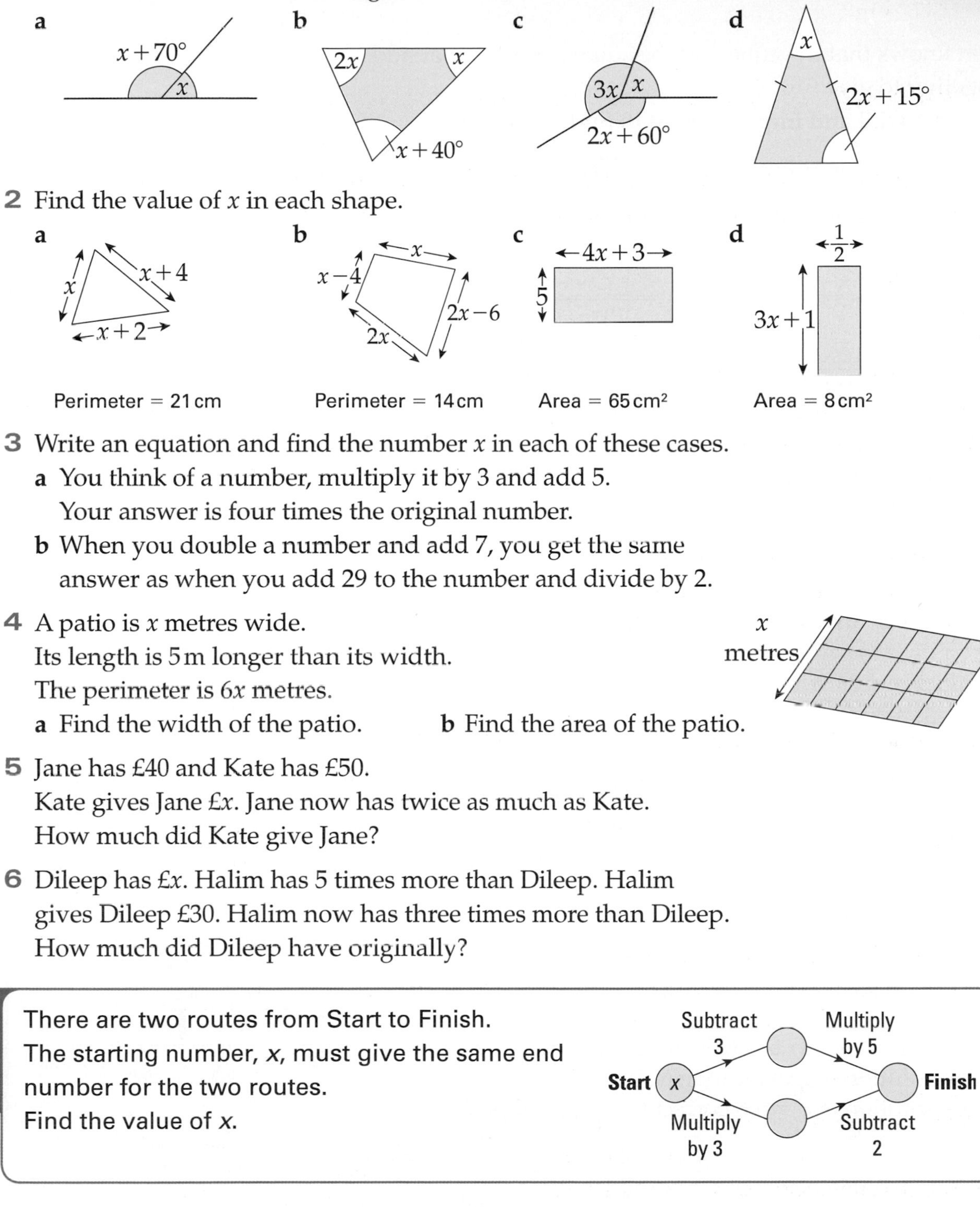

1 Find the value of x in each diagram.

a **b** **c** **d**

2 Find the value of x in each shape.

a Perimeter = 21 cm

b Perimeter = 14 cm

c Area = 65 cm²

d Area = 8 cm²

3 Write an equation and find the number x in each of these cases.

a You think of a number, multiply it by 3 and add 5.
Your answer is four times the original number.

b When you double a number and add 7, you get the same answer as when you add 29 to the number and divide by 2.

4 A patio is x metres wide.
Its length is 5 m longer than its width.
The perimeter is $6x$ metres.

a Find the width of the patio. **b** Find the area of the patio.

5 Jane has £40 and Kate has £50.
Kate gives Jane £x. Jane now has twice as much as Kate.
How much did Kate give Jane?

6 Dileep has £x. Halim has 5 times more than Dileep. Halim gives Dileep £30. Halim now has three times more than Dileep.
How much did Dileep have originally?

puzzle

There are two routes from Start to Finish.
The starting number, x, must give the same end number for the two routes.
Find the value of x.

Trial and improvement

- Solve equations using trial and improvement

Keywords
Improve
Trial and improvement

Ben knows that the cube and the square of a number add together to give 576.

p. 184

He uses **trial and improvement** to find the number.

The equation to solve is $x^3 + x^2 = 576$.

He makes a guess (or trial) and then **improves** on it.

Try	x^3	x^2	$x^3 + x^2$	Comment
$x = 2$	8	4	12	$12 < 576$, far too low
$x = 10$	1000	100	1100	$1100 > 576$, too high
$x = 7$	343	49	392	$392 < 576$, too low
$x = 8$	512	64	576	Spot on!

The solution is $x = 8$.

- Trial and improvement often gives a decimal solution.

example

Solve the equation $x^2 + x = 50$.
Give your answer correct to 1 decimal place.

Take $x = 6$ as your first trial and then improve on it.

Try	x^2	x	$x^2 + x$	Comment
$x = 6$	36	6	42	$42 < 50$, too low
$x = 7$	49	7	56	$56 > 50$, too high
$x = 6.5$	42.25	6.5	48.75	$48.75 < 50$, too low
$x = 6.6$	43.56	6.6	50.16	$50.16 > 50$, too high

The solution must be between 6.5 and 6.6.

Try the midpoint: $x = 6.55$.

$$6.55^2 + 6.55 = 42.9025 + 6.55$$
$$= 49.4525$$

$49.4525 < 50$, so $x = 6.55$ is also too low.
The solution is greater than 6.55.
The solution is $x = 6.6$ correct to 1 decimal place.

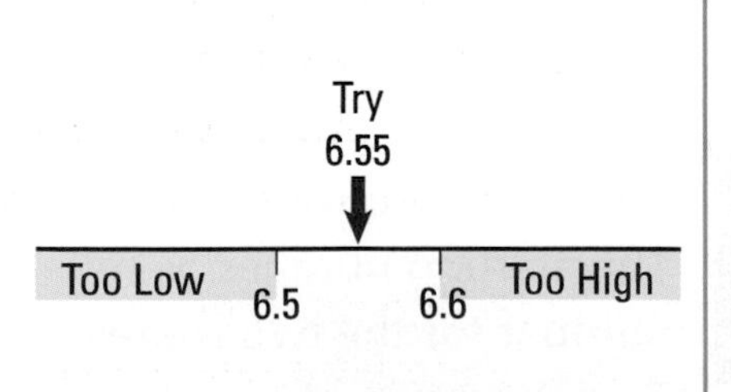

- You can use a computer spreadsheet instead of a calculator to construct your table of values.

	A	B	C	D
1	Try	x^2	x	$x^2 + x$
2	6	= A2 * A2	= A2	= B2 + C2
3	7	= A3 * A3	= A3	= B3 + C3

LEVEL 6

Grade D–C

Exercise 4f

1 Use this table to solve the equation $x^3 - x^2 = 294$.
Try $x = 5$ as your first trial.

Try	x^3	x^2	$x^3 - x^2$	Comment
$x = 5$				

2 Make your own tables to solve these equations.

a $x^2 - x = 272$ (Try $x = 10$) **b** $x^3 + x = 738$ (Try $x = 5$) **c** $x^3 + x^2 = 1872$ (Try $x = 10$)

d $x^2 + 5x = 176$ **e** $x^3 - 8x = 287$ **f** $x^4 - 3x^2 = 1188$

3 Use this table to solve the equation $x^3 - x = 150$.
Give your answer correct to 1 decimal place.

Try	x^3	x	$x^3 - x$	Comment
$x = 5$				

4 Make your own tables to solve these equations correct to 1 decimal place.

a $x^3 + x = 100$ (Try $x = 4$) **b** $x^2 - x = 50$ (Try $x = 7$) **c** $x + x^2 = 80$ (Try $x = 8$)

d $x^2 = 30$ **e** $x^3 = 30$ **f** $x^2 - 2x = 30$

g $x^4 + 4x = 700$ **h** $(x + 1)(x + 2) = 60$ **i** $x + \sqrt{x} = 25$

5 **a** When a number, n, its square and its cube are all added together the total is 584. Find the number n.

b If the total of n, n^2 and n^3 is 600, find the value of n correct to one decimal place.

6 This rectangle is 4 cm longer than it is wide. Its area is 70 cm².
Find its width, z, by solving the equation $z(z + 4) = 70$.
Use this table to help you with a first try of $z = 6$.

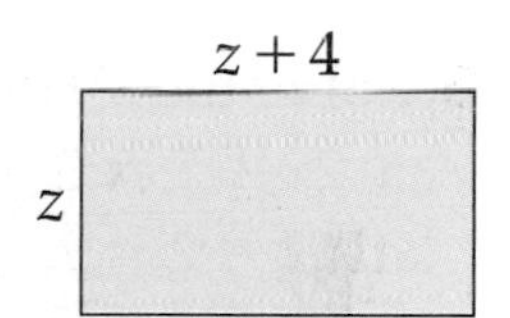

Try	z	$z + 4$	$z(z + 4)$	Comment
$z = 6$				

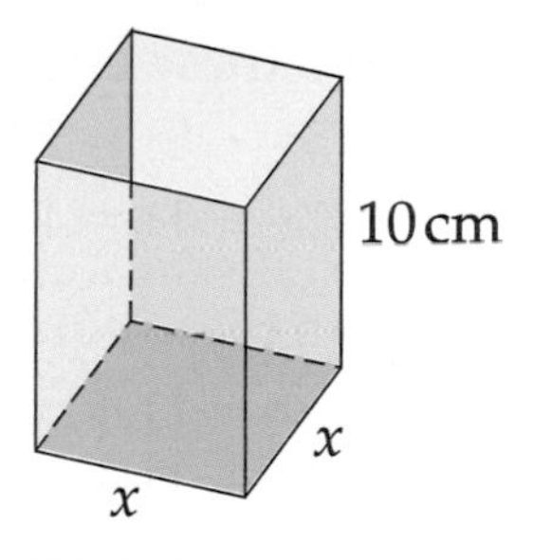

7 A plant pot has a square base of side x cm and four rectangular sides of height 10 cm.
Find the value of x if the total area of these five shapes is

a 500 cm² **b** 400 cm².

challenge

n is an odd number.
The next odd number after n is $n + 2$.

a Write down the next odd number after $n + 2$.

b These three odd numbers are multiplied together to give 117 453.
Find their values.
Use a calculator or computer spreadsheet to help you.

4 Consolidation

4a

1 Match the words in the box with the descriptions **a** to **d**.

Equation	Formula	Function	Identity

a The cost, £C, of L litres of oil is $C = 5 + \frac{1}{2}L$.
b $2(4x + 1) = 22$
c The output, y, and input, x, are related by $y = 3x - 1$.
d $2(4x + 1) \equiv 8x + 2$

2 **a** Substitute $x = 6$ to find P when $P = x^2 + 4$.
b Simplify $3(2x - 1) + 2(x + 2)$.
c Use this function machine to find the output, y, when $x = 8$.
d Solve $5x = 3x + 8$.

$x \rightarrow \boxed{\div 4} \rightarrow \boxed{+5} \rightarrow y$

4b

3 Use inverse operations to solve these equations.
a $x + 5 = 7$ **b** $x - 8 = 2$ **c** $3x = 18$ **d** $\frac{x}{2} = 5$

4 Solve these equations. Each solution takes two steps.
a $2x + 3 = 11$ **b** $2x - 3 = 11$ **c** $6x + 1 = 19$
d $\frac{x}{2} + 1 = 4$ **e** $\frac{x}{2} - 1 = 4$ **f** $\frac{x}{3} + 2 = 7$

5 Solve these equations. Take care with the signs and fractions.
a $2x + 7 = 3$ **b** $3x - 8 = -2$ **c** $2x + 1 = 6$
d $4x - 2 = 7$ **e** $-1 = 5x + 8$ **f** $4 = \frac{x}{4} - 1$

4c

6 Solve these equations.
a $2(3x + 5) = 22$ **b** $5(2x + 4) = 30$ **c** $7(3x - 2) = 28$
d $3(2x - 1) = 12$ **e** $16 = 2(4x + 3)$ **f** $18 = 6(2 + 3x)$

7 Solve these equations. You will need to collect like terms.
a $2(3x + 1) + 3(4x + 2) = 44$ **b** $5(3x - 2) + 2(x + 7) = 55$
c $4(4x + 1) + 3(5 - x) = 32$ **d** $2(x + 3) + 3(4 - 2x) = 16$
e $2(x - 1) + 8(x + 3) = 2$ **f** $5(2x + 7) + 6(2 - x) = 43$

8 Solve these equations. Remember how to multiply positive and negative numbers.
a $5(2x + 3) - 3(2x + 4) = 15$ **b** $3(6x + 1) - 2(7x - 4) = 43$
c $3(3x + 4) - 2(2x + 1) = 30$ **d** $9(2x + 1) - 3(5x - 3) = 18$
e $3(2 + 4x) + 3(5 - x) = 30$ **f** $7(2 + 5x) + 4(8 - 7x) = 60$

9 Solve these equations which have unknowns on both sides.

a $5x + 7 = 3x + 15$ **b** $4x - 1 = 2x + 13$ **c** $2(3x + 2) = 5(x + 3)$
d $3(3x + 2) = 8x + 5$ **e** $4(2x - 1) = 6x + 8$ **f** $4(2x - 1) = 6x - 8$
g $x + 4 = 13 - 2x$ **h** $2x + 6 = 9 - x$ **i** $2x - 6 = 9 - x$
j $8x - 4 = 6x + 1$ **k** $x + 5 = 12 - x$ **l** $2(2x - 1) = 3x - 7$

10 Solve these equations.

a $\frac{5x + 1}{2} = 2x + 3$ **b** $\frac{5x - 1}{2} = 2x + 3$ **c** $\frac{7x + 2}{4} = x + 2$
d $2x - 3 = \frac{8x + 2}{5}$ **e** $3x - 1 = \frac{7x - 2}{3}$ **f** $\frac{1}{2}(3x - 1) = 2x - 1$

11 Cerys thinks of a number.
She doubles it, subtracts 5 and then trebles the result.
Her final answer is four times her original number.
What number did Cerys think of?

12 **a** The triangle has a perimeter of $6x$.
Find the value of x.
b For this rectangle
i find the value of x
ii work out the perimeter.

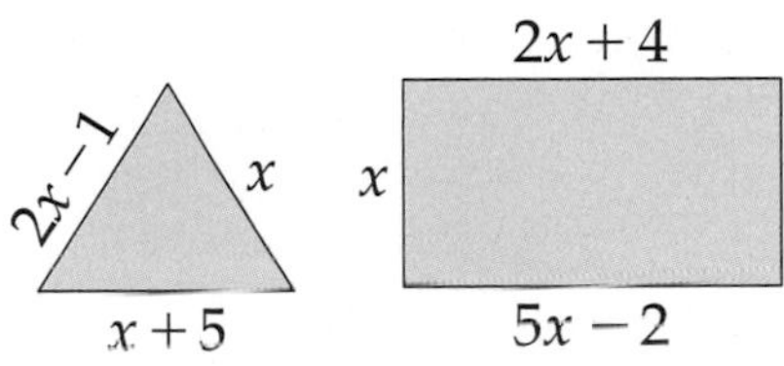

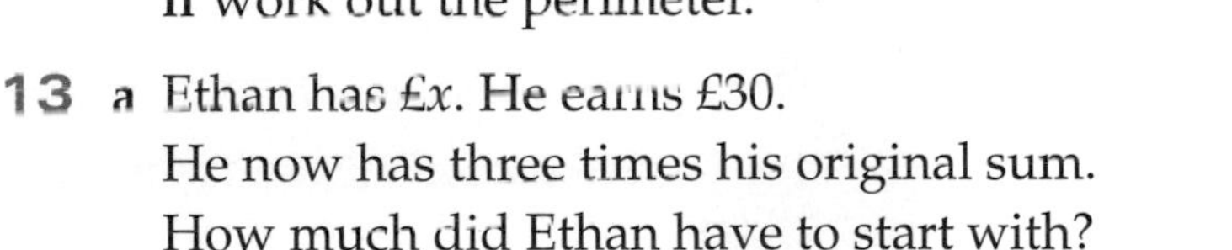

13 **a** Ethan has £x. He earns £30.
He now has three times his original sum.
How much did Ethan have to start with?
b April has £x and June has £20.
They add what they have and then share it out equally.
April now has £4 more than she started with.
How much did April have to start with?

14 A rectangular sheet of metal has a rectangular hole cut in it.
This diagram gives the dimensions in metres.
The area which is left is $11x$ m².
Find the value of x and the area of the original sheet.

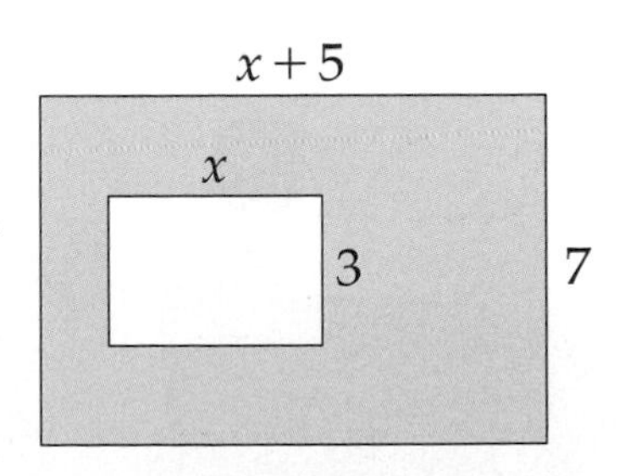

15 Use this table to solve $x^2 + x = 48$.
Give your answer correct to 1 decimal place.
Try $x = 6$ as your first trial.

Try	x^2	x	$x^2 + x$	Comment
$x = 6$				

Maths life

Investigating crime

Forensic experts have used mathematical techniques to solve crimes for a long time. Even now when we have DNA as evidence, the techniques used in this case study are still very valuable.

The Weekly Bugle

Incident on Park Street

A speeding car narrowly missed a cyclist after it skidded 53 metres along Park Street and overshot the junction with Fisher Row. The driver and passenger of the car were seen running from the scene.

A local resident said 'He must have been doing at least 80 mph. It's lucky the cyclist wasn't killed'.

Police investigating the incident are keen to trace the driver and passenger of the car.

POLICE LINE DO NOT CROSS POLICE

DETECTIVE AGENCY

FINGERPRINTS

Police often look for fingerprints when investigating crimes and have over 7 million sets of fingerprints on record.

Take your own fingerprints

- Scribble an area using a soft pencil.
- Press your finger firmly on the pencilled area
- Stick a small piece of clear sticky tape on your finger.
- Remove the tape and stick it on a piece of paper to see your fingerprint.
- Make a copy of each of your fingerprints from both hands.

What similarities and differences can you see in your prints?

Are some prints more similar than others?

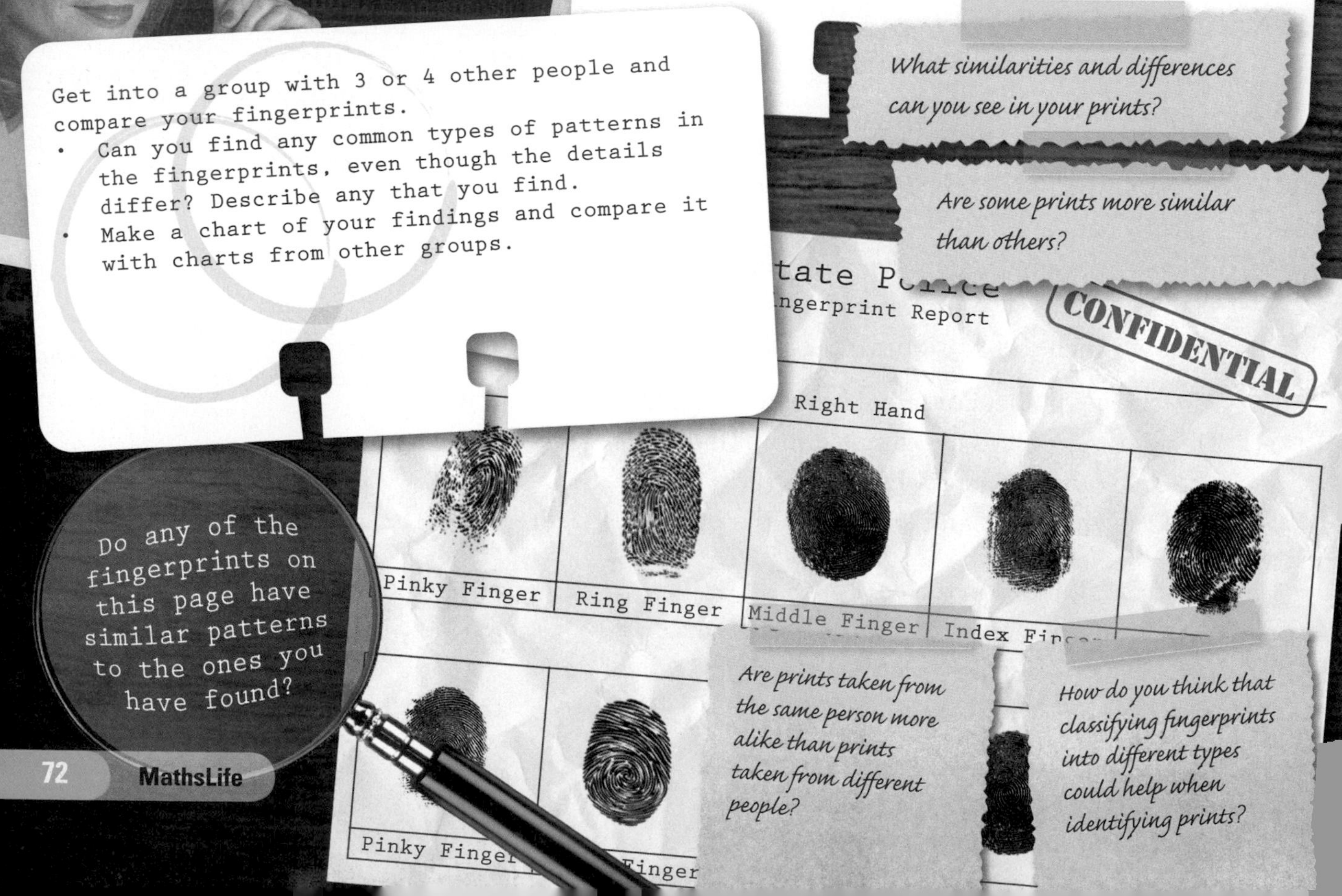

Get into a group with 3 or 4 other people and compare your fingerprints.

- Can you find any common types of patterns in the fingerprints, even though the details differ? Describe any that you find.
- Make a chart of your findings and compare it with charts from other groups.

Do any of the fingerprints on this page have similar patterns to the ones you have found?

Are prints taken from the same person more alike than prints taken from different people?

How do you think that classifying fingerprints into different types could help when identifying prints?

TYRE MARKS

CONFIDENTIAL

The length of the tyre marks left by a skidding car depends on its speed when it started skidding. These are typical values for a tarmac road surface and dry weather conditions.

Initial speed	length of tyre marks
10 mph	1.5 metres
15 mph	3.3 metres
20 mph	5.9 metres
25 mph	9.3 metres
30 mph	13.3 metres
35 mph	18.1 metres
40 mph	23.7 metres
45 mph	30 metres

- Use the data to draw a graph of the length of the tyre marks against speed.
- Join the points with a smooth line.
- What type of relationship does the graph show?

Extend your graph to get an approximate initial speed for the car in the news article.

- *What happens to the length of the tyre marks as the speed doubles?*
- *What happens as the speed trebles?*

- *Is the relationship between the speed and the length of the skid a linear one?*

The relationship between speed and the length of the skid is given by the equation

$$\text{speed} = \sqrt{90 \times \text{length} \times \text{friction}}$$

where friction is the drag factor of the road

- The tarmac road has a drag factor of 0.75
- Was the resident right in thinking that the car was doing at least 80 mph?
- You could use the equation to set up a spreadsheet.

- *How far would the car have skidded if it had been on a concrete road surface with a drag factor of 0.9?*

- *How far would it have skidded if it had been on snow with a drag factor of 0.3?*

- *How quickly would it have been travelling if it skidded for 53 metres on a concrete road?*

4 Summary

Assessment criteria

- Construct and solve linear equations **Level 6**
- Use systematic trial and improvement methods to find approximate solutions to equations **Level 6**

Level 6

1 Ian hasn't got a cube root button on his calculator.
Use trial and improvement, to show Ian how to find $\sqrt[3]{380}$ to one decimal place.

p. 182

Bethan's answer ✔

Try	x^3	Comment
$x = 7$	343	too low
$x = 8$	512	too high
$x = 7.5$	421.875	too high
$x = 7.2$	373.248	too low
$x = 7.3$	389.017	too high
$x = 7.25$	381.078125	too high

Bethan narrows the search to between 7.2 and 7.3

She knows $\sqrt[3]{380}$ is nearer to 7.2 than 7.3

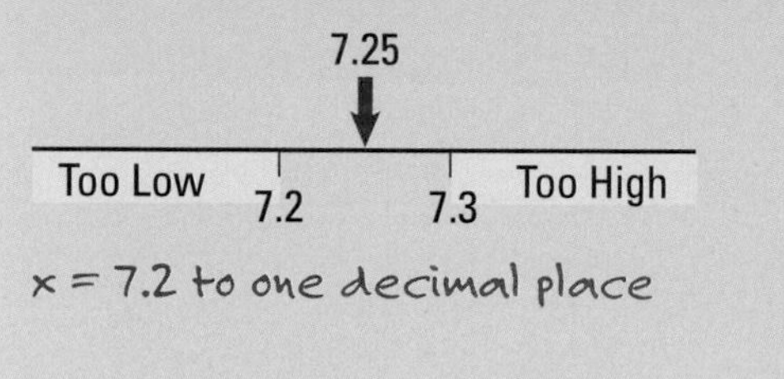

$x = 7.2$ to one decimal place

Level 6

2 a Look at this equation.

$$14y - 51 = 187 + 4y$$

Is $y = 17$ the solution to the equation?
Show how you know.

b Look at this equation.

$$3y^2 = 2601$$

Is $y = 17$ the solution to the equation?
Show how you know.

Key Stage 3 2005 5–7 Paper 2

5 Statistics

Surveys

Surveys are used all the time in day to day life, from finding out which foods we like to eat and which TV programmes we watch to looking at who we vote for in elections.

What's the point? Surveys help companies know what we'd most like to buy or politicians know what we want to see change.

Check in

Level 5

1 This pie chart shows the audience share for the main UK television channels.

Explain the key features of the chart.

Others
BBC 1
BBC 2
ITV
Five
C4/S4C

2 This time-series graph shows the changes in the audience share for different television channels over time. Comment on the main features of the graph.

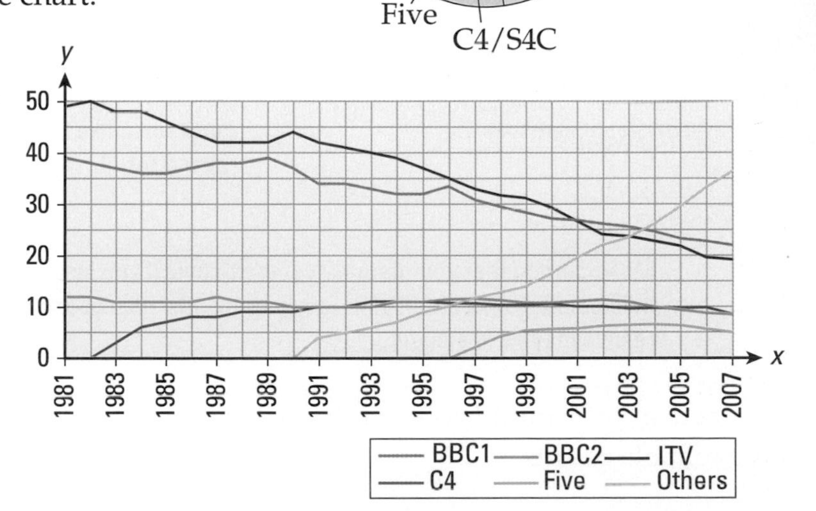

5a Planning a project

LEVEL 6/7

- Suggest a problem to explore using statistical methods
- Identify possible primary or secondary sources
- Think about the sample size and degree of accuracy

Keywords
Conjecture
Data
Degree of accuracy
Primary
Sample
Sample size
Secondary
Source

- You need to think carefully when you plan a data-handling project.
  - Decide questions to investigate, and make a **conjecture**.
  - Identify the information you need to investigate your conjecture.
  - Identify suitable **sources** of **primary** or **secondary** data.
  - Think about the **sample size** and **degree of accuracy**.

A **conjecture** is a specific idea that you can use your **data** to test.

example

Students in class 9A were asked to carry out a statistical project based on their school sports day.
Suggest a conjecture that they could investigate and explain how they could plan the data collection.

Conjecture: *Taller people tend to do better in the long jump.*

To investigate, collect paired data: the height of a number of long jumpers at the sports day and the distance they jumped. This is primary data.
Collect data for every competitor (sample size), measuring both height and distance to the nearest centimetre (degree of accuracy).

Both height and distance are continuous data. They are rounded as they are collected.

Make sure you collect enough data. Small samples may give misleading results.

but

Don't collect too much data as this can take a lot of time and make processing all the results more difficult.

Make certain that your data is representative. If you just collect information from your family or friends, then your results may be misleading.

In practice, you should collect the smallest set of data that will give reliable results.

Exercise 5a

1 Students in class 9A planned a project at their school sports day. Here are some of the conjectures they suggested.

a This year's results will be better than last year's.

b The weather has a big effect on sports results.

c Some people are better at sport than others.

For each one, explain why it is not a good conjecture and suggest improvements.

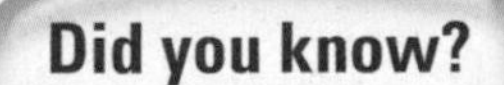

A census is a survey of all the people living in a country. The earliest complete UK census is for England and Wales in 1841.

2 Students in class 9B were asked to choose their own topics for a data-handling project.

These are some of their conjectures.

> The number of children taken to school by car is increasing.

> Year 9 students spend more time on homework than Year 7 students.

> Girls send and receive more text messages than boys.

> Teenagers smoke more now than they did 10 years ago.

For each of these conjectures, suggest one source of primary or secondary data that could be used.

Explain your choices.

You could collect primary data in a survey or experiment.
You could find secondary data on the internet or in a book.

3 Rebecca and Jason are measuring people's heights for a science project.

Rebecca says, 'We need accurate results so we should measure people to the nearest millimetre.'

Jason says, 'That will be too fiddly and take too much time. Let's just measure people to the nearest 10 cm.'

What do you think? Explain your answer.

challenge

This claim appeared in an advertisement for a new type of cat food.

Do you think this claim is fair?

What questions would you want to ask the advertisers?

Explain how the cat food manufacturers could collect primary data to check the claims that appear in the advertisement.

5b Data collection

LEVEL 6

- Design a survey or experiment to collect data
- Design, trial and improve data-collection sheets

Keywords
Continuous
Categorical
Data-collection sheet
Discrete
Questionnaire
Survey

A **data-collection sheet** is important when you are carrying out a **survey** or recording the results of an experiment.

- Think carefully about the different types of **data**.

Categorical data can be described.
Eye colour, Gender

Discrete data can only have certain values.
Number of houses, Shoe size

Continuous data can have any value in a range.
Height, Length

example

Carla and Wasim are investigating data from the long-jump competition. They want to find out how a jumper's height, age and gender change the distance jumped.
Design a suitable data-collection sheet and explain how the data should be collected.

A separate line of data is collected for each competitor.

Name	M/F	DoB	Height	Distance

When each person fills in a sheet of their own it is a **questionnaire**. When you fill in answers for several people on each page it is a data-collection sheet.

This data-collection sheet contains both categorical and numerical data.

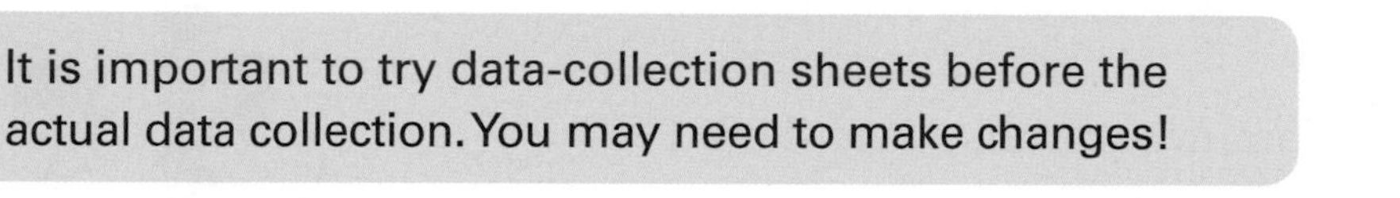

- It is important to try data-collection sheets before the actual data collection. You may need to make changes!

example

Carla and Wasim went to a practice session before the sports day to try out their data collection sheet but …
- each jumper had three attempts and they did not have enough space on their form
- they tried to measure people's heights after each jump and record their date of birth but did not have enough time.

What changes could they make?

Record the school year instead of the date of birth for each person.

Name	M/F	Year	Height	Distance

Add space to record three distances and circle the best one for each jumper.
Get the names of the competitors in advance.
Measure and record the heights in advance, perhaps as competitors arrive for the event.

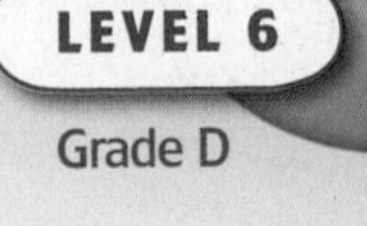

Grade D

Exercise 5b

1 Mei-ling is carrying out a survey and needs to collect this information from each person she interviews.
- First name, second name, post code
- Gender, date of birth
- How they travel to work, journey distance and duration

Design a data collection sheet that she could use in her survey.

Make the form easy to use by giving options to choose from if possible.

2 These questions were included in a questionnaire.
There is a problem with each of them!

How old are you? (Tick one box) ☐ Young ☐ Middle-aged ☐ Old

Do you watch a lot of television? ☐ Yes ☐ No

How many people live in your house? (Tick one box)
☐ 0 ☐ 1–2 ☐ 2–3 ☐ 3+

a Explain what the problems are with each question.
b Design an improved version of this section of the questionnaire.

3 Alisdair is collecting information about driving habits.
He wants to see if men and women tend to drive different types of vehicle.
Here is part of his data collection sheet.

	Tally	Frequency
Male drivers		
Female drivers		
Large cars		

a Explain why this data collection sheet will not work properly.
b Design an improved version.

4 Klara wants to know how people feel about this statement; 'Being vegetarian is good for your health'
Which of these two methods of collecting data would be better in your opinion, and why?

a Mark a cross on this scale to show your opinion.

Disagree ←――――――――→ Agree

b Tick one of these boxes.

Strongly disagree	Disagree	Cannot decide or no opinion	Agree	Strongly agree

discussion

Here are some more recommendations about how to design a questionnaire.
Why is each one important?
a Keep the questionnaire short and simple.
b Make questions precise and easy to understand.
c Ask for one piece of information at a time.
d Start with easier questions and go on to harder ones.

5c Frequency tables

LEVEL 6

- Use two-way tables to organise data
- Use frequency tables to organise data

Keywords
Categorical *Discrete*
Class intervals *Numerical*
Continuous *Tally*
Two- way table

- A **two-way table** can be useful for displaying discrete data.

This table shows how many boys and girls studied French and German in Year 10.

	French	German
Boys	26	54
Girls	55	32

- You can use a **frequency table** to organise your data.

example

These are the ages (in years) of 20 long-jump competitors.

15 14 15 15 16 16 16 14 15 15
16 15 16 14 15 15 16 16 16 15

Draw a frequency table for this set of data.

This is **discrete numerical** data.
You can use a **tally** to produce a simple frequency table.

Age	Tally	Frequency
14					3
15	~~||||~~ ||||	9
16	~~||||~~ |||	8

You can organise a set of **categorical** data in the same simple way.

- For **continuous** data, you need to pick suitable **class intervals.**

example

These are the heights, in centimetres, of 30 athletes.

174 174 173 178 168 171 172 178 176 179
172 179 177 178 173 182 170 174 175 176
180 173 179 176 177 170 182 174 182 174

Draw a frequency table for this set of data.

Height (cm)	Tally	Frequency
165–169			1
170–174	~~||||~~ ~~||||~~ |||	13
175–179	~~||||~~ ~~||||~~ ||	12
180–184	||||	4

This is one possible way of organising the class intervals.

Choose a way of dividing up the data. Use between 3 and 10 intervals.

Another way of labelling these classes would be Height (h cm): $165 \leqslant h < 170$, etc.

Exercise 5c

1 Samta asked boys and girls in her class which sport they had chosen. She recorded either: B (boy) or G (girl) and H (hockey) or B (Basketball).

BH	BB	BB	GH	GH	BB	GB	GH	GB	BB
GH	BB	BB	GB	GB	GH	GB	BH	BB	BB
GB	GH	GH	BB	BH	BB	BB	GH	BH	GB

BB means a boy had chosen basketball.

Draw a two-way table for this data set.

Use a tally to make sure you include all of the data.

2 Here are the shoe sizes of 60 Year 9 boys.

8	4	7	7	9	7	6	4	8	6
5	7	4	6	6	8	6	5	5	9
6	5	7	7	6	5	7	7	4	5
9	6	6	8	8	4	5	6	7	5
5	6	6	4	6	8	7	6	6	5
7	4	6	6	7	8	4	5	7	5

Construct a tally and frequency table for this set of data.

3 32 students measured their height in centimetres to the nearest 0.1 cm.

169.1	161.0	167.1	169.1	164.7	164.5	176.1	165.9
176.0	157.7	165.9	180.0	161.0	164.3	183.0	165.2
160.7	170.5	159.9	168.0	169.7	169.0	171.6	160.8
177.0	180.4	168.2	176.6	164.5	172.6	163.2	174.4

Construct a frequency table for this set of data using class intervals for the height (h cm) of $155 \leqslant h < 160$, $160 \leqslant h < 165$, …

4 32 people were weighed, in kilograms, to the nearest 0.1 kg.

72.6	67.3	58.2	59.2	67.4	63.6	71.7	61.8
78.5	80.9	53.5	44.7	52.8	58.9	58.0	53.8
59.2	51.5	69.8	47.0	56.6	58.7	70.2	60.3
63.1	63.0	67.9	55.7	74.0	67.1	53.1	75.4

Construct a frequency table for this set of data using suitable class intervals.

challenge

The shoe sizes and heights, in centimetres, of 32 people were measured and recorded in the form (shoe size, height).

(4, 161)	(4, 160)	(7, 166)	(5, 161)	(4, 155)	(8, 167)
(3, 158)	(5, 161)	(4, 157)	(6, 162)	(5, 158)	(7, 165)
(4, 159)	(7, 168)	(6, 166)	(5, 164)	(5, 160)	(3, 159)
(5, 160)	(3, 155)	(9, 169)	(8, 169)	(3, 154)	(6, 163)
(6, 165)	(5, 159)	(5, 164)	(7, 164)	(6, 162)	(8, 171)
(9, 170)	(3, 154)				

Construct a two-way table for this set of data.

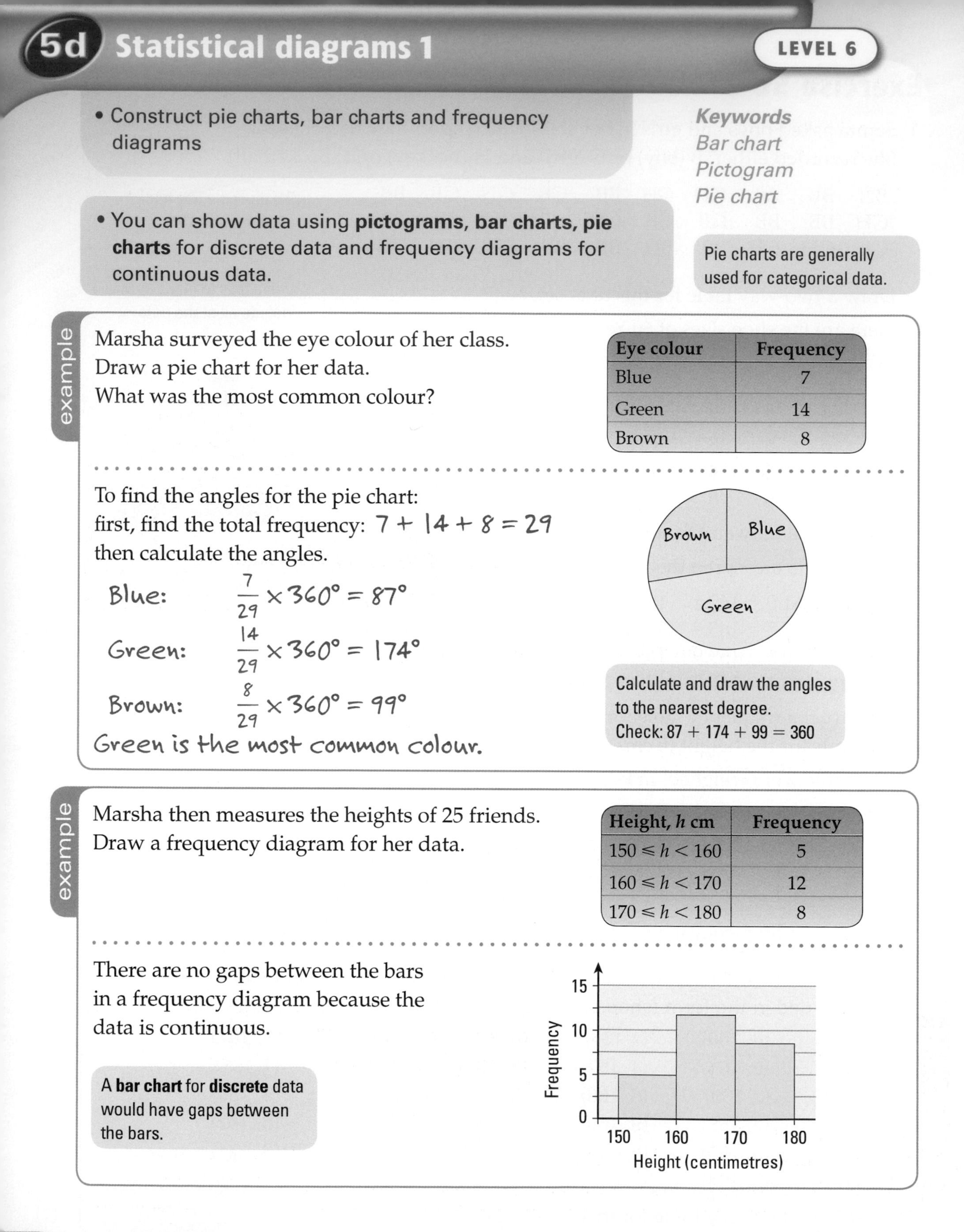

5d Statistical diagrams 1

LEVEL 6

- Construct pie charts, bar charts and frequency diagrams

Keywords
Bar chart
Pictogram
Pie chart

- You can show data using **pictograms, bar charts, pie charts** for discrete data and frequency diagrams for continuous data.

Pie charts are generally used for categorical data.

example

Marsha surveyed the eye colour of her class.
Draw a pie chart for her data.
What was the most common colour?

Eye colour	Frequency
Blue	7
Green	14
Brown	8

To find the angles for the pie chart:
first, find the total frequency: $7 + 14 + 8 = 29$
then calculate the angles.

Blue: $\frac{7}{29} \times 360° = 87°$

Green: $\frac{14}{29} \times 360° = 174°$

Brown: $\frac{8}{29} \times 360° = 99°$

Green is the most common colour.

Calculate and draw the angles to the nearest degree.
Check: $87 + 174 + 99 = 360$

example

Marsha then measures the heights of 25 friends.
Draw a frequency diagram for her data.

Height, h cm	Frequency
$150 \leq h < 160$	5
$160 \leq h < 170$	12
$170 \leq h < 180$	8

There are no gaps between the bars in a frequency diagram because the data is continuous.

A **bar chart** for **discrete** data would have gaps between the bars.

Grade D

Exercise 5d

1 This pictogram shows the number of cars in Aspen School car park on three consecutive mornings.

Day	
Monday	
Tuesday	
Wednesday	

Key: = 10 vehicles

Horizontal charts have the scale across the page and the bars horizontal.

Draw a horizontal bar chart for this set of data.

2 This table shows the colours of the cars in Aspen School car park on Thursday morning.

Colour	Frequency
Silver/Grey	18
Red	8
Blue	11
White	9

Draw a pie chart to represent this set of data.
What was the most common colour?

3 These are average temperatures for Glasgow in one year.
Draw a vertical bar chart for this set of data.

Month	Jan	Feb	Mar	Apr	May	Jun	Jul	Aug	Sep	Oct	Nov	Dec
Average max temp (°C)	5	11	14	18	19	21	23	25	19	14	11	6

Describe the pattern of the diagram.

4 These are the weights of some gym members.
Draw a frequency diagram for this set of data.

Weight, w kg	Frequency
$60 \leq w < 65$	2
$65 \leq w < 70$	19
$70 \leq w < 75$	24
$75 \leq w < 80$	9

investigation

This table shows the favourite subjects of students in class 9X.

Subject	Maths	English	Science	Art	PE
Frequency	6	8	7	6	4

Represent this set of data as

a a bar chart **b** a pie chart.

Explain the advantages and disadvantages of each chart.

Which chart was easiest to draw?
What features are easiest to see with each chart?

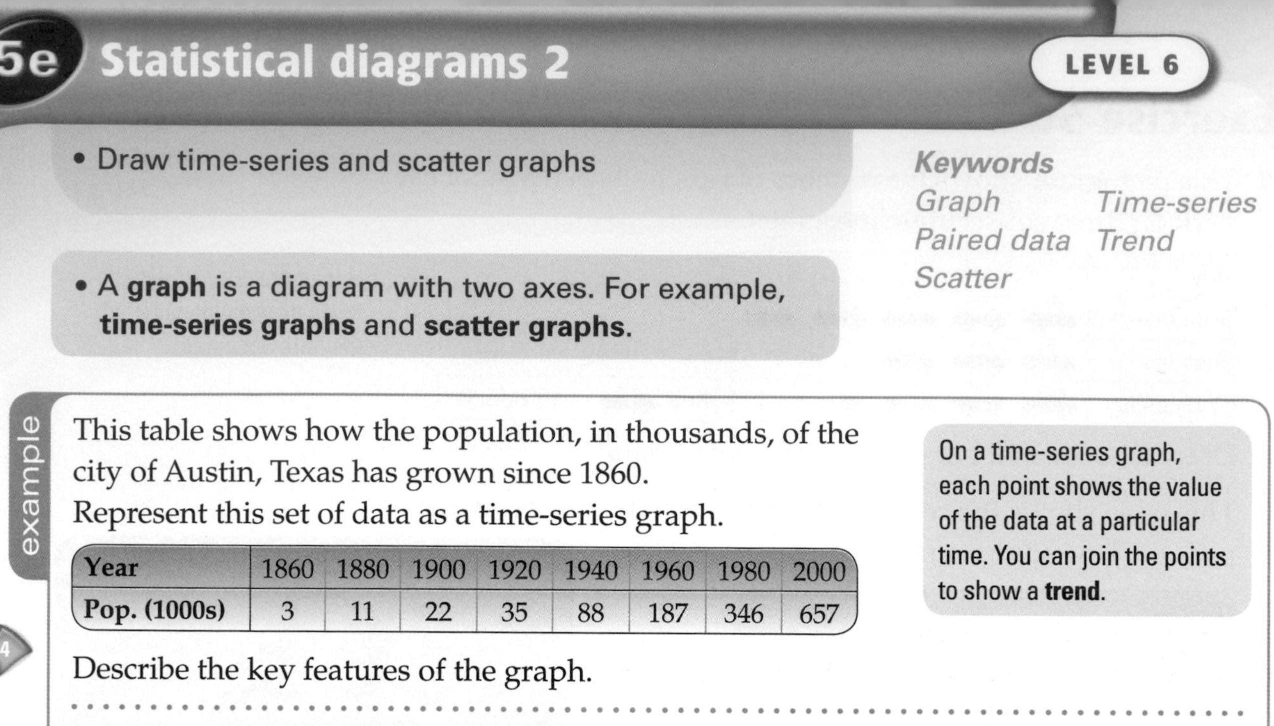

5e Statistical diagrams 2

LEVEL 6

- Draw time-series and scatter graphs

Keywords
Graph *Time-series*
Paired data *Trend*
Scatter

- A **graph** is a diagram with two axes. For example, **time-series graphs** and **scatter graphs.**

example

This table shows how the population, in thousands, of the city of Austin, Texas has grown since 1860.
Represent this set of data as a time-series graph.

Year	1860	1880	1900	1920	1940	1960	1980	2000
Pop. (1000s)	3	11	22	35	88	187	346	657

p. 144

Describe the key features of the graph.

On a time-series graph, each point shows the value of the data at a particular time. You can join the points to show a **trend**.

Population of Austin, 1860–2000

Population (thousands): 0, 200, 400, 600, 800
Year: 1860, 1880, 1900, 1920, 1940, 1960, 1980, 2000

The population increases slowly until the second half of the 20th century, when it increases at a greater rate.

- A scatter graph can show any set of **paired data**.

example

The table shows the experience and the annual salary for 10 computer programmers.
Draw a scatter graph for this set of paired data.

p. 204

Salary (£K): 0, 20, 40, 60
Experience (years): 5, 10, 15

× Experience and salary

Each point shows the salary and the number of years' experience for a person.

Experience (years)	1	3	5	2	12	10	7	2	15	11
Salary (£K)	18	24	28	22	52	38	36	19	50	47

Exercise 5e

1 Look at the second example on page 84.
Describe the key features of the scatter graph.
What is the trend?

2 Draw a time-series graph for this set of data.

Aspen High School: Year 9 students achieving Level 5 or above in mathematics								
Year	2002	2003	2004	2005	2006	2007	2008	2009
%	68%	73%	75%	79%	78%	82%	85%	87%

Describe the trend in the results.

3 Draw a scatter graph for this set of data.
Plot both sets of data on the same graph but use a different symbol to plot each data set, for example, dots and crosses.

Mathematics and science test scores for 12 students												
Student	A	B	C	D	E	F	G	H	I	J	K	L
Maths	29	28	47	17	48	41	29	19	24	27	31	43
Science	20	33	38	12	50	34	34	31	28	19	23	44

Do students do equally well in both Maths and Science?

4 Draw a time-series graph for this set of data about smoking in Britain.

Percentages of adults (aged 16 or over) smoking.								
Year	1974	1978	1982	1986	1990	1994	1998	2002
Men	51	45	38	35	31	28	30	27
Women	41	37	33	31	29	26	26	25

Plot the data on the same graph but with different symbols.

Describe the trend shown in the graph.

challenge

This table shows the median heights for boys aged 4 to 18 years.

Age	4	6	8	10	12	14	16	18
Height (cm)	102	115	128	138	149	164	174	176

a Plot this set of data as a time-series graph.

b Plot these boys' heights as points on the same graph.
Are any of the boys particularly tall or short for their age?
Explain your answer.

Name	Ben	Theo	Neil	Mike
Age	13	8	15	7
Height (cm)	180	126	155	118

5f Calculating averages

LEVEL 6

- Calculate averages for sets of data and choose the ones most appropriate for a particular problem.

Keywords
Assumed mean
Mean
Median
Mode
Range

- Averages are used to summarise a set of data.
  - **Mode**: the most common value
  - **Median**: the middle value when the data is put in order
  - **Mean**: add all the values and divide by number of items

example

The table shows the gender, age and amount of money spent by 12 customers in a coffee shop.
Calculate a suitable average for each type of data recorded.

Gender	F	F	F	M	F	M
Age	15	15	14	21	23	18
Spend	£1.85	£1.45	£1.85	£2.75	£3.05	£1.85

Gender	F	F	M	M	F	M
Age	14	11	42	14	16	16
Spend	£1.45	0	£8.45	0	£2.75	£3.05

It is possible that one father paid the bill for himself and two children.

Gender: The mode is Female.
This is the only average that can be found.

Age: Any average is possible but the median is a good choice.

11 14 14 14 15 15
16 16 18 21 23 42

Median age is $(15 + 16) \div 2 = 15.5$ years.

The mean of the ages would be affected by the one large value (42) and the mode is too variable.

Money spent: The mean is a good choice.
Mean spend = £28.50 ÷ 12 = £2.38

- To work out what is a suitable average, think about.
  - how easy it is to calculate
  - how well it summarises all the data
  - if it would be affected by one very large or small value.

- You can also use the **range** of values to help you summarise the data.
  Range = maximum value − minimum value

Exercise 5f

1 Find the mean, median and mode of each of these sets of data.

a 8, 5, 5, 7, 9 **b** 6, 7, 24, 9, 14, 9 **c** 4, 3, 2, 8, 6, 5, 8, 5

d 1.4, 1.8, 1.7, 1.6, 1.5 **e** -2, 4, 0, 4, -3, 2, 0

2 A volunteer working at a charity television event took these donations over the telephone.

£5	£15	£10	£7	£5	£5
£12	£15	£5	£500	£20	£10

a Find the mode, mean and median of this set of data.

b Are each of the averages you calculated representative of the whole data?
Explain your answer and say which average you would use in this case.

3 This table shows the number of words on each of the first eight pages of a book.

Page	1	2	3	4	5	6	7	8
No. of words	30	125	159	133	121	147	128	133

a Find the mode, mean and median of this set of data.

b Are each of the averages you found representative of the whole data?
Explain your answer.

c Find the range of this set of data.

d Which average would you use to represent the data?
Explain why.

4 This frequency table shows the ages of people attending a computer club.

Age	14	15	16
Frequency	8	11	4

a Find the mode of this set of data.

b Find the median age of the people attending the club.

c Find the mean of the ages.

The mode is the age with the greatest frequency.
The median is the value in the middle position.
To find the mean, calculate the total of all the ages ($14 \times 8, \ldots$) and divide by the total of all the frequencies.

challenge

This bar chart shows the number of points awarded to students in class 9X in a sports competition.

Calculate the mode, median and mean of this set of data.
Show all of your working.

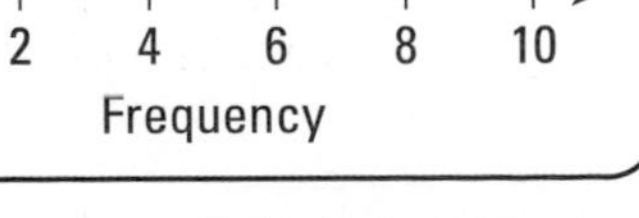

5 Consolidation

5a

1 Students in class 9B were given a choice of topics for a statistics project.
For each of the topics, suggest one conjecture that could be made and tested.

a Healthy lifestyles
b Travel to school
c Leisure and recreation

2 What makes a good conjecture?
Write a list of key points that would help somebody to devise a suitable conjecture to investigate in a statistical enquiry.

5b

3 This question was included in a questionnaire.

How much television do you watch?

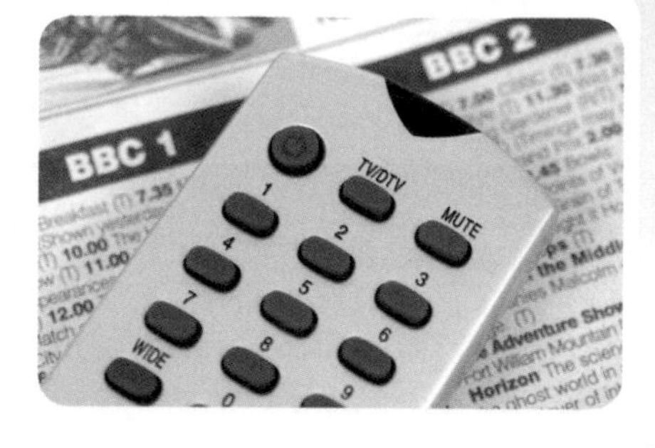

a Explain why the answers to this question might not be easy to analyse.
b Write a better version of this question.

5c

4 Marie records the ages of 30 people in a survey.

15	23	45	71	19	8	16	17	24	35
28	17	19	24	33	11	52	26	31	28
44	63	32	34	28	31	47	32	29	28

Construct a frequency table for this set of data with the ages organised into suitable groups.

5 Jack measures the heights, in centimetres, of 40 seedlings in a scientific experiment.

13.5	13.6	13.7	12.9	14.0	13.6	13.2	12.6	13.5	13.8
13.2	13.7	13.7	13.2	13.1	13.1	14.2	13.2	13.8	13.2
14.5	13.7	13.9	13.8	14.4	13.9	13.5	13.3	13.0	13.4
13.5	14.1	13.5	13.5	13.7	12.9	14.0	13.6	14.1	12.7

Construct a frequency table for this set of data.

You might find it easier to select class intervals for the data, eg. $12.5 \leq h < 13.0$

6 This table shows the sports options chosen by students in class 9Y.

Option	Football	Hockey	Rounders	Tennis
Frequency	9	11	7	4

a Draw a bar chart for this set of data.

b Draw a pie chart for the same set of data.

7 Draw a frequency diagram for this set of continuous data.

Length, l mm	Frequency
$120 \leq l < 130$	48
$130 \leq l < 140$	27
$140 \leq l < 150$	16
$150 \leq l < 160$	2

8 The table shows the growth of the population of New York City.
Draw a time-series graph for this set of data.

Year	1800	1850	1900	1950	2000
Population (thousands)	79	696	3437	7891	8008

9 This table shows the scores of 12 students in their Mathematics and French tests.
Draw a scatter graph for this set of data.

Student	A	B	C	D	E	F	G	H	I	J	K	L
Maths	32	41	26	17	27	43	29	17	24	31	42	28
French	31	22	25	21	37	26	32	29	14	25	18	35

10 This frequency table shows the number of points awarded to competitors in an athletics competition.

Points	0	1	2	3	4	5
Frequency	13	28	41	39	21	7

Find the mean, median and mode of this set of data.
Show all of your working.

5 Summary

Assessment criteria

- Construct pie charts, bar charts and frequency diagrams **Level 6**
- Design and use two-way tables **Level 6**

Level 6

1 In a survey, some people were asked

Would you like to eat an apple or an orange?

Here are the results:

Type of fruit	Number of people
Apple	15
Orange	14
Neither	11

Nick wants to draw a pie chart to show the results.
What angles should he draw for each category?

Alexander's answer ✔

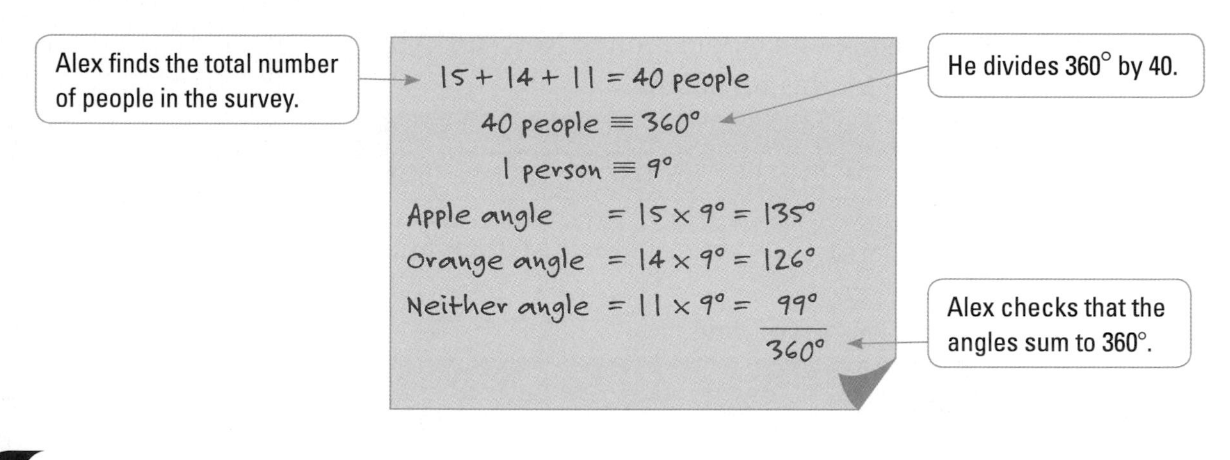

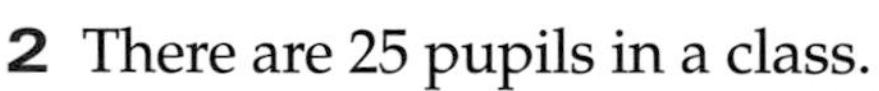

Level 6

2 There are 25 pupils in a class.
The table shows the information about their test results in Maths and English.

		English		
		Level 5	Level 6	Level 7
Maths	Level 5	0	1	1
	Level 6	2	7	0
	Level 7	2	1	4
	Level 8	0	1	6

a How many pupils had the same level in both Maths and English?
b How many pupils had a higher level in Maths than in English?

Key Stage 3 2008 5–7 Paper 1

6 Geometry

Measures

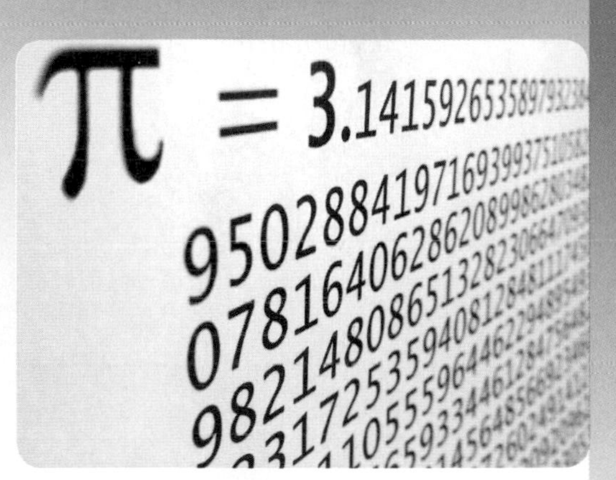

π = 3.141 592 653 589 793 238 462 643 ...

In 1873 the English mathematician, William Shanks, published the value of π to 707 decimal places. It had taken him 15 years to do the calculations. Unfortunately the last 180 digits were wrong due to an arithmetical mistake!

Now computers can calculate π to millions of decimal places but it is still impossible to know or predict all the digits of π.

What's the point? π is used in mathematical formulae involving circles. The value of π you use depends on the accuracy of the measurements and the accuracy you need for your answers.

Check in

Level 5

36

1 Calculate the perimeter and area of these shapes.

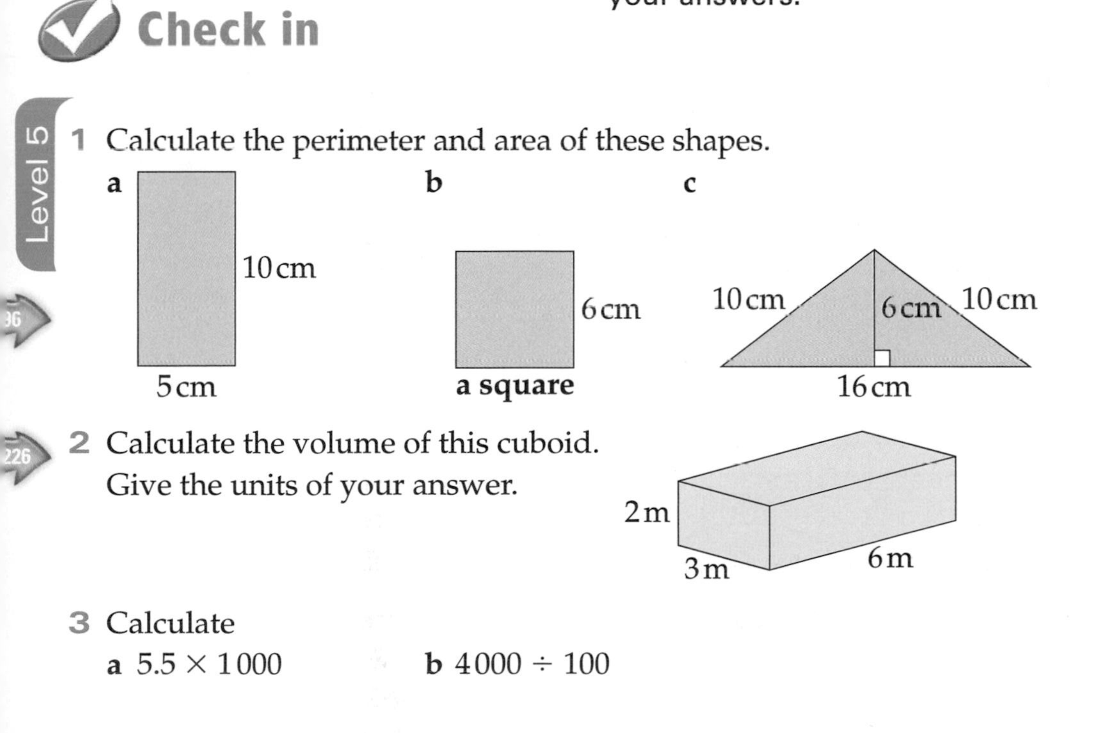

226

2 Calculate the volume of this cuboid.
Give the units of your answer.

3 Calculate

a 5.5×1000 b $4000 \div 100$

6a Measures 1

LEVEL 5/6

- Know the appropriate metric units to measure length, area, capacity and mass
- Convert between metric units

Keywords
Area *Mass*
Capacity *Metric*
Length *Volume*

- You can measure **length** using the **metric** units.

millimetre (mm) metre (m)
centimetre (cm) kilometre (km).

1 cm = 10 mm
1 m = 100 cm
1 km = 1000 m

- **Area** is the amount of surface a shape covers.

square centimetre (cm^2)
square metre (m^2)
hectare (ha)
square kilometre (km^2).

$1\,cm^2 = 100\,mm^2$
$1\,m^2 = 10\,000\,cm^2$
$1\,ha = 10\,000\,m^2$
$1\,km^2 = 1\,000\,000\,m^2$

- **Capacity** is the amount of liquid a container holds.
- **Volume** is the amount of space inside a 3-D shape.

millilitre (ml) cubic centimetre (cm^3)
centilitre (cl) cubic metre (m^3).
litre

1 litre = 1000 ml = 100 cl
1 litre = $1000\,cm^3$
$1\,m^3$ = 1000 litres
$1\,m^3 = 1\,000\,000\,cm^3$

- **Mass** is how heavy something is.

milligram (mg) kilogram (kg)
gram (g) tonne (t).

1 g = 1000 mg
1 kg = 1000 g
1 t = 1000 kg

The height of a male giraffe is about 5 m.

The area of a giraffe's foot is about $700\,cm^2$.

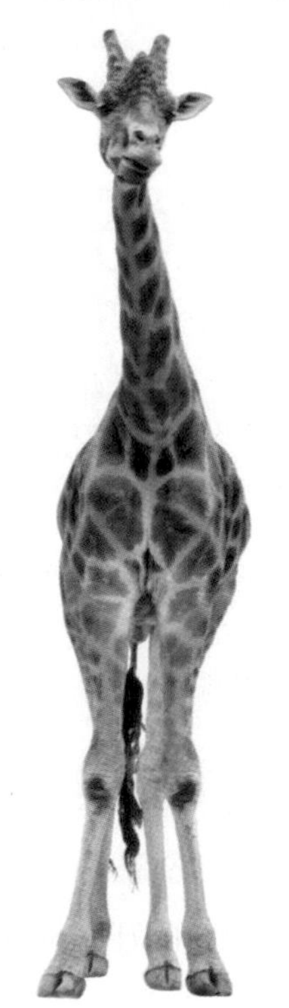

A giraffe only needs 2 litres of water a day.

The mass of a male giraffe is about 1.3 tonnes.

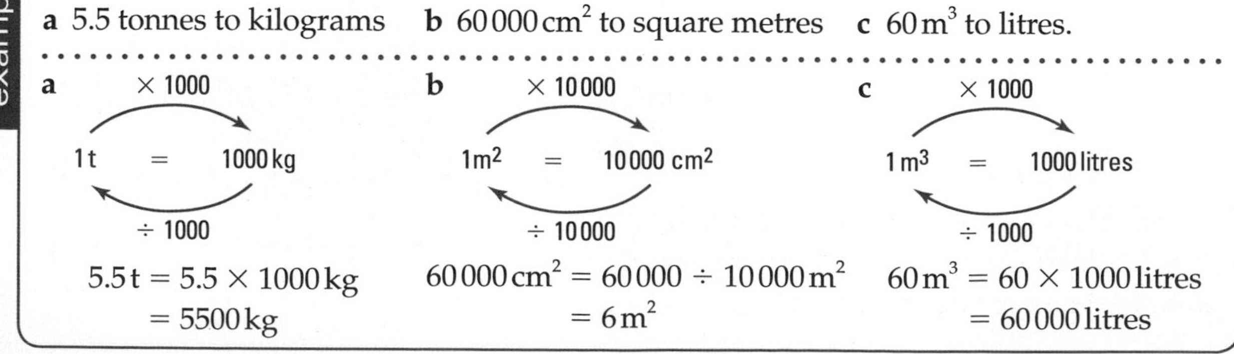

Convert

a 5.5 tonnes to kilograms **b** $60\,000\,cm^2$ to square metres **c** $60\,m^3$ to litres.

a

$5.5\,t = 5.5 \times 1000\,kg$
$= 5500\,kg$

b

$60\,000\,cm^2 = 60\,000 \div 10\,000\,m^2$
$= 6\,m^2$

c

$60\,m^3 = 60 \times 1000$ litres
$= 60\,000$ litres

Grade D

Exercise 6a

1 Choose the most sensible estimate for

a the mass of an apple	10 g	100 g	1 kg
b the area of a table	1 cm^2	1 m^2	1 ha
c the diagonal length of a computer monitor	50 mm	5 cm	50 cm
d the capacity of a can of drink	33 ml	33 cl	33 litres
e the distance from Madrid to Lisbon	600 cm	600 m	600 km
f the mass of a van	90 kg	900 kg	9 t
g the volume of a house brick.	140 cm^3	1400 cm^3	14 000 cm^3

2 Convert these metric measurements to the units in brackets.

a 480 cm (m) b 4.5 cm^2 (mm^2)

c 5000 m^2 (ha) d 4 000 000 cm^3 (m^3)

e 75 cl (litres) f 8 m^2 (cm^2)

g 0.75 kg (g) h 650 m (km)

i 0.5 m^3 (cm^3) j 750 kg (tonnes)

3 A rectangular football pitch measures 90 metres by 50 metres. Calculate the area in

a square metres b hectares.

4 A trough is in the shape of a cuboid measuring 120 cm by 60 cm by 35 cm.

a Calculate the volume in cubic centimetres.

b How many litres of water will fill the trough?

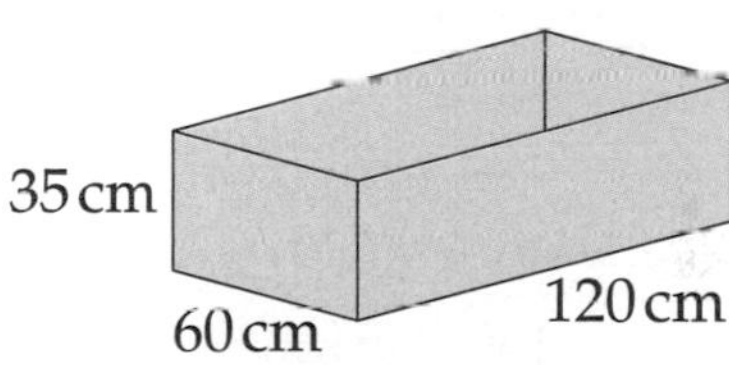

Did you know?

The area of the UK is $\frac{1}{4}$ million square kilometres.

Russia is the world's largest country with an area of 17 million square kilometres.

Be careful to count how many zeros you have.

activity

Fold a sheet of A4 paper in half. This is now A5 paper. Folding a sheet of A5 paper gives A6 size, and so on.

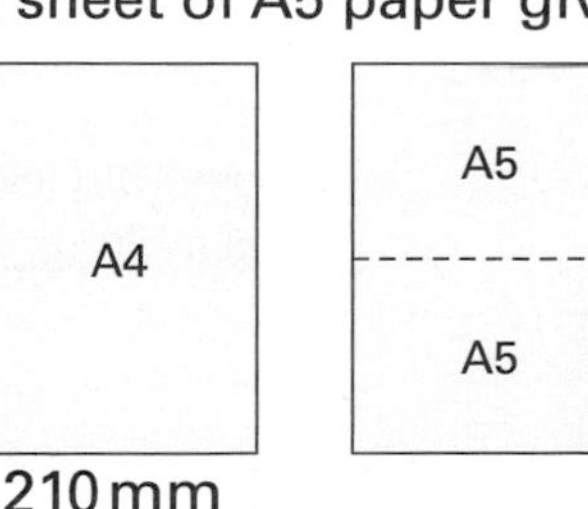

A sheet of A4 paper measures 297 mm by 210 mm. Copy and complete the table with the length and width of the paper sizes A1 to A8.

Size	Measurements
A1	
A2	
A3	
A4	297 mm × 210 mm
A5	
A6	
A7	
A8	

6b Measures 2

LEVEL 6

- Know rough metric equivalents for imperial measures in daily use
- Know that a measurement is not exact

Keywords
Capacity *Mass*
Imperial *Measurement*
Length *Metric*
Degree of accuracy

You may still use some of the **imperial** units of **measurement**.

- You can measure **length** using
  inch (in) 12 in = 1 ft
  foot (ft) 3 ft = 1 yd
  yard (yd)
  mile.

1 inch ≈ 2.5 cm
1 yard ≈ 1 metre
5 miles ≈ 8 km

- You can measure **capacity** using
  pint 8 pints = 1 gallon
  gallon.

1 gallon ≈ 4.5 litres
1 pint ≈ 0.6 litre
1 pint ≈ 600 ml

- You can measure **mass** using
  ounce (oz) 16 oz = 1 lb
  pound (lb).

1 oz ≈ 30 g
1 kg ≈ 2.2 lb

example

Use approximations to convert

a 60 miles to kilometres **b** 240 ml to pints.

a
5 miles = 8 km
1 mile = 8 ÷ 5 km
60 miles = 60 × 8 ÷ 5 km
= 480 ÷ 5 km
= 96 km

b
1 pint ≈ 600 ml (× 600 from pints to ml; ÷ 600 from ml to pints)

240 ml = 240 ÷ 600 pints
= 0.4 pints

- When you measure a quantity, the measurement can never be exact. You give the measurement to the appropriate **degree of accuracy**.

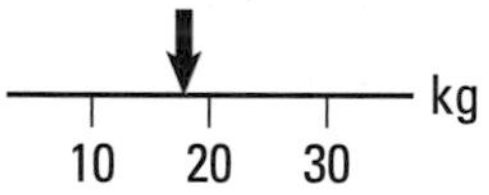

The measurement can be given as 20 kg.

7b

The population of Tahiti is 151 000.
The area of China is 36 000 km².
The length of the Humber Bridge is 2220 m.
The Loch Ness Monster is worth £5 000 000 a year to tourism in Scotland.

None of these measurement are exact.

Exercise 6b

Use approximations to answer these questions.

1 Which measurement is larger?
Explain your reasoning.

a 1 mile or 1 kilometre **b** 1 pound (lb) or 1 kilogram
c 1 inch or 1 centimetre **d** 1 pint or 1 litre
e 1 ounce or 1 gram

2 Convert these imperial measurements to the **metric** units in brackets.

a 6 oz (g) **b** 16 feet (m) **c** 10 gallons (ml)
d 87.5 in (cm) **e** 93.5 lb (kg) **f** 36 in (m)
g 47 miles (km) **h** 4.5 pints (ml)

3 The distances, in kilometres, between four places in France are shown on the chart.

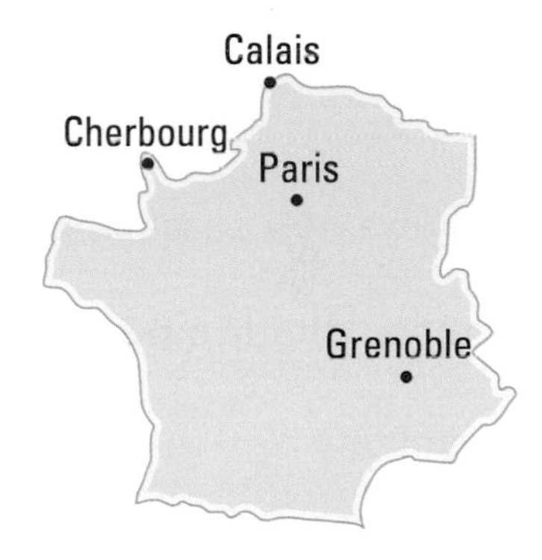

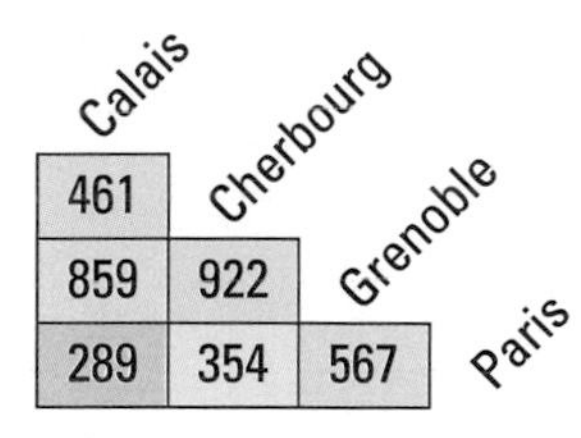

Calais			
461	Cherbourg		
859	922	Grenoble	
289	354	567	Paris

Convert the distances to miles.

4 Convert these metric measurements to the imperial units in brackets.

a 450 g (oz) **b** 10 cm (in) **c** 9 litres (pints)
d 36 litres (gallons) **e** 90 cm (feet) **f** 1.7 m (in)
g 3.5 kg (lb) **h** 150 ml (pints)

activity

Change each saying to a metric equivalent.

a Give him an inch and he will take a yard.
b You can't get a quart into a pint pot.
c A miss is a good as a mile.
d I wouldn't touch it with a ten-foot barge pole.
e An ounce of prevention is worth a pound of cure.

1 quart = 2 pints

Find some more sayings with imperial units and change them to their metric equivalents.

6c Area of a 2-D shape

LEVEL 6

- Calculate the area of a triangle, a parallelogram and a trapezium
- Calculate the area of shapes made from rectangles and triangles

Keywords
Area *Trapezium*
Base *Triangle*
Parallelogram
Perpendicular height

You can calculate the **area** of a rectangle and a **triangle**.

- Area of a rectangle $= l \times w$

- Area of a triangle $= \frac{1}{2} \times b \times h$

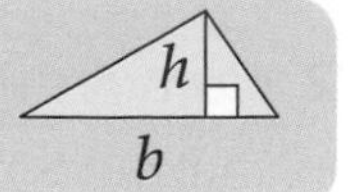

You can divide a **parallelogram** into two congruent triangles.

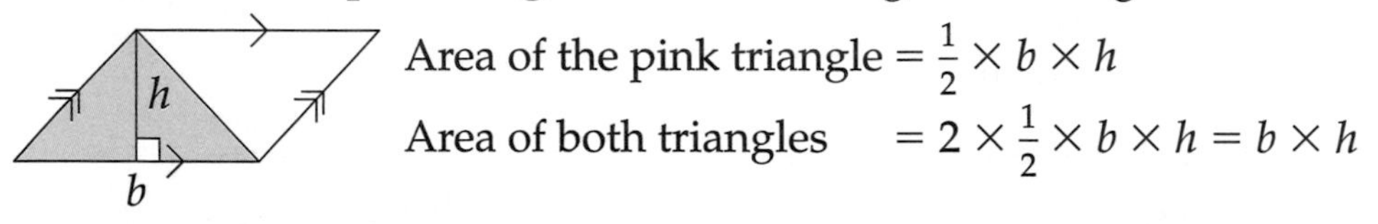

Area of the pink triangle $= \frac{1}{2} \times b \times h$

Area of both triangles $= 2 \times \frac{1}{2} \times b \times h = b \times h$

- Area of a parallelogram = **base × perpendicular height**

You can divide a **trapezium** into two triangles.

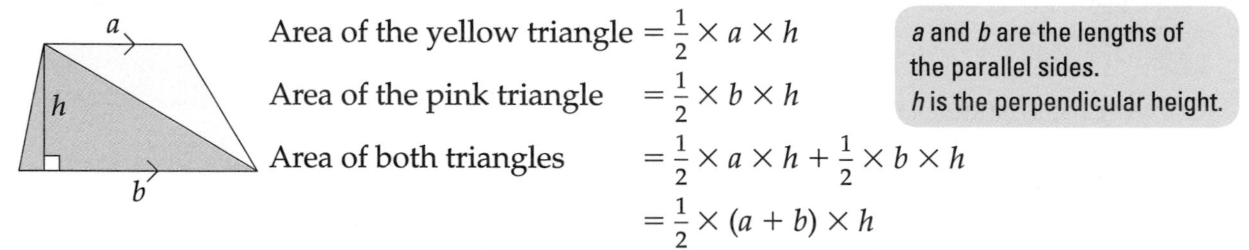

Area of the yellow triangle $= \frac{1}{2} \times a \times h$

Area of the pink triangle $= \frac{1}{2} \times b \times h$

Area of both triangles $= \frac{1}{2} \times a \times h + \frac{1}{2} \times b \times h$

$= \frac{1}{2} \times (a + b) \times h$

a and *b* are the lengths of the parallel sides.
h is the perpendicular height.

- Area of a trapezium $= \frac{1}{2} \times (a + b) \times h$

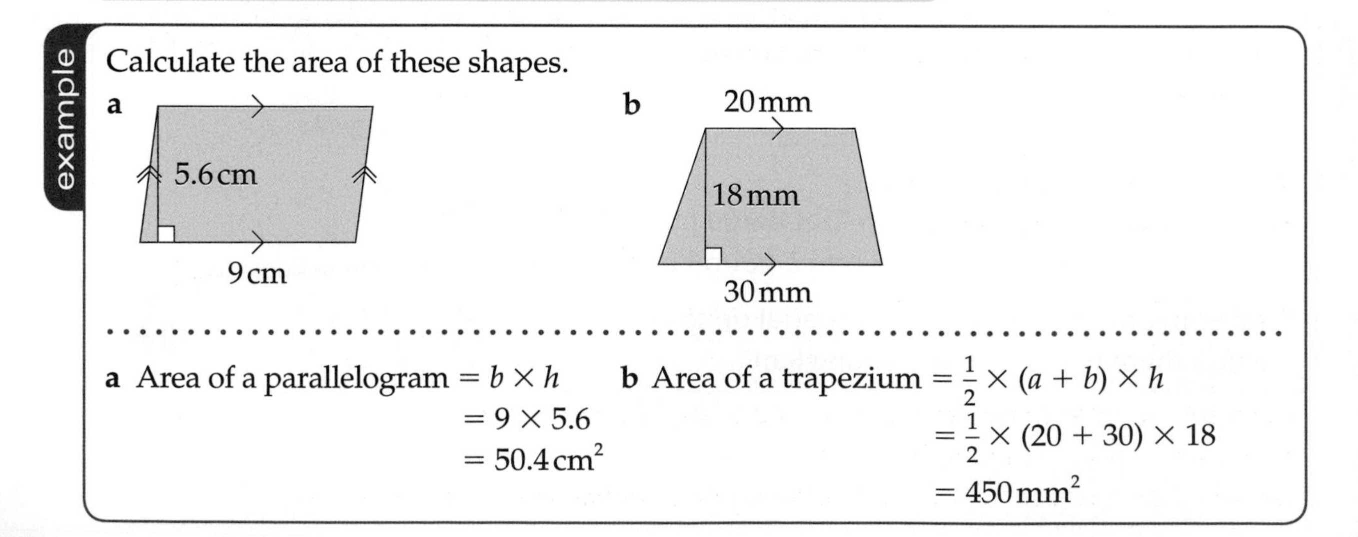

example

Calculate the area of these shapes.

a (parallelogram: 5.6 cm, 9 cm)

b (trapezium: 20 mm, 18 mm, 30 mm)

a Area of a parallelogram $= b \times h$
$= 9 \times 5.6$
$= 50.4\,\text{cm}^2$

b Area of a trapezium $= \frac{1}{2} \times (a + b) \times h$
$= \frac{1}{2} \times (20 + 30) \times 18$
$= 450\,\text{mm}^2$

Exercise 6c

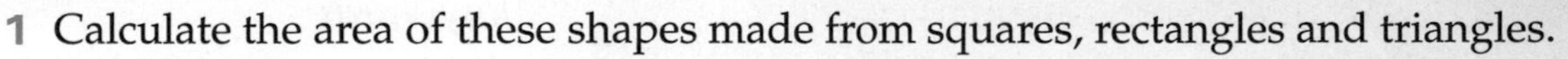

1 Calculate the area of these shapes made from squares, rectangles and triangles.

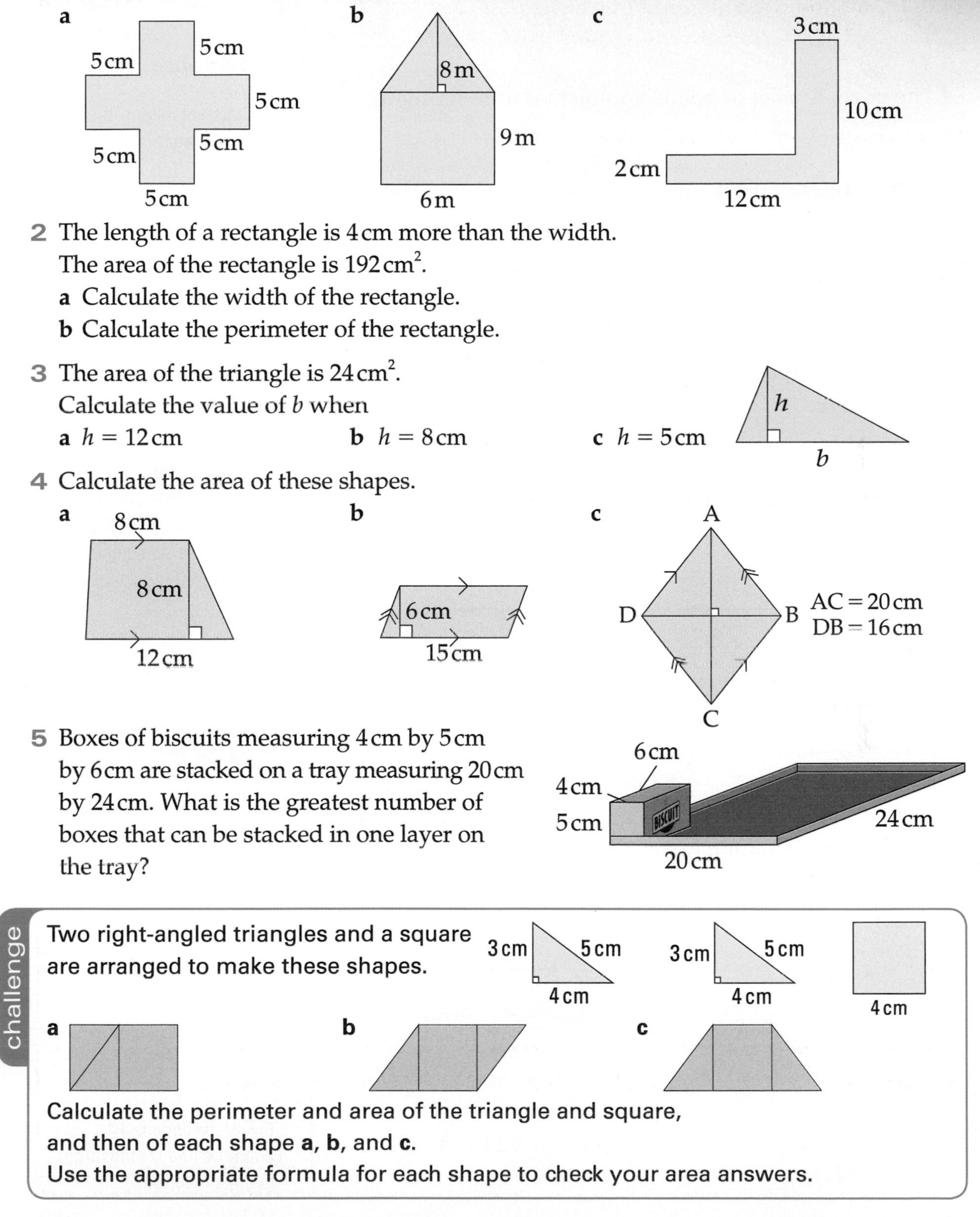

2 The length of a rectangle is 4 cm more than the width.
The area of the rectangle is 192 cm^2.

a Calculate the width of the rectangle.

b Calculate the perimeter of the rectangle.

3 The area of the triangle is 24 cm^2.
Calculate the value of b when

a $h = 12$ cm **b** $h = 8$ cm **c** $h = 5$ cm

4 Calculate the area of these shapes.

5 Boxes of biscuits measuring 4 cm by 5 cm by 6 cm are stacked on a tray measuring 20 cm by 24 cm. What is the greatest number of boxes that can be stacked in one layer on the tray?

challenge

Two right-angled triangles and a square are arranged to make these shapes.

Calculate the perimeter and area of the triangle and square, and then of each shape **a**, **b**, and **c**.
Use the appropriate formula for each shape to check your area answers.

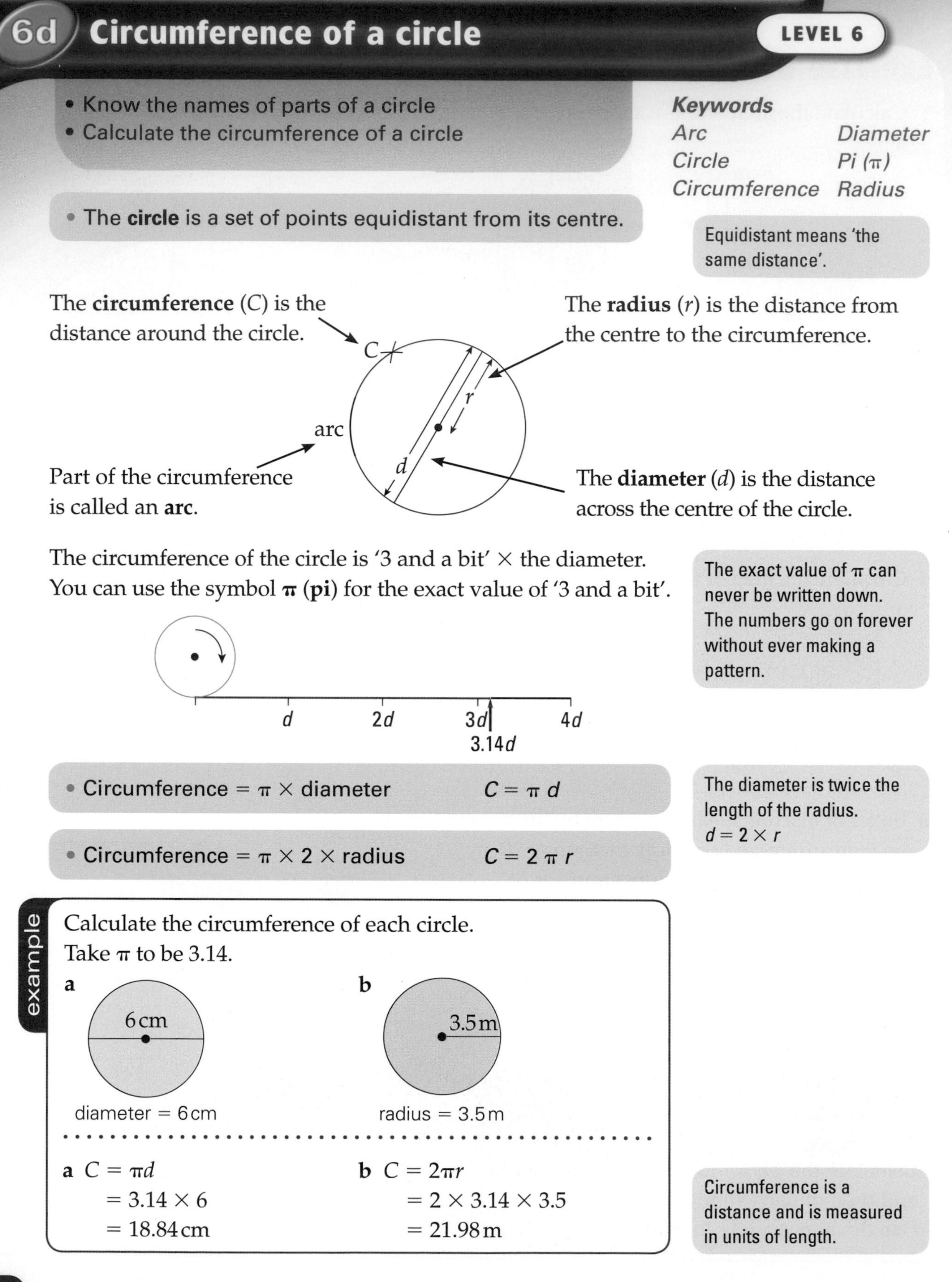

6d Circumference of a circle

LEVEL 6

- Know the names of parts of a circle
- Calculate the circumference of a circle

Keywords
Arc *Diameter*
Circle *Pi (π)*
Circumference *Radius*

- The **circle** is a set of points equidistant from its centre.

Equidistant means 'the same distance'.

The **circumference** (C) is the distance around the circle.

The **radius** (r) is the distance from the centre to the circumference.

Part of the circumference is called an **arc**.

The **diameter** (d) is the distance across the centre of the circle.

The circumference of the circle is '3 and a bit' × the diameter.
You can use the symbol **π (pi)** for the exact value of '3 and a bit'.

The exact value of π can never be written down. The numbers go on forever without ever making a pattern.

- Circumference = π × diameter $C = \pi d$
- Circumference = π × 2 × radius $C = 2\pi r$

The diameter is twice the length of the radius. $d = 2 \times r$

example

Calculate the circumference of each circle.
Take π to be 3.14.

a

diameter = 6 cm

b

radius = 3.5 m

a $C = \pi d$
$= 3.14 \times 6$
$= 18.84$ cm

b $C = 2\pi r$
$= 2 \times 3.14 \times 3.5$
$= 21.98$ m

Circumference is a distance and is measured in units of length.

Exercise 6d

d is the diameter.
r is the radius.

Use $\pi = 3.14$ for all the questions on this page.

1 Calculate the circumference of these circles.

a $d = 8$ cm **b** $d = 20$ cm
c $r = 4.5$ cm **d** $r = 9$ m

2 The London Eye wheel has a diameter of 135 metres. Calculate the distance you would travel in one complete revolution.

3 The diameter of a wheel on a bicycle is 70 cm.

a Calculate the circumference.
b Work out the number of rotations of the wheel during a journey of one kilometre.

4 Calculate the perimeter of these shapes.

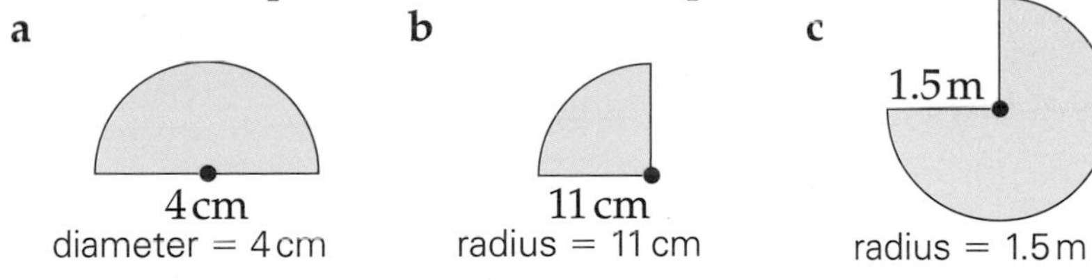

5 A regular hexagon fits inside a circle of radius 5 m.

a Calculate
  i the perimeter of the hexagon
  ii the circumference of the circle.
b Explain why you know the perimeter of the hexagon is less than the circle's circumference.

6 The circumference of the top of the pie is 36 cm. What is the diameter?

Did you know?

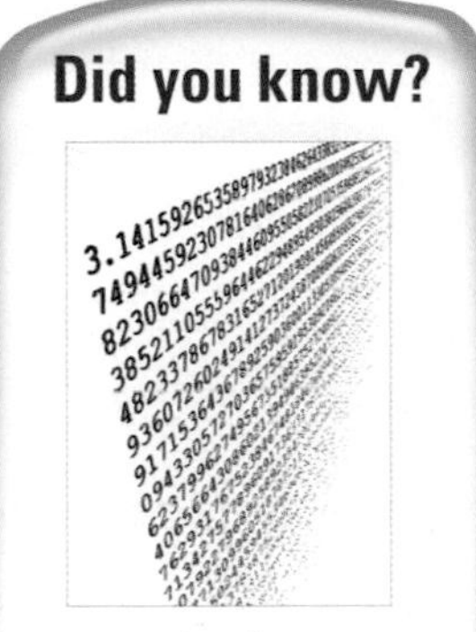

In 2002, scientists at the University of Tokyo calculated π to over one trillion (one million million) decimal places. The computer calculation took 25 days.

activity

Make a collection of circular objects, for example, a coin, a plate.
Use a ruler and string to measure the diameter and circumference of your objects.
Copy and complete the table.

Object	Diameter	Circumference	$\pi \times$ diameter

You should find that the answers in the last two columns are approximately the same for each object.

You could work out the difference between the last two columns to see how accurate your measurements were!

Area of a circle

LEVEL 6

- Know the names of parts of a circle
- Calculate the area of a circle

Keywords
Chord *Sector*
Diameter *Segment*
Pi (π) *Semicircle*
Radius

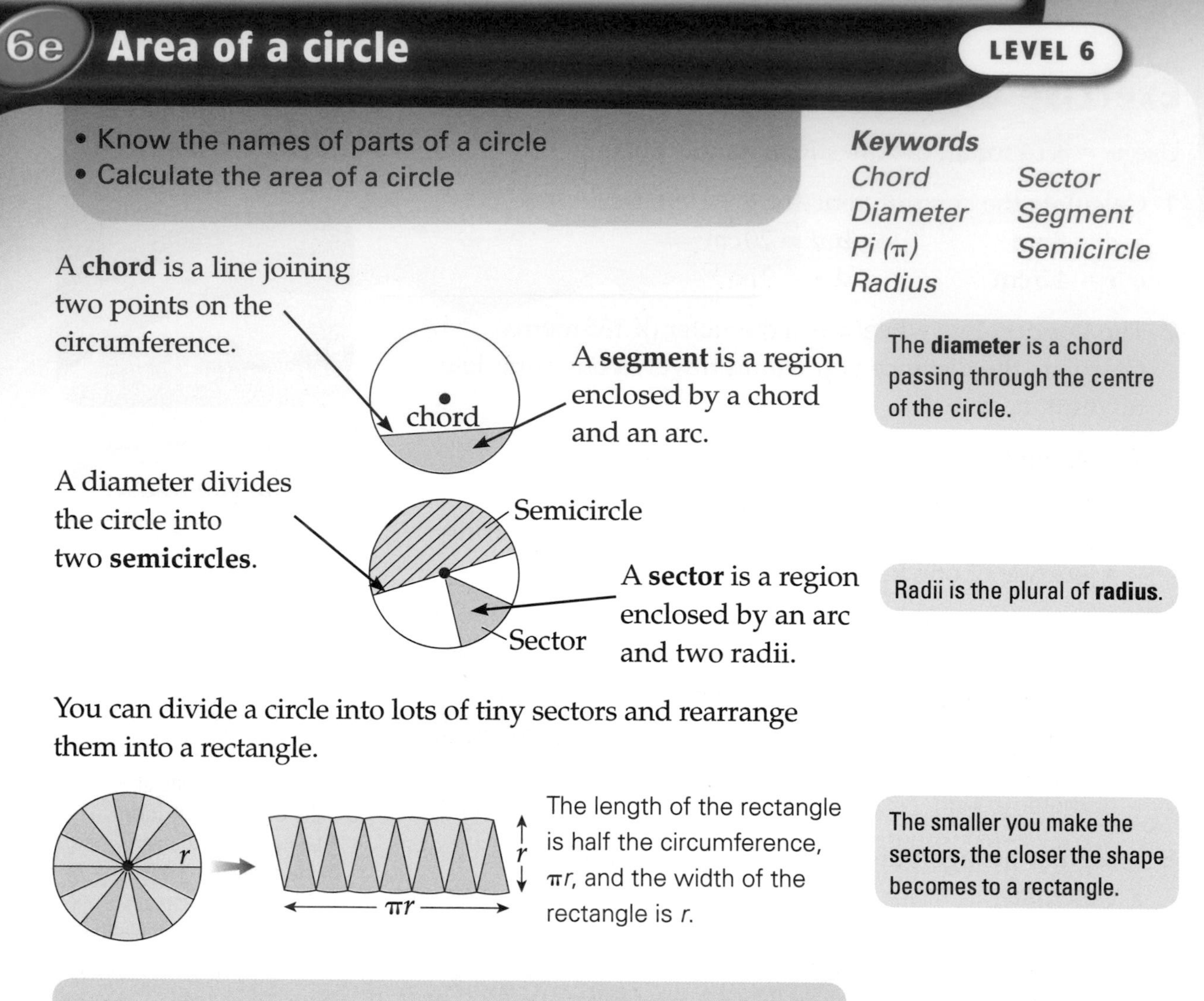

The **diameter** is a chord passing through the centre of the circle.

Radii is the plural of **radius**.

You can divide a circle into lots of tiny sectors and rearrange them into a rectangle.

The length of the rectangle is half the circumference, πr, and the width of the rectangle is r.

The smaller you make the sectors, the closer the shape becomes to a rectangle.

- Area of a circle = π × radius × radius

$$\text{Area} = \pi r^2$$

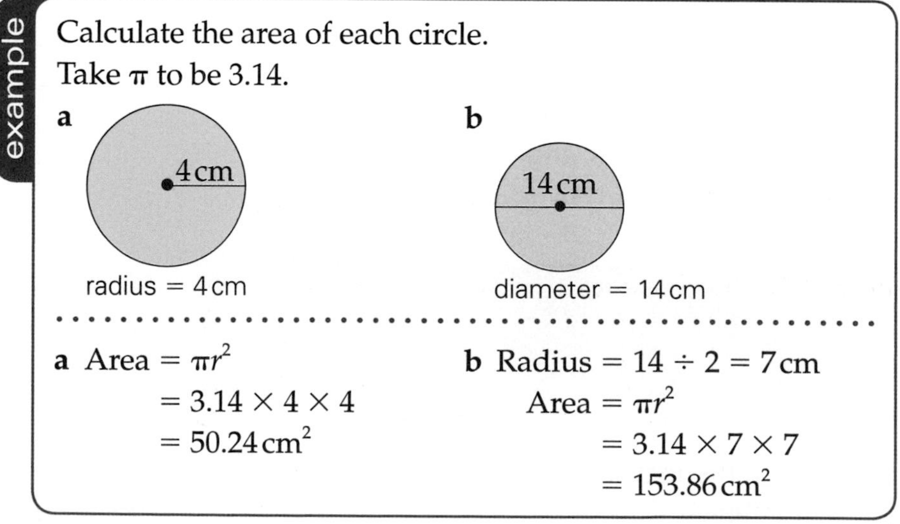

example

Calculate the area of each circle.
Take π to be 3.14.

a radius = 4 cm

b diameter = 14 cm

a Area $= \pi r^2$
$= 3.14 \times 4 \times 4$
$= 50.24\text{ cm}^2$

b Radius $= 14 \div 2 = 7\text{ cm}$
Area $= \pi r^2$
$= 3.14 \times 7 \times 7$
$= 153.86\text{ cm}^2$

Area is measured in square units.

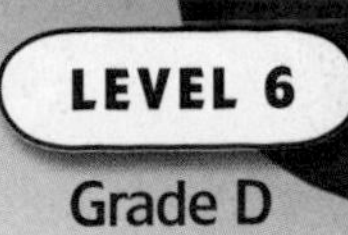

Exercise 6e

Grade D

Use $\pi = 3.14$ for all the questions on this page.

r is the radius.

1 Calculate the area of these circles.

a $r = 10\,\text{cm}$ **b** $r = 20\,\text{cm}$

c $r = 9\,\text{cm}$ **d** $r = 2.5\,\text{m}$

2 A circular patio has a diameter of 3.5 metres. Calculate the area of the paving stones.

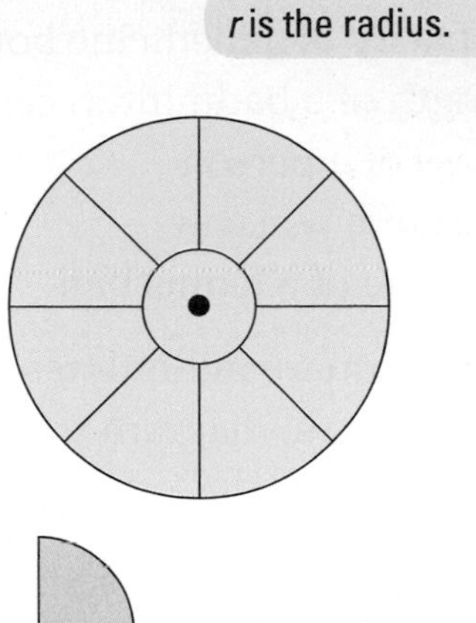

3 These shapes are based on a circle of radius 6 cm. Calculate the area of each shape.

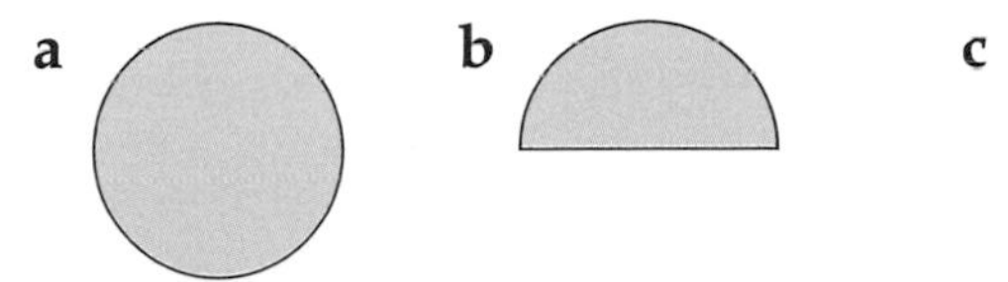

The shape in part **c** is called a quadrant.

4 The large circle has a radius of 8 cm.
Calculate the blue area and the green area for each shape.
Show your working out.

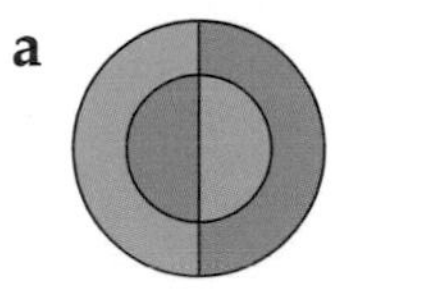

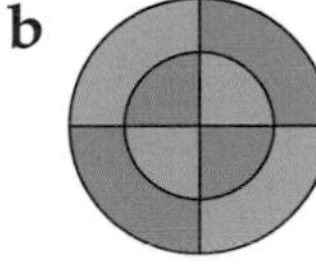

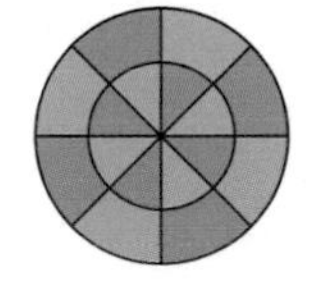

5 A circumscribed circle of radius 5 cm is drawn round a square.
Calculate the area of

a the square

b the circle

c the shaded region.

5 cm

Circumscribed means it is drawn touching the corners of the shape.

challenge

a Use compasses to construct a right-angled triangle with lengths 6 cm, 8 cm and 10 cm.

b Construct the angle bisectors and the inscribed circle.

c Measure the radius of the circle.

d Calculate the area of the circle.

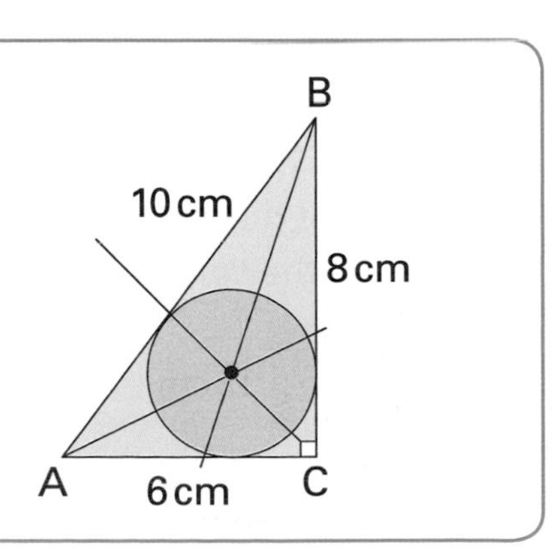

p. 52

6a

1 Choose the most sensible estimate for these.

a the capacity of a medicine bottle	20 ml	200 ml	2 litres
b the length of a badminton court	13.4 cm	13.4 m	13.4 km
c the mass of a person	6 kg	60 kg	600 kg
d the area of a window	1 mm^2	1 cm^2	1 m^2
e the volume of a tennis ball	14 cm^3	140 cm^3	1400 cm^3

2 How many square millimetres are there in one square centimetre? Draw an accurate diagram to show your working.

3 Convert these metric measurements to the units in brackets.

a 67 mm (cm) **b** 850 g (kg)
c 8 m^3 (cm^3) **d** 1 km (mm)
e 400 g (kg) **f** 7.5 ha (m^2)
g 3.5 m (mm) **h** 75 000 cl (litres)
i 5 m^2 (cm^2) **j** 18 tonnes (kg)

6b

4 Convert these imperial measurements to the metric units in brackets using approximations.

a 2.5 oz (g) **b** 7 pints (ml)
c 12 in (cm) **d** 40 in (cm)
e 154 lb (kg) **f** 35 miles (km)
g 8.5 pints (litres) **h** 2.5 gallons (ml)

5 Convert these metric measurements to the imperial units in brackets using approximations.

a 160 cm (in) **b** 3.9 litres (pints)
c 84 km (miles) **d** 48 kg (lb)
e 45 g (oz) **f** 49.5 litres (gallons)
g 8.4 m (feet) **h** 2100 ml (pints)

6c

6 The area of the rectangle and the triangle are the same. Calculate the value of h.

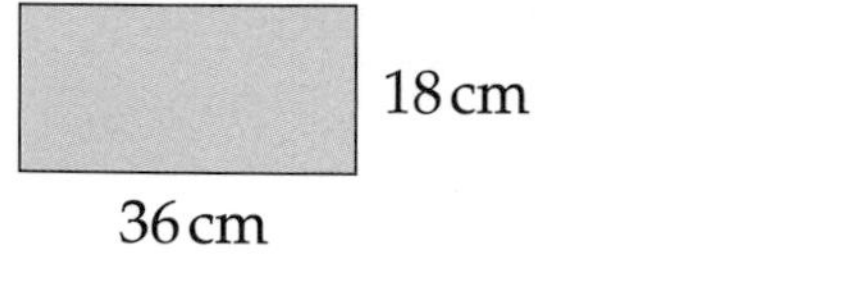

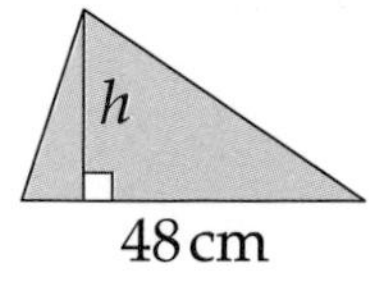

6c

7 Calculate the area of these shapes.
State the units of your answers.

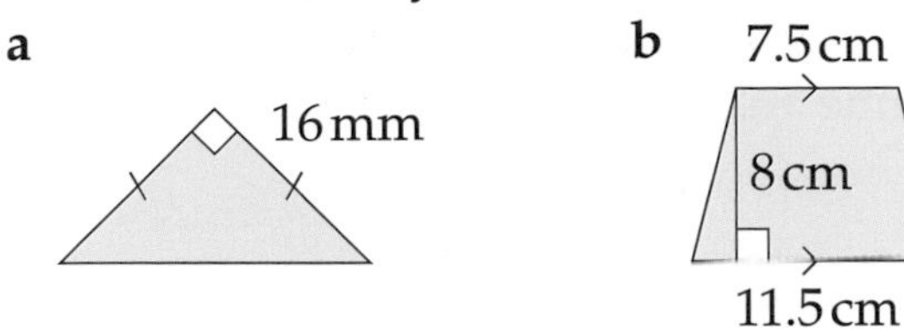

6d

8 Calculate the circumference of these circles.
Use $\pi = 3.14$.

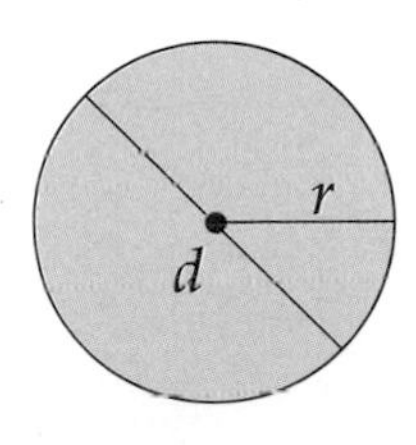

a $r = 6$ cm
b $r = 8.5$ m
c $d = 15$ cm
d $d = 11$ cm
e $r = 2.75$ cm

9 A coin with a diameter of 25 mm is rolled along a table.
Calculate

a the circumference
b the distance travelled in metres during 20 complete rotations.

Use $\pi = 3.14$.

6e

10 Calculate the area of these circles.
Use $\pi = 3.14$.

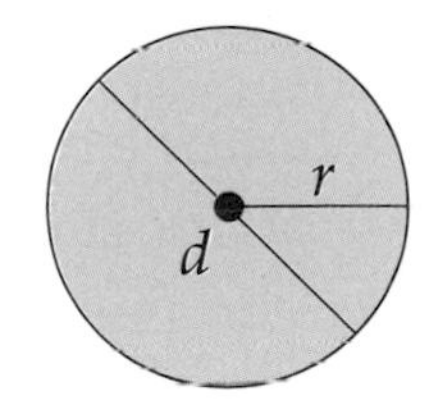

a $r = 7$ cm
b $r = 3.5$ m
c $r = 9.5$ cm
d $d = 11$ cm
e $d = 25$ cm

11 A circumcircle is drawn for a regular hexagon.
The hexagon has a perimeter of 36 cm.
Calculate the area of the circle.
Use $\pi = 3.14$.

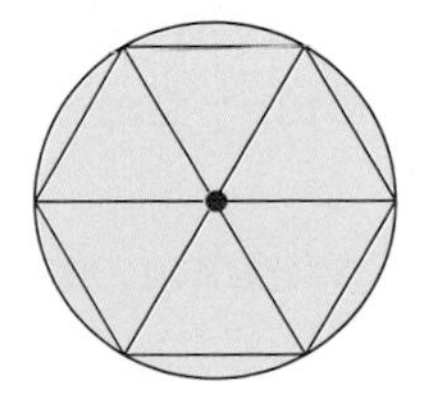

6 Summary

Assessment criteria

- Use the formula for the area of a rectangle and a parallelogram **Level 6**
- Know and use the formulae for the circumference and the area of a circle **Level 6**

Level 6

1 The triangle and the parallelogram have the same area.

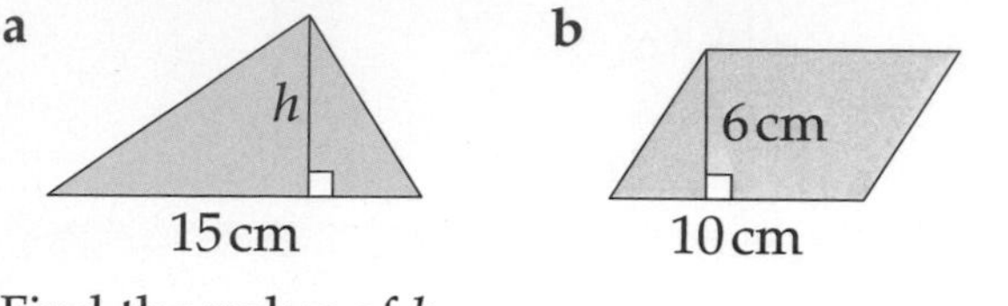

Find the value of h.

Ritu's answer ✔

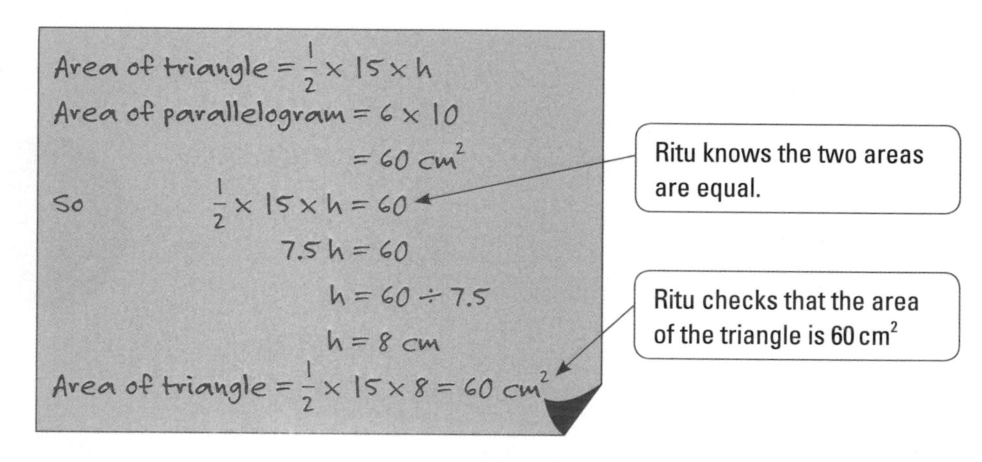

Level 6

2 a The cross-section of a cylindrical cotton reel is a circle. The diameter of this circle is 3 cm. What is the circumference of this circle?

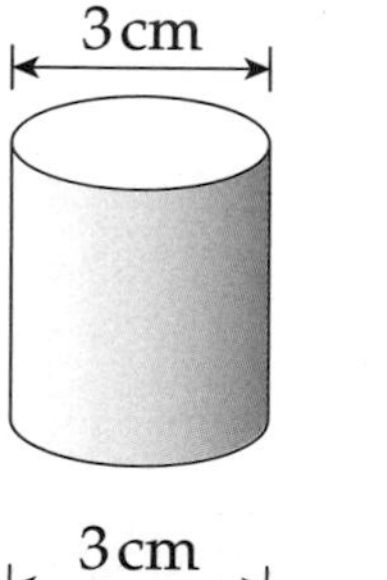

b 91 metres of cotton goes round the cotton reel. About how many times does the cotton go round the reel? Show your working, and give your answer to the nearest ten.

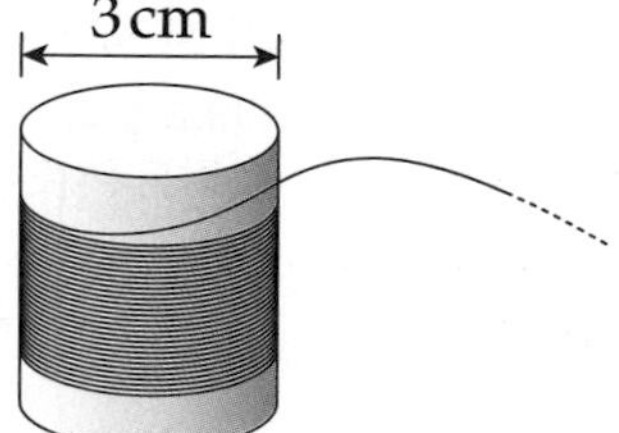

Key Stage 3 2004 5–7 Paper 2

7 Number

Calculations

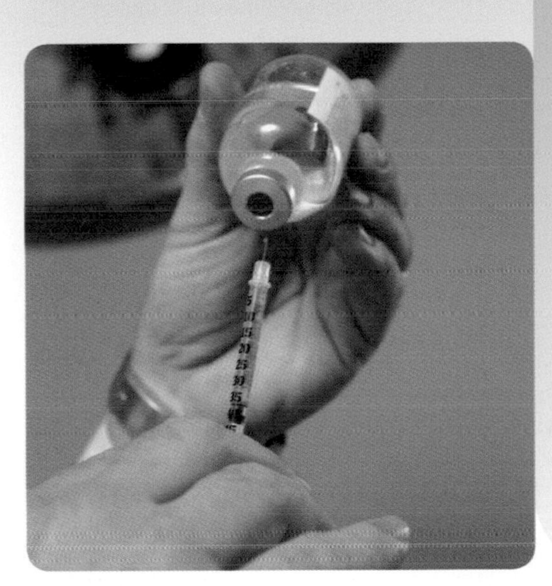

Doctors and nurses often have to work out doses of medication to give to patients. In an emergency they must do this very quickly.

What's the point? Even if they use a calculator they must still be able to approximate the answer themselves and spot if they have made a mistake. This requires a good knowledge of mental arithmetic. A dose that is too high or too low could have disastrous consequences for the patient.

Check in

Level 4

1 Calculate

a 2.9×100 **b** $38.6 \div 10$ **c** $42 \div 0.1$ **d** 42×0.1

2 Round each of these numbers to the nearest **i** 100 **ii** 10 **iii** 1 decimal place.

a 2456.78 **b** 928.2735

3 Calculate these using an appropriate method.

a $5.6 + 3.9$ **b** $9.3 - 2.9$ **c** $13.8 + 4.9$ **d** $18.3 - 9.4$

4 Calculate these using an appropriate method.

a 13×11 **b** 43×25 **c** 322×23 **d** 11×2.8

5 Calculate these using an appropriate method.
Give your answer to 1dp as appropriate

a $126 \div 8$ **b** $240 \div 15$ **c** $170 \div 9$ **d** $500 \div 17$

6 Work out these calculation using the order of operations.

a $(3^2 + 5) \times 2$ **b** $\dfrac{4^2 \times (7 - 2)}{10}$

7a Powers of 10

LEVEL 6

- Multiply and divide numbers by powers of 10
- Multiply and divide numbers written in index form

Keywords
Index notation
Power
Standard form

- You can write all **powers** of 10 using **index notation**.

The power is also called the index. It tells you how many times 10 is multiplied by itself.

1 thousand (kilo) $= 1000 = 10 \times 10 \times 10 = 10^3$

1 hundred $= 100 = 10 \times 10 = 10^2$

1 ten $= 10 = 10^1$

1 unit $= 1 = 10^0$

1 tenth $= \frac{1}{10} = 0.1 = \frac{1}{10^1} = 10^{-1}$

1 hundredth (centi) $= \frac{1}{100} = 0.01 = \frac{1}{10^2} = 10^{-2}$

1 thousandth (milli) $= \frac{1}{1000} = 0.001 = \frac{1}{10^3} = 10^{-3}$

Any number to the power of zero is 1.

Negative powers represent fractions.

- You can multiply and divide by powers of 10 by moving the digits the correct number of decimal places.

example

Calculate these.

a 2.5×10^3 **b** $0.27 \div 0.1$ **c** 2.6×0.01

Re-write the calculations.

a $2.5 \times 10^3 = 2.5 \times 1000$

b $0.27 \div 0.1 = 0.27 \div \frac{1}{10}$

c $2.6 \times 0.01 = 2.6 \times \frac{1}{100}$

Simplify the calculations.

a $= 2500$

b $= 0.27 \times 10 = 2.7$

c $= 2.6 \div 100 = 0.026$

Dividing by $\frac{1}{10}$ is the same as multiplying by 10.

Multiplying by $\frac{1}{100}$ is the same as dividing by 100.

- You can multiply and divide numbers written in **index form**.

example

Calculate these.

a $10^3 \times 10^2$ **b** $10^4 \div 10^1$

a $10^3 \times 10^2 = (10 \times 10 \times 10) \times (10 \times 10) = 10^5$

p. 184

b $10^4 \div 10^1 = \dfrac{10 \times 10 \times 10 \times 10}{10} = 10 \times 10 \times 10 = 10^3$

The indices are added when multiplying. $10^3 \times 10^2 = 10^{3+2} = 10^5$

The indices are subtracted when dividing. $10^4 \div 10^1 = 10^{4-1} = 10^3$

Exercise 7a

1 Calculate these.

a 3×100 **b** $16 \div 10$ **c** $1.2 \times 10\,000$ **d** $3.7 \div 100$

e $180 \div 10$ **f** 13.2×100 **g** $75 \div 100$ **h** 0.93×1000

2 Calculate these.

a 37×0.1 **b** $78 \div 0.01$ **c** 5.1×0.1 **d** $9.3 \div 0.1$

e $8.3 \div 0.01$ **f** $0.48 \div 0.1$ **g** 0.54×0.01 **h** 483×0.01

3 Here are six number cards. Copy these statements and fill in the missing numbers using the cards.

10 100 1000 0.1 0.01 0.001

a $3 \times \square = 300$ **b** $0.43 \div \square = 43$ **c** $78 \div \square = 7.8$ **d** $2.1 \div \square = 21$

e $3 \times \square = 0.03$ **f** $0.02 \div \square = 20$ **g** $570 \times \square = 57$ **h** $3200 \div \square = 3.2$

4 Jenny works out $3.4 \times 23.4 = 79.56$ using a calculator.

a Use this information to work out these calculations without using a calculator.

i 34×23.4 **ii** 3.4×2.34 **iii** 34×234

b What other multiplications can you work out using Jenny's calculation?

5 2.5×10^3 is written in **standard form.**

Each of these numbers has been written in standard form.
Work out the size of each of the numbers.

a 2.7×10^3 **b** 5.6×10^4 **c** 1.3×10^5

d 6.2×10^4 **e** 4.1×10^6 **f** 2.7×10^2

g 3.6×10^3 **h** 1.4×10^4 **i** 1.7×10^5

6 Simplify these leaving your answer as a single power of the number.

a $10^2 \times 10^2$ **b** $10^4 \div 10^2$ **c** $10^3 \times 10^4$

d $10^5 \div 10^2$ **e** $10^3 \times 10^2$ **f** $10^5 \div 10^2$

g $10^7 \div 10^3$ **h** $10^5 \times 10$ **i** $10^6 \div 10^2$

Did you know?

1 cm

10 000 μm

A micron is used to measure really small lengths. One micron is a millionth of a metre. This is 1×10^{-6} m.

investigation

Hannah says that to multiply by a power of 10 you just look at the power and move the digits that number of places to the left.

a Investigate Hannah's method for multiplying by 10^2 and 10^3.

b Does Hannah's method work for dividing by powers of 10?

c Does Hannah's method work for negative powers of 10?

Rounding

LEVEL 5/6

- Round whole numbers to a given power of 10
- Round decimals to 2 decimal places
- Use rounding to make estimates

Keywords
Decimal places
Estimate
Rounding

- When you **round** a number, look at the next digit to see whether to round up or down.

If the next digit is 5 or more, the number is rounded up. If it is less than 5, the number is rounded down.

example

A young elephant has a mass of 229.476 kg.
What is the mass of the elephant to

a the nearest 100 kg
b the nearest 1 kg
c 2 decimal places?

In each case look at the next digit.

a 229.476 kg to the nearest 100 kg
$\approx$ 200 kg

Look at the tens digit: 2.
Round down to nearest 100.

200 229.476 300

b 229.476 kg to the nearest 1 kg
$\approx$ 229 kg

Look at the tenths digit: 4.
Round down to nearest 1.

229 229.476 230

c 229.476 kg to 2 decimal places
$\approx$ 229.48 kg

Look at the thousandths digit: 6.
Round up to 2 **decimal places**.

229.47 229.476 229.48

- You use **rounding** to make **estimates** in real-life examples.

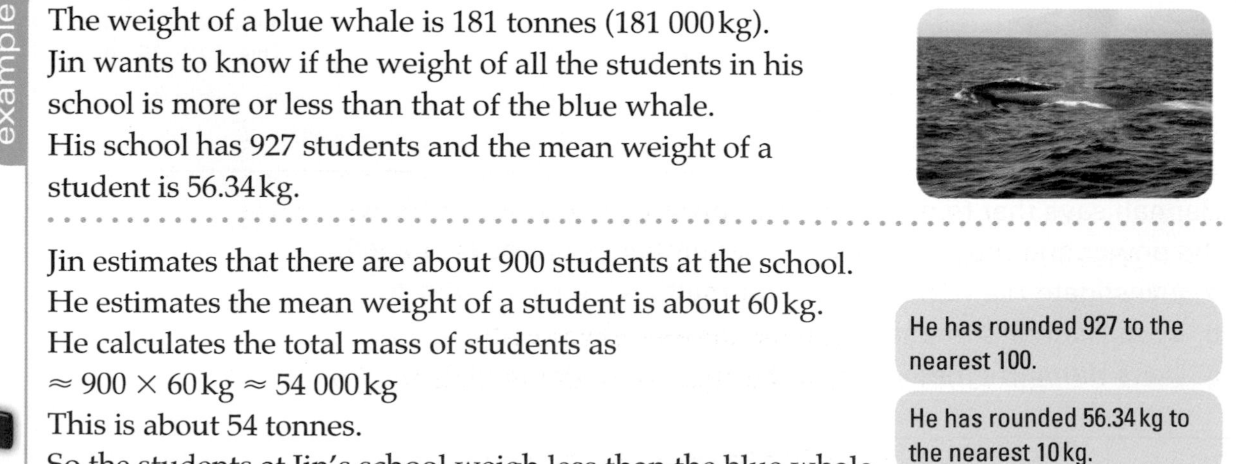

example

The weight of a blue whale is 181 tonnes (181 000 kg).
Jin wants to know if the weight of all the students in his school is more or less than that of the blue whale.
His school has 927 students and the mean weight of a student is 56.34 kg.

Jin estimates that there are about 900 students at the school.
He estimates the mean weight of a student is about 60 kg.
He calculates the total mass of students as
$\approx 900 \times 60\,\text{kg} \approx 54\,000\,\text{kg}$
This is about 54 tonnes.
So the students at Jin's school weigh less than the blue whale.

He has rounded 927 to the nearest 100.

He has rounded 56.34 kg to the nearest 10 kg.

p. 94

Exercise 7b

1 Round each of these numbers to the nearest
i 1000 **ii** 100 **iii** 10.

a 3108 **b** 5677 **c** 9843 **d** 3992
e 13 175 **f** 26 394 **g** 3587.6 **h** 1965.384

2 Round each of these numbers to the nearest
i whole number **ii** 1 decimal place **iii** 2 decimal places.

a 4.356 **b** 6.283 **c** 7.418 **d** 9.027
e 3.4035 **f** 17.6362 **g** 128.4347 **h** 0.7085

3 Use a calculator to do each of these calculations.
Write the answers to 2 decimal places.

a $1 \div 3$ **b** $5 \div 16$ **c** $13 \div 7$ **d** $3 \div 11$
e $7 \div 8$ **f** $4896 \div 1000$ **g** $8 \div 13$ **h** $17 \div 12$

4 Solve each of these problems using rounding to estimate the answer.
Do not use a calculator.

a Which is heavier:
a group of 29 women with an average weight of 58.3 kg or
a group of 21 men with an average weight of 78.6 kg?
Explain and justify your answer.

b Heather weighs 48.6 kg.
Each day she eats a chocolate bar with a mass of 225 g.
In about how many days will Heather eat her own weight in chocolate bars?

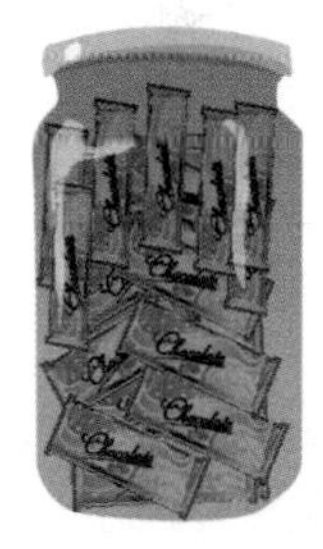

5 Each of these measurements has already been rounded.
Write the greatest and smallest value each measurement could be.

a A giraffe is 6 m tall (to the nearest metre).
b A man is 1.8 m tall (to 1 dp)
c A VW Golf car is 1200 kg (to the nearest 100 kg)

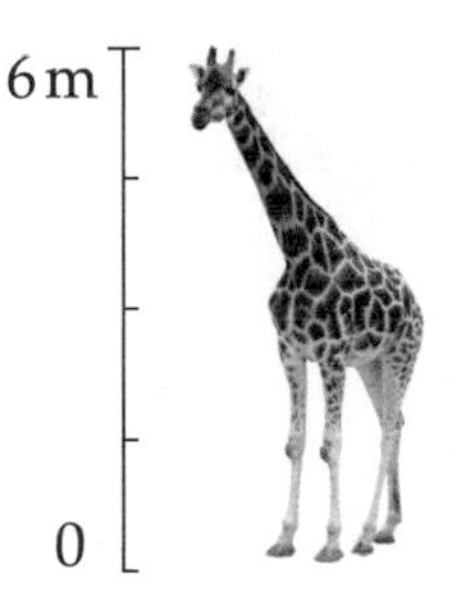

challenge

A swimming club decided to raise money for charity by swimming the equivalent distance from London to Newcastle – 457.4 km.
The length of the swimming pool is 24.8 m.
The average time to swim one length was 63 seconds.

a Estimate the number of lengths equivalent to the distance from London to Newcastle.
b Estimate the total time it takes to swim this equivalent distance.

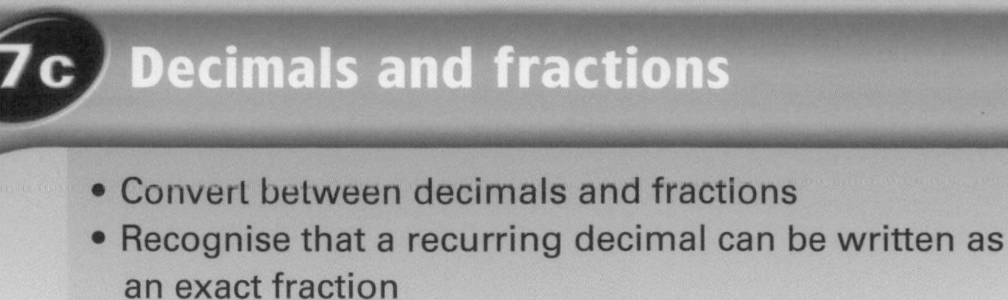

7c Decimals and fractions

LEVEL 6/7

- Convert between decimals and fractions
- Recognise that a recurring decimal can be written as an exact fraction
- Order fractions

Keywords
Place value
Recurring decimal
Terminating decimal

- To convert a terminating decimal into a fraction use **place value.**

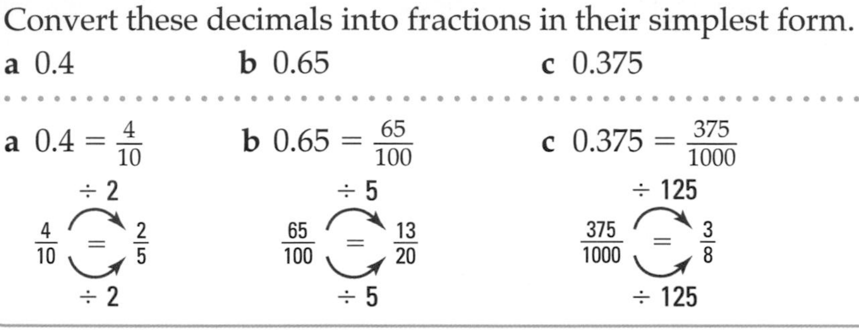

example

Convert these decimals into fractions in their simplest form.

a 0.4 **b** 0.65 **c** 0.375

a $0.4 = \frac{4}{10}$ **b** $0.65 = \frac{65}{100}$ **c** $0.375 = \frac{375}{1000}$

$\frac{4}{10} = \frac{2}{5}$ (÷ 2) $\frac{65}{100} = \frac{13}{20}$ (÷ 5) $\frac{375}{1000} = \frac{3}{8}$ (÷ 125)

A **terminating decimal** has an exact number of decimal places. $\frac{1}{4} = 0.25$

1 dp = tenths
2 dp = hundredths
3 dp = thousandths

- You can convert a fraction into a decimal.

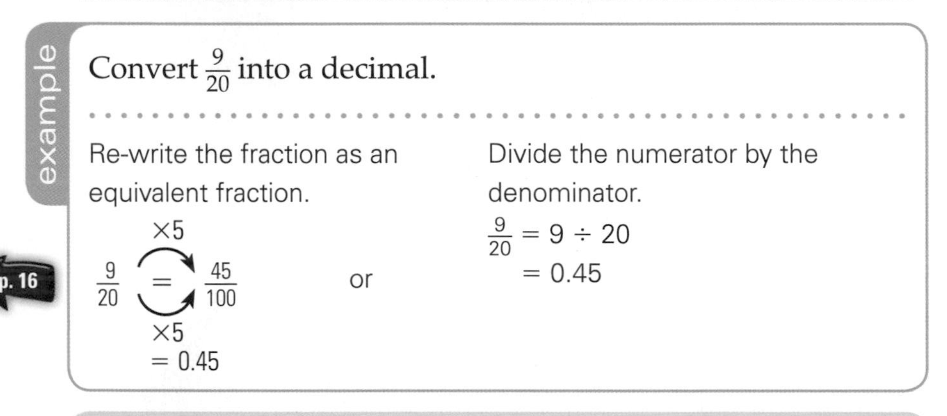

example

Convert $\frac{9}{20}$ into a decimal.

Re-write the fraction as an equivalent fraction.

$\frac{9}{20} = \frac{45}{100}$ (×5)
$= 0.45$

or

Divide the numerator by the denominator.

$\frac{9}{20} = 9 \div 20$
$= 0.45$

p. 16

- You can compare and order fractions by converting them into decimals.

example

Put these fractions and decimals in order, lowest first.

$\frac{5}{11}$ $\frac{2}{5}$ 0.44

$\frac{5}{11} = 5 \div 11$
$= 0.454545...$

$\frac{2}{5} = 2 \div 5$
$= 0.4$

Put the decimals in order

0.4 0.44... $0.\dot{4}\dot{5}$

Put the decimals and fractions in order.

$\frac{2}{5}$ 0.44 $\frac{5}{11}$

A **recurring decimal** has an infinite number of repeating digits. $\frac{1}{3} = 0.333\,333...$

You use dots to show which digits repeat.
$0.454545... = 0.\dot{4}\dot{5}$

Exercise 7c

1 Write these decimals as fractions in their simplest form.

a 0.6 **b** 0.48 **c** 0.25 **d** 0.74 **e** 0.125

f 0.585 **g** 1.5 **h** 1.05 **i** 2.25 **j** 1.56

2 Write these fractions as decimals without using a calculator.

a $\frac{7}{10}$ **b** $\frac{13}{20}$ **c** $\frac{11}{25}$ **d** $\frac{23}{50}$ **e** $\frac{31}{25}$

f $\frac{6}{5}$ **g** $\frac{27}{20}$ **h** $\frac{17}{40}$ **i** $\frac{12}{16}$ **j** $\frac{64}{80}$

3 Change these fractions into decimals using an appropriate method.
Give your answers to 2 decimal places where appropriate.

a $\frac{11}{16}$ **b** $\frac{7}{32}$ **c** $\frac{3}{11}$ **d** $\frac{6}{7}$ **e** $\frac{7}{6}$

f $\frac{11}{19}$ **g** $\frac{9}{7}$ **h** $\frac{11}{15}$ **i** $\frac{8}{13}$ **j** $\frac{23}{21}$

4 Which of these fractions are smaller than $\frac{1}{12}$?
Do not use a calculator. Explain and justify your answers.

a $\frac{1}{16}$ **b** $\frac{1}{8}$ **c** $\frac{3}{24}$ **d** $\frac{1}{4}$ **e** $\frac{4}{50}$

5 Copy these pairs of numbers.
Place $<$ or $>$ between these pairs of numbers to show which number is larger.

a $0.6 \square \frac{5}{7}$ **b** $\frac{5}{12} \square \frac{4}{7}$ **c** $\frac{6}{7} \square 0.83$ **d** $0.19 \square \frac{3}{16}$

e $\frac{2}{9} \square 0.25$ **f** $0.55 \square \frac{7}{13}$ **g** $\frac{1}{9} \square 0.12$ **h** $0.165 \square \frac{3}{19}$

6 Put these fractions and decimals in order from lowest to highest.

a $\frac{2}{7}$ 0.4 $\frac{4}{11}$ 0.33

b $\frac{1}{5}$ $\frac{3}{11}$ 0.3 0.2929...

7 a Hannah has £0.45. Jameela has $\frac{6}{8}$ of £1. Who has more money? Explain and justify your answer.

b To make a cake Gary uses 1.6 kg of flour. To make a different cake Farah uses $1\frac{4}{5}$ kg of flour. Who uses more flour?

8 Write three decimal numbers, each with 1 decimal place, between $\frac{3}{7}$ and $\frac{3}{4}$.

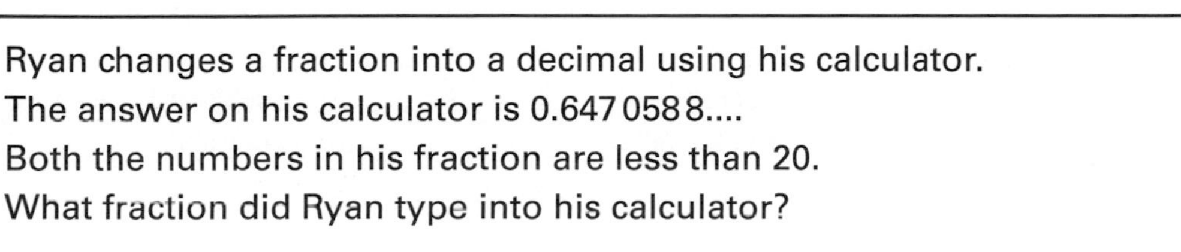

puzzle

Ryan changes a fraction into a decimal using his calculator.
The answer on his calculator is 0.647 058 8....
Both the numbers in his fraction are less than 20.
What fraction did Ryan type into his calculator?

7d Adding and subtracting decimals

LEVEL 5/6

- Consolidate and extend a range of mental strategies for addition and subtraction
- Consolidate and develop standard written methods for addition and subtraction

Keywords
Compensation
Partitioning
Written method

- Try to work out additions and subtractions in your head. You could use **partitioning** or **compensation**.

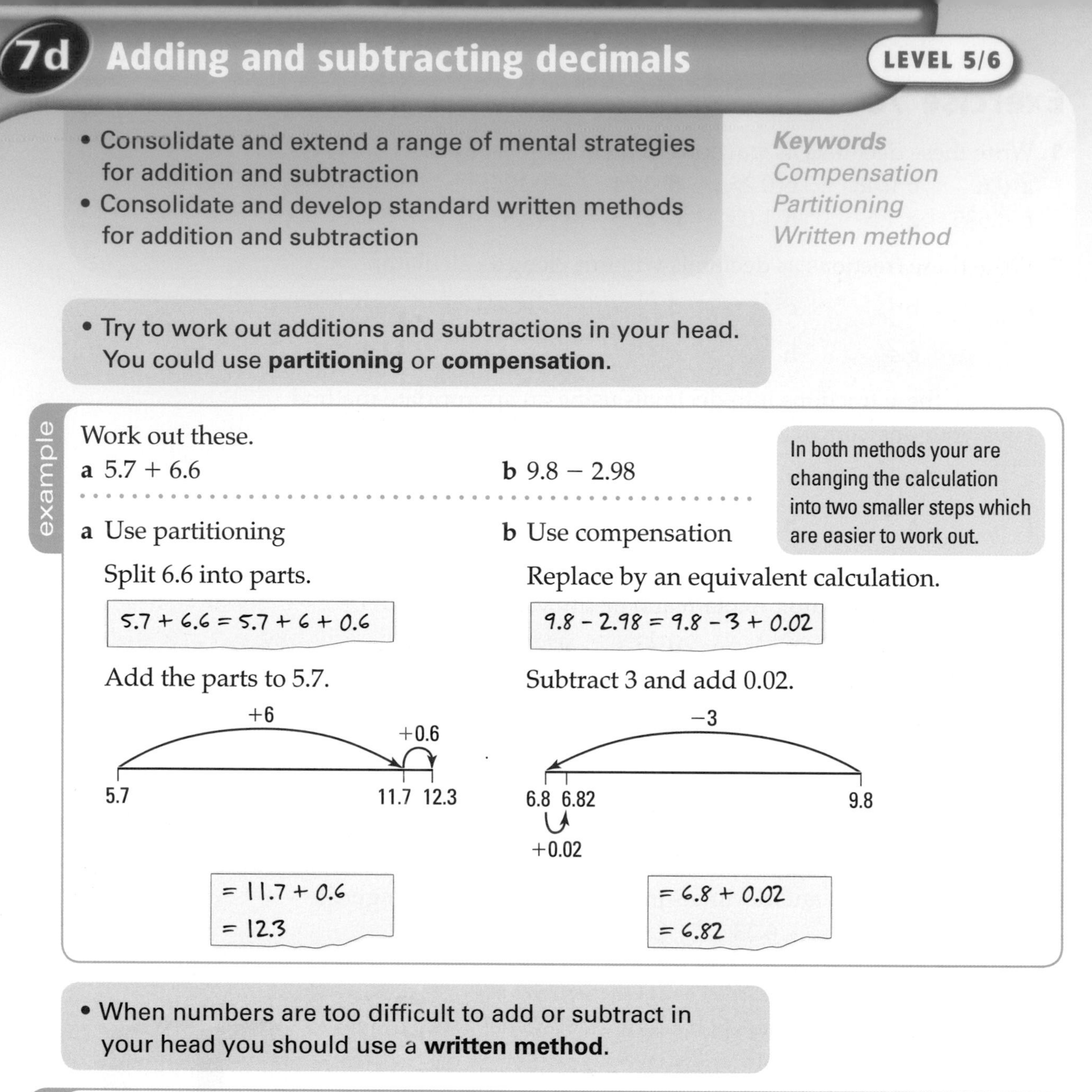

- When numbers are too difficult to add or subtract in your head you should use a **written method**.

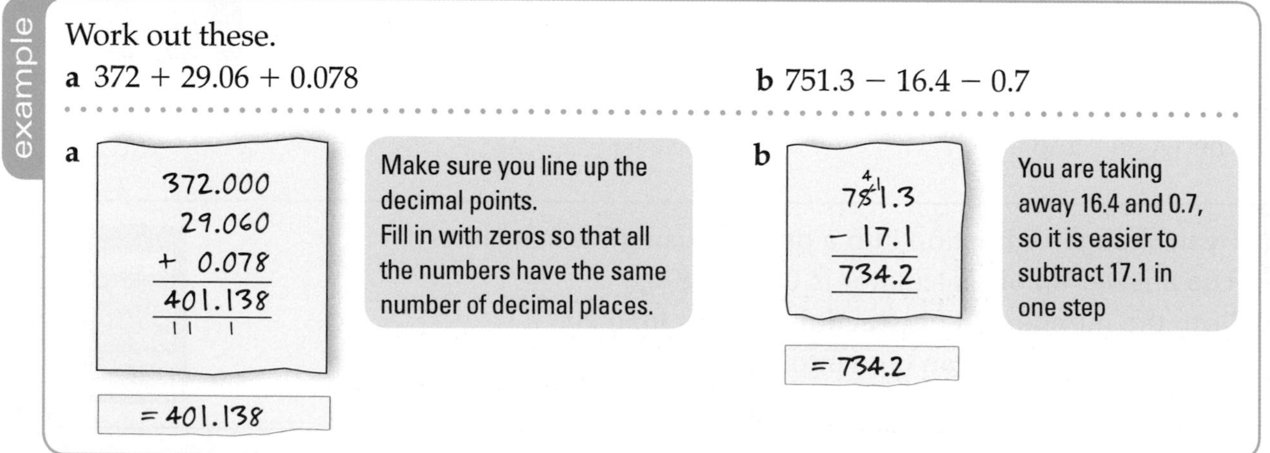

Exercise 7d

1 Work out these using a mental method.

a 8.8 + 5.6 **b** 13.4 − 4.9 **c** 13.6 + 4.7 **d** 12.8 + 6.7
e 15.6 − 7.9 **f** 12.2 − 3.8 **g** 4.7 + 6.5 **h** 11.4 − 6.95

2 Choose an appropriate method to work out these.

a 15.4 + 6.8 **b** 3.57 + 5.9 **c** 8.9 + 4.35 **d** 8.2 + 7.95
e 13.4 − 2.9 **f** 9.86 − 7.9 **g** 4.85 − 7.5 **h** 7.1 + 6.8 + 5.3

3 Copy and complete these number sentences.

a 4.15 + □ = 6 **b** 3.8 + □ = 20 **c** □ + 9.3 = 15 **d** 6.95 + □ = 30

4 Work out these using a written method.

a 534.8 + 95.1 **b** 357.42 + 43 **c** 28.45 + 52.6
d 171.2 − 95.6 **e** 423.9 − 38.64 **f** 758.93 − 409.6

5 Work out these using an appropriate method.

a 5.83 + 635.4 + 9 **b** 84.6 + 216.8 + 52.38 **c** 9.14 + 0.6 + 4 + 0.86
d 624.5 + 38.36 + 0.089 **e** 45.3 + 279.6 − 28.7 **f** 1456.3 + 42.36 − 7.9
g 146.3 − 37 − 45.8 **h** 58.6 + 284.6 − 36.46

6 Here are the masses of some items on the planet Pewn.

Fuzz
785.8 kg

Flyer
589 kg

Burper
1.25 kg

Slurp
0.057 kg

Adder
0.76 kg

Pewnen
67.8 kg

a Calculate the total mass of these.
  i A Pewnen in a Flyer
  ii A Pewnen eating two Burpers and a Slurp
  iii A Fuzz with two Pewnens and a Flyer with three Pewnens
  iv A Fuzz with a Pewnen and an Adder

b How much greater is the mass of a Fuzz than the combined mass of a Flyer with two Pewnens?

problem

Here are six numbers.

6.4 12.75 3.9 4.56 7.85 5.6

You can use each number only once in each question.

a Which four numbers have a total of 30.9?
b Which three numbers can be subtracted from 28 to make 1?
c How can you add and subtract all six numbers to make 12.94?
d By adding and subtracting the six numbers, what is the closest number to zero that you can make?

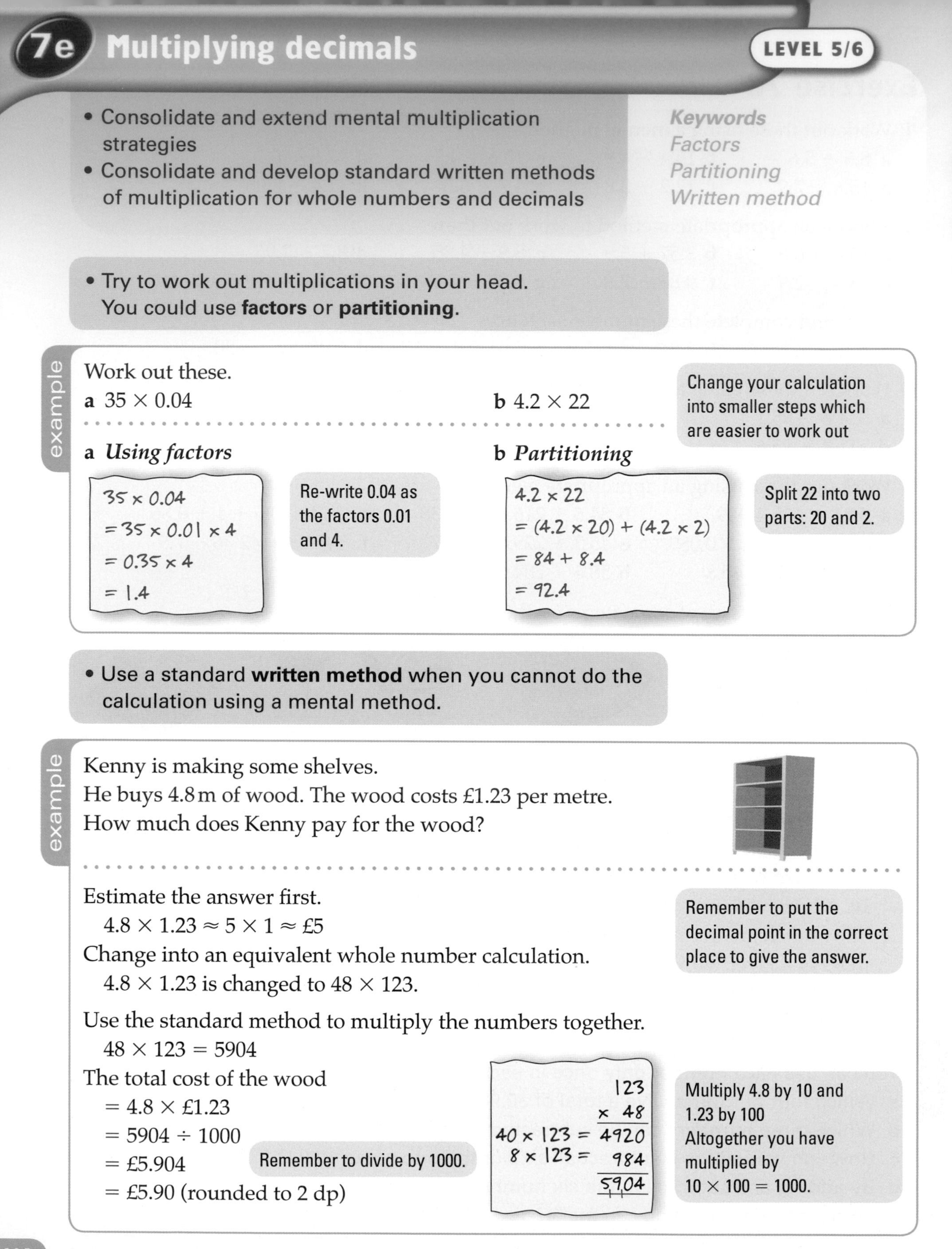

7e Multiplying decimals

LEVEL 5/6

- Consolidate and extend mental multiplication strategies
- Consolidate and develop standard written methods of multiplication for whole numbers and decimals

Keywords
Factors
Partitioning
Written method

- Try to work out multiplications in your head. You could use **factors** or **partitioning**.

example

Work out these.

a 35×0.04 **b** 4.2×22

Change your calculation into smaller steps which are easier to work out

a ***Using factors***

35×0.04
$= 35 \times 0.01 \times 4$
$= 0.35 \times 4$
$= 1.4$

Re-write 0.04 as the factors 0.01 and 4.

b ***Partitioning***

4.2×22
$= (4.2 \times 20) + (4.2 \times 2)$
$= 84 + 8.4$
$= 92.4$

Split 22 into two parts: 20 and 2.

- Use a standard **written method** when you cannot do the calculation using a mental method.

example

Kenny is making some shelves.
He buys 4.8 m of wood. The wood costs £1.23 per metre.
How much does Kenny pay for the wood?

Estimate the answer first.
$4.8 \times 1.23 \approx 5 \times 1 \approx £5$
Change into an equivalent whole number calculation.
4.8×1.23 is changed to 48×123.

Remember to put the decimal point in the correct place to give the answer.

Use the standard method to multiply the numbers together.
$48 \times 123 = 5904$

The total cost of the wood
$= 4.8 \times £1.23$
$= 5904 \div 1000$
$= £5.904$
$= £5.90$ (rounded to 2 dp)

Remember to divide by 1000.

```
                123
              ×  48
40 × 123 =     4920
 8 × 123 =      984
               5904
```

Multiply 4.8 by 10 and 1.23 by 100
Altogether you have multiplied by
$10 \times 100 = 1000$.

LEVEL 5/6

Grade D–C

Exercise 7e

1 Work out these using a mental method.

a 6.4 × 3.1 **b** 3.4 × 0.05 **c** 3.6 × 1.2 **d** 4.5 × 0.03

2 Work out these using a written method.

a 17 × 52 **b** 43 × 82 **c** 315 × 6 **d** 623 × 4

e 143 × 24 **f** 13 × 625 **g** 516 × 32 **h** 44 × 444

3 Work out these using an appropriate method.

a 21 × 4.2 **b** 14 × 0.2 **c** 15 × 1.44 **d** 29 × 12.1

4 Latifa works out 28 × 139 = 3892.

a Use Latifa's answer to work out these calculations.

i 28 × 1.39 **ii** 0.28 × 13.9

iii 280 × 1390 **iv** 28 000 × 0.0139

b What other multiplications can you work out?
Can you work out any divisions?

5 Work out these using a written method.
Remember to do a mental estimate first.

a 5 × 4.13 **b** 6 × 4.52 **c** 13 × 6.2 **d** 27 × 5.3

e 18 × 0.35 **f** 26 × 0.62 **g** 38 × 4.13 **h** 19 × 12.7

i 27 × 5.23 **j** 33 × 6.84 **k** 69 × 8.35 **l** 3.6 × 17.4

m 4.3 × 16.8 **n** 4.7 × 2.85 **o** 3.8 × 1.54 **p** 6.3 × 5.24

6 **a** Hanif is a baker.
He buys a large 7.5 kg jar of jam.
The jam costs £1.88 per kilogram.
How much does the jar of jam cost?

b Ismail buys a big piece of cheese with a mass of 1.6 kg.
The cheese costs £7.69 per kilogram.
How much does Ismail pay for the piece of cheese?

c Cat food costs £0.32 per 100 g pouch.
Karen's cat eats 2.5 pouches per day.

i How much does Karen need to spend on cat food each week?

ii How much will Karen spend on cat food in a year?

investigation

Connor is given these digits. 3 4 5 6 7
He is asked to find a way of multiplying these digits together to make the smallest possible product. Connor starts with 34 × 56 × 7.

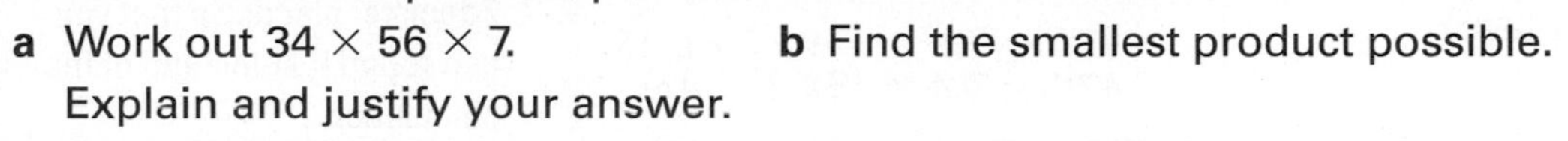

a Work out 34 × 56 × 7.
Explain and justify your answer.

b Find the smallest product possible.

c Find the largest product possible.

d Try using a different set of five numbers.

Dividing decimals

LEVEL 5/6

- Consolidate and extend mental division strategies
- Use a standard written method of division for whole numbers and decimals

Keywords
Divisor
Partitioning
Using factors
Written method

- Try to work out divisions in your head. You could use **factors** or **partitioning**.

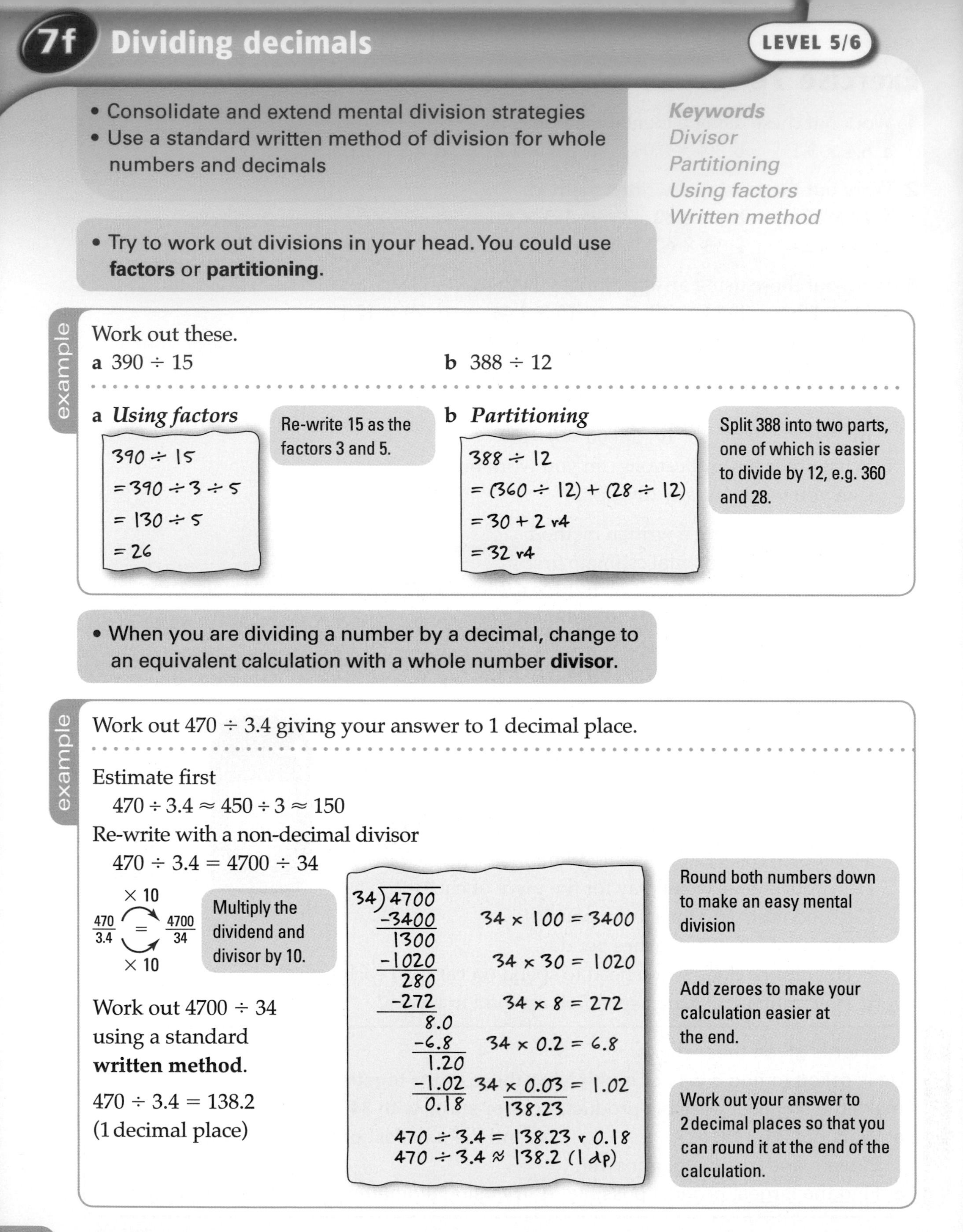

example

Work out these.

a $390 \div 15$ **b** $388 \div 12$

a ***Using factors***

$390 \div 15$
$= 390 \div 3 \div 5$
$= 130 \div 5$
$= 26$

Re-write 15 as the factors 3 and 5.

b ***Partitioning***

$388 \div 12$
$= (360 \div 12) + (28 \div 12)$
$= 30 + 2$ r4
$= 32$ r4

Split 388 into two parts, one of which is easier to divide by 12, e.g. 360 and 28.

- When you are dividing a number by a decimal, change to an equivalent calculation with a whole number **divisor**.

example

Work out $470 \div 3.4$ giving your answer to 1 decimal place.

Estimate first

$470 \div 3.4 \approx 450 \div 3 \approx 150$

Re-write with a non-decimal divisor

$470 \div 3.4 = 4700 \div 34$

$\frac{470}{3.4} = \frac{4700}{34}$ (× 10, × 10)

Multiply the dividend and divisor by 10.

Work out $4700 \div 34$ using a standard **written method**.

$470 \div 3.4 = 138.2$
(1 decimal place)

```
34)4700
  -3400     34 × 100 = 3400
   1300
  -1020     34 × 30 = 1020
    280
   -272     34 × 8 = 272
      8.0
     -6.8   34 × 0.2 = 6.8
      1.20
     -1.02  34 × 0.03 = 1.02
      0.18           138.23
```

$470 \div 3.4 = 138.23$ r 0.18
$470 \div 3.4 \approx 138.2$ (1 dp)

Round both numbers down to make an easy mental division

Add zeroes to make your calculation easier at the end.

Work out your answer to 2 decimal places so that you can round it at the end of the calculation.

LEVEL 5/6

Grade D–C

Exercise 7f

1 Work out these using an appropriate mental method.

a $102 \div 6$ **b** $117 \div 9$ **c** $192 \div 12$
d $345 \div 15$ **e** $504 \div 12$ **f** $360 \div 15$

2 Work out these using an appropriate mental method.
Give your answer with a remainder where appropriate.

a $250 \div 12$ **b** $300 \div 13$ **c** $350 \div 14$ **d** $500 \div 15$
e $495 \div 16$ **f** $230 \div 19$ **g** $221 \div 17$ **h** $700 \div 12$

3 Work out these using an appropriate method.
Give your answer to 1 decimal place where appropriate.

a $228 \div 6$ **b** $352 \div 8$ **c** $408 \div 17$ **d** $608 \div 19$
e $16.8 \div 7$ **f** $57.6 \div 9$ **g** $43.2 \div 16$ **h** $97.2 \div 18$
i $55 \div 8$ **j** $152 \div 7$ **k** $225 \div 16$ **l** $433 \div 18$
m $36.5 \div 6$ **n** $48.7 \div 9$ **o** $74.5 \div 17$ **p** $39.6 \div 19$

4 Work out these using an appropriate method.
Give your answer to 1 decimal place where appropriate.

a $792 \div 3.6$ **b** $952 \div 2.8$ **c** $646 \div 1.9$ **d** $697 \div 4.1$
e $500 \div 3.7$ **f** $580 \div 2.5$ **g** $470 \div 1.4$ **h** $506 \div 2.2$
i $473 \div 3.8$ **j** $323 \div 0.7$ **k** $517 \div 2.3$ **l** $963 \div 0.9$

5 Give your answers either with a remainder or as a decimal to 1 decimal place, depending upon the problem.

a Usman runs 100 m in 9.7 seconds.
What is his speed in metres per second?

How many metres does he travel in each second?

b Victor drives his car from Ayton to Betaville.
He travels a distance of 140 km and uses 8.8 litres of petrol.
How many kilometres does his car travel on each litre of petrol?

c Winnie buys eight pots of honey.
The total mass of the honey is 7.6 kg. The total cost of the honey is £24.32.

i How much does 1 kg of honey cost?
ii How much honey is there in 1 pot?

investigation

Penny says that multiplying always makes things bigger and dividing always makes things smaller.

a Start with the number 360.

i Multiply 360 by 1.4. **ii** Multiply 360 by 0.8.
iii Divide 360 by 1.4. **iv** Divide 360 by 0.8.

Write what you notice.

b Repeat for a different starting number.

7g Using a calculator

LEVEL 6

- Know and use the order of operations, including powers and the use of brackets
- Use a range of function keys appropriately on a calculator

Keywords
Brackets
Function key
Order of operations
Powers

- You follow the **order of operations** to do calculations.

Brackets first.	B
Then **powers** or **square roots**.	I
Then **multiplications** and **divisions**.	DM
Then **additions** and **subtractions**.	AS

Brackets → Indices → Multiply, Divide → Add, Subtract

- Scientific calculators understand the order of operations. However you must type in the calculation correctly.

example

Calculate $\dfrac{7 + 4^2}{\sqrt{2 \times 8}}$

You can re-write the calculation as a division using brackets.

$\dfrac{7 + 4^2}{\sqrt{2 \times 8}} = (7 + 4^2) \div \sqrt{(2 \times 8)}$

$= (7 + 4^2) \div (\sqrt{(16)}\,)$ — inner brackets

$= (7 + 16) \div (4)$ — powers and roots inside brackets

$= 23 \div 4$ — division

$= 5.75$

example

[x/y] **Fraction key**

Calculate $\frac{2}{3} + \frac{4}{5}$.

[2] [x/y] [3] [+] [4] [x/y] [5] [=]

The answer is $\frac{22}{15}$.

example

[(-)] **Sign change key**

Calculate 5.6×-3.4^2

[5] [.] [6] [×] [(] [(-)] [3] [.] [4] [)] [x²] [=]

Put -3.4 inside an extra pair of brackets to work out $(-3.4)^2$ and not 3.4^2 with a negative sign in front of it.

The answer is 64.736.

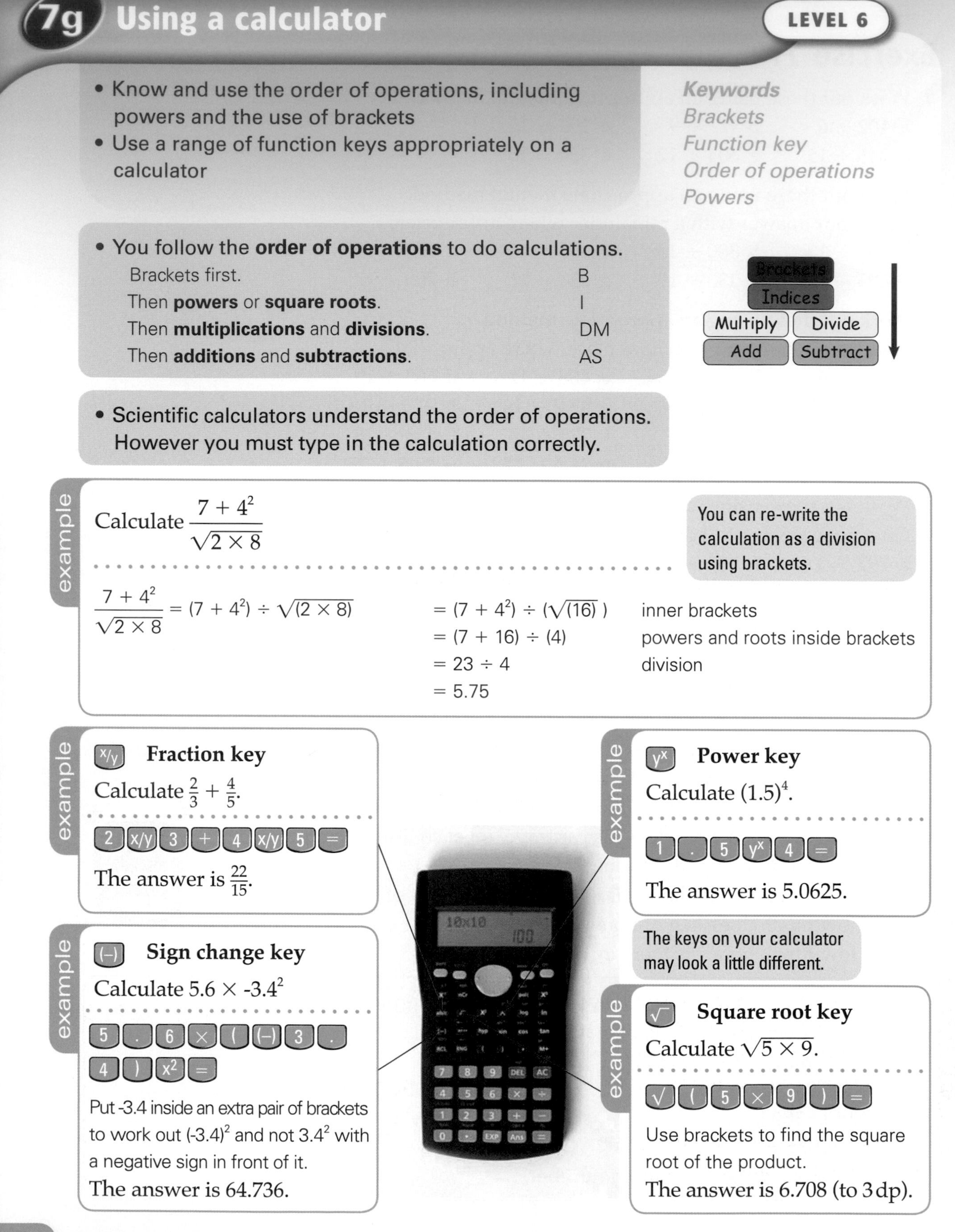

example

[y^x] **Power key**

Calculate $(1.5)^4$.

[1] [.] [5] [y^x] [4] [=]

The answer is 5.0625.

The keys on your calculator may look a little different.

example

[√] **Square root key**

Calculate $\sqrt{5 \times 9}$.

[√] [(] [5] [×] [9] [)] [=]

Use brackets to find the square root of the product.

The answer is 6.708 (to 3 dp).

Exercise 7g

1 **i** Two answers are given for each question. Choose the correct answer.

Question	Answer X	Answer Y
a $(5 + 3^2) \times 2$	28	128
b $(10 + 3)^2 - 1$	18	168
c $8 - 5^2$	9	-17
d $(-5)^2 + 8$	33	-17
e $160 \div (8 \times 5) - (2 \times 3)^2$	40	-32
f $(2 \times 3^2) \div 3 \times 2$	12	3

ii Explain your method and reasoning for each answer.

iii Explain the mistake made for each incorrect answer.

iv Check your answers using a calculator.
Be careful to type the operations in correctly.

2 Calculate these, giving your answer to 1 decimal place where appropriate.

a $\dfrac{(7-2)^2}{\sqrt{4-1}}$ **b** $\dfrac{(4^2-2)(7-3)^2}{(11-7)^2}$ **c** $\dfrac{(8-5)^2\sqrt{30-5}}{(6-3)^3}$

3 Calculate these, giving your answer to 2 decimal places where appropriate.

a $\left(\frac{2}{5} + \frac{3}{8}\right)^2$ **b** $\sqrt{120 - 3.8^2} + 11.7$ **c** $17 \times (6.5 - 5.6)^4$

4 Erik is trying to solve two puzzles.
He must use each of the numbers 2, 3, 4, 5 and 6 only once to make each mathematical calculation correct.

$\dfrac{\sqrt{\square + \square\square}}{\square} + \square = 6$ $\dfrac{\square^4 \times \square \times \square}{\square \times \square} = 10$

Copy and complete each calculation so that it is correct.
Use your calculator to help you.

investigation

Nina is trying to make all the whole numbers from 1 to 10 using exactly four 4s.
So far she has only got one answer.

$4(4 \div 4) + 4 = 8$

a Find the other numbers using exactly four 4s.
You must use all four 4s in each calculation.
You may use any of the operations including powers and square roots.
Write all calculations using the correct order of operations.

b Investigate numbers bigger than 10.

7h Interpreting the display

LEVEL 7

- Use rounding to check whether an answer is of the correct order of magnitude
- Interpret the display on a calculator in different contexts
- Convert between units by finding whole number remainders after division

Keywords
Divisor
Mental estimate
Remainder

- When you use a calculator for a division you may have a **remainder**. It can be written as a whole number, a fraction or a decimal.

Decide how best to write and interpret the remainder in the context of the problem.

example

At the local supermarket giant baked beans are on special offer.
You can buy a six-pack of tins for £8.
Xin buys a six-pack.
How much did she pay for each tin of beans?

Estimate first: $8 \div 6 \approx 8 \div 4 = 2$
Using a calculator: $8 \div 6 = 1.3333\ldots$
Because the answer is money, interpret the answer as a decimal and round it to 2 decimal places.
Answer: Each tin cost £1.33.

You could write the answer

- as a fraction: $\frac{£8}{6} = \frac{£4}{3} = £1\frac{1}{3}$.
  We don't usually write amounts of money as fractions.
- as a remainder: £1 r 2.
  This doesn't make sense.

- You can convert decimal remainders into whole numbers by multiplying by the **divisor**, especially when converting between units.

example

Convert 5000 seconds into minutes and seconds.

Estimate first: $5000 \div 60 \approx 5000 \div 50 = 100$
Using a calculator, convert the seconds into minutes.

$5000 \div 60 = 83.333\ldots$

p. 18

Multiply the remainder by the divisor.

$0.333\ldots \text{ minutes} = 0.333\ldots \times 60 \text{ seconds}$
$= 20 \text{ seconds}$

5000 seconds = 83 minutes and 20 seconds

You divide by 60 to change seconds into minutes.

Change the remainder into a whole number by multiplying by 60.

Exercise 7h

1 Without using a calculator choose the most likely answer for each question by doing a mental estimate.

p. 108

a $(38)^2 =$ 54 872 or 1444 or 76

b $130 \div 0.45 =$ 58.5 or 244.2 or 288.9

In each case explain the reasoning behind your choice.

2 Calculate these divisions using your calculator. Give the answer in the form stated.

a £30 ÷ 7 (a decimal to 2 decimal places)

b 30 cakes ÷ 7 (with a whole number remainder)

c 30 pies ÷ 7 (a fraction)

3 Solve these problems.
Give your answer in a form appropriate to the question.

a Dale sells free range eggs.
She has 155 eggs. She packs them into boxes of 12.
How many boxes of eggs does she need to pack the eggs?

b At a charity event, 12 competitors eat a total of 155 pizzas.
Each competitor eats exactly the same amount of pizza.
How much pizza did each person eat?

4 Convert these measurements to the units in brackets.

a 2458 cm (into m and cm)

b 3876 seconds (into minutes and seconds)

c 43 155 mm (into m, cm and mm)

5 Solve these problems.
Give your answer in a form appropriate to the question.

a Igor buys 7 kg of sugar.
He wants to put the sugar into 1.5 kg jars.
How many jars will he need?
How much sugar will there be in the last jar?

b The Year 9 students at Oxford Sports College are going on a trip to a theme park.
There are 189 students and 16 staff going on the trip.
Each coach can hold 45 people.
How many coaches should be ordered?

Did you know?

The first hand-held calculators were released in the late 1960s. They could perform addition, subtraction, multiplication and division and could display 12 digit numbers.

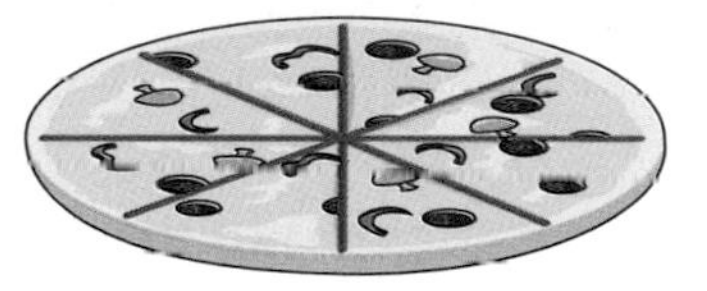

puzzle

Convert 99 999 999 seconds into years, weeks, days, hours, minutes and seconds.

7 Consolidation

7a

1 Calculate these.

a 46×0.1 **b** $158 \div 0.01$ **c** 2.3×0.1 **d** $17.2 \div 0.1$

e $36.2 \div 0.01$ **f** $0.03 \div 0.1$ **g** 0.362×0.01 **h** 1273×0.01

2 Each of these numbers has been written in standard form.
Work out the size of each of the numbers.

a 3.6×10^2 **b** 4.8×10^5 **c** 1.02×10^4 **d** 3.1×10^7

e 2.15×10^3 **f** 1.87×10^2 **g** 2.4×10^{-1} **h** 6.3×10^{-2}

7b

3 Round each of these numbers to the nearest

i whole number **ii** 1 decimal place **iii** 2 decimal places.

a 3.467 **b** 7.175 **c** 9.326 **d** 4.613

e 8.2073 **f** 13.4735 **g** 137.5653 **h** 3.4914

4 Estimate the answer to each of these problems.

a The Eiffel tower has a mass of 8.56 million kilograms.
The mass of Blackpool Tower is 2 345 979 kg.
Approximately how many times heavier is the Eiffel Tower compared to Blackpool Tower?

b Which is heavier, five male lions each weighing 208 kg each or nine female lions weighing 134 kg each?

7c

5 Write these decimals as fractions in their simplest form.

a 0.8 **b** 0.76 **c** 0.75 **d** 0.77 **e** 0.875

f 0.325 **g** 1.4 **h** 1.35 **i** 3.75 **j** 2.16

6 Change these fractions into decimals using an appropriate method.
Give your answers to 2 decimal places where appropriate.

a $\frac{13}{20}$ **b** $\frac{9}{16}$ **c** $\frac{5}{11}$ **d** $\frac{8}{15}$ **e** $\frac{7}{10}$

f $\frac{12}{25}$ **g** $\frac{17}{23}$ **h** $\frac{11}{22}$ **i** $\frac{14}{21}$ **j** $\frac{21}{30}$

7d

7 Work out these using a written method.

a $452.7 + 86.6$ **b** $753.68 + 67$ **c** $82.65 + 58.4$

d $939.8 - 45.9$ **e** $687.1 - 72.46$ **f** $852.17 - 690.4$

8 Work out these using an appropriate method.

a $4.27 + 475.6 + 3$ **b** $26.4 + 894.2 + 58.72$

c $65.7 + 831.4 - 82.3$ **d** $4567.4 + 68.74 - 23.8$

e $364.3 - 73 - 54.4$ **f** $42.4 + 526.4 - 74.69$

7e

9 Work out these using a written method.
Remember to do a mental estimate first.

a 6×3.97 **b** 4×6.58 **c** 24×4.8 **d** 43×5.7
e 38×0.75 **f** 44×0.48 **g** 53×6.97 **h** 32×18.3
i 35×7.87 **j** 61×4.26 **k** 73×2.78 **l** 7.4×13.6
m 6.7×14.2 **n** 6.3×8.25 **o** 7.2×1.66 **p** 4.7×6.86

10 Nigella buys 3.2 kg of olives.
The olives cost £4.78 per kilogram.
How much do the olives cost Nigella?

7f

11 Work out these using an appropriate method.
Give your answer to 1 decimal place where appropriate.

a $756 \div 4.2$ **b** $756 \div 3.8$ **c** $756 \div 2.1$ **d** $754 \div 5.8$
e $754 \div 5.9$ **f** $754 \div 6$ **g** $414 \div 1.8$ **h** $414 \div 1.9$
i $414 \div 2$ **j** $386 \div 0.6$ **k** $386 \div 0.5$ **l** $406 \div 0.7$

12 Boris runs 60 m in 5.9 seconds.
a What is his speed in metres per second?
b How long would it take Boris to run 100 m at this speed?

How many metres does he travel in each second?

7g

13 Calculate these giving your answer to 1 decimal place where appropriate.

a $\dfrac{(5+6)^3}{\sqrt{35+41}}$ **b** $\dfrac{(4+3^2)(2-5)^2}{(18-3)^2}$ **c** $\dfrac{(12-3.5)^2\sqrt{28-4.5}}{(7-2.5)^2}$

14 Calculate these giving your answer to 2 decimal places where appropriate.

a $\left(\frac{4}{15}+\frac{5}{3}\right)^2$ **b** $\sqrt{45-4.8^2+13.2}$ **c** $14 \times (2.4-0.63)^3$

7h

15 Calculate these divisions using your calculator.
Give the answer in the form specified.

a 48 kg ÷ 9 (a decimal to 2 decimal places)
b 48 sheep ÷ 9 (a whole number remainder)
c 48 pizzas ÷ 9 (a fraction)

16 Convert these measurements to the units in brackets

a 3867 seconds (into minutes and seconds)
b 4126.7 m (into km, m and cm)
c 3675 ml (into litres and ml)
d 7395 minutes (into days, hours and minutes)

Maths Life

Online auction

A group of friends are going to make bracelets and necklaces to sell on an online auction site.

- What would it cost if they needed 200 red beads of each size?
- Would it cost the same if they needed 100 black and 100 plain beads of each size?
- Which supplier should they use?

- Explain how the choice of colours could affect the overall cost of each item.

diameter x length 8mm x 16mm beads

diameter x length 12mm x 9mm beads

They have found the cost of materials from two suppliers:

(1)

NATURAL BEAD COMPANY

Postage and packing: £3.50 for any size of order

8 x 16mm beads	12 x 9mm beads
8p per bead	5p per bead
£1.30p per 20	80p per 20
£2.90 per 50	£1.80 per 50
£4.80 per 100	£3.00 per 100
£8.00 per 250	£5.00 per 250

Leather thread	Waxed cord
50p per metre	10p per metre
£11.95 per 50m	£4.95 per 100m

(2)

BEAD-E-IZE

Free postage and packing. Minimum order charge of £10

8 x 16mm beads	12 x 9mm beads
7p per bead	4p per bead
£1.50p per 25	85p per 25
£6.75 per 150	£3.75 per 150
£19.00 per 500	£10.75 per 500

Leather thread	Waxed cord
45p per metre	11p per metre
£19.00 per 80m	£1.95 per 20m
	£9.50 per 200m

Waxed cord

Leather thread

- What length should they make the bracelet and the necklace?
- What length would they need to allow for tying the necklace or bracelet?

- What is the largest number of beads they would need for each item?
- What is the smallest number of beads they would need for each item if the designs have beads all the way round?

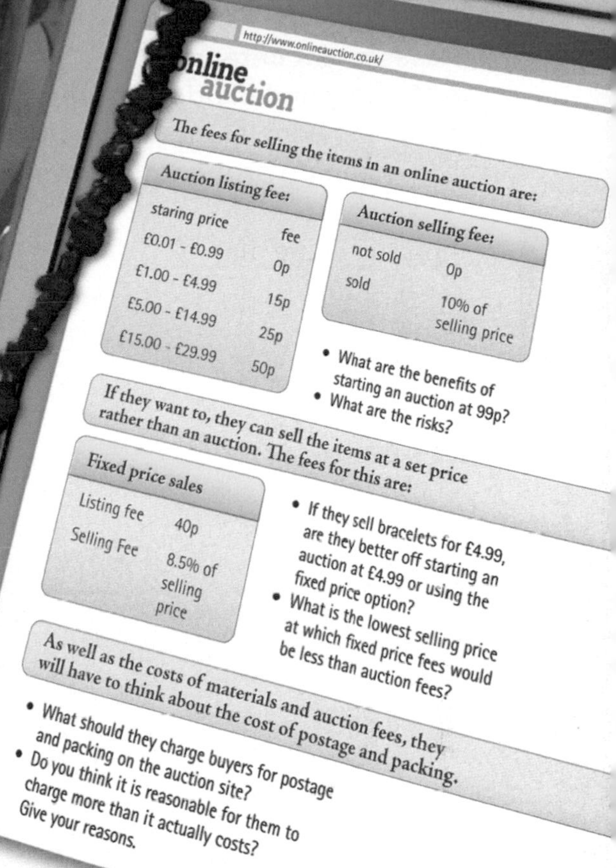

http://www.onlineauction.co.uk/

online auction

The fees for selling the items in an online auction are:

Auction listing fee:

staring price	fee
£0.01 - £0.99	0p
£1.00 - £4.99	15p
£5.00 - £14.99	25p
£15.00 - £29.99	50p

Auction selling fee:

not sold	0p
sold	10% of selling price

- What are the benefits of starting an auction at 99p?
- What are the risks?

If they want to, they can sell the items at a set price rather than an auction. The fees for this are:

Fixed price sales

Listing fee	40p
Selling Fee	8.5% of selling price

- If they sell bracelets for £4.99, are they better off starting an auction at £4.99 or using the fixed price option?
- What is the lowest selling price at which fixed price fees would be less than auction fees?

As well as the costs of materials and auction fees, they will have to think about the cost of postage and packing.

- What should they charge buyers for postage and packing on the auction site?
- Do you think it is reasonable for them to charge more than it actually costs? Give your reasons.

Your challenge!

Decide what you would do if you were setting up this business. Think about things such as:

- What designs you would make.
- How many of each item you would make. Making more can save money on materials but lose more if the items don't sell.
- What the items would cost to make.
- How much you would sell them for.
- Whether you would sell as an auction or at a fixed price.
- How much profit you would hope to make.
- How much you would initially spend to get started. You might want to limit the amount so that you don't lose too much money if your items don't sell.

Present your decisions as a business plan, setting out all the details and the reasons for the decisions you make.

Give some examples of ideas you rejected and your reasons for rejecting them.

7 Summary

Assessment criteria

- Multiply and divide numbers by powers of 10 **Level 6**
- Use the equivalence of fractions, decimals and percentages to compare proportions **Level 6**

Level 6

1 Find the value of

a 4.3×10^3

b $4.3 \div 10^3$

Peter's answer ✔

a $4.3 \times 10^3 = 4.3 \times 10 \times 10 \times 10$

$= 4.3 \times 1000$

$= 4300$

b $4.3 \div 10^3 = 4.3 \div 1000$

T	U	•	$\frac{1}{10}$	$\frac{1}{100}$	$\frac{1}{1000}$	$\frac{1}{10\,000}$
	4	•	3			
	0	•	0	0	4	3

$= 0.0043$

Peter knows $4 \times 1000 = 4000$ and so $4.3 \times 1000 = 4300$

Peter moves the digits 3 places to the right to make the number smaller.

Level 6

2 a Some of the fractions below are smaller than $\frac{1}{9}$.
Write them down.

$\frac{1}{10}$ $\frac{4}{9}$ $\frac{1}{2}$ $\frac{1}{100}$ $\frac{1}{8}$

b To the nearest per cent, what is $\frac{1}{9}$ as a percentage?
Choose the correct percentage,

0.9% 9% 10% 11% 19%

c Copy and complete the sentence below by writing a fraction.
$\frac{1}{9}$ is half of ________

Key Stage 3 2007 5–7 Paper 1

8 Algebra

Graphs

The steepness of a line is measured by its gradient. Hills and mountains also have a gradient. If a road goes up a down a steep hill you will see a road sign telling you the gradient either as a ratio or as a percentage.

What's the point? This sign shows a gradient of 20%. This is the same as a ratio of 1 : 5. Every time the car travels 5 units horizontally it also goes up 1 unit vertically. Your knowledge of maths can tell you how steep the hill is going to be.

Check in

Level 4

1 The total mass m g of x light bulbs, including their packaging, is given by this rule.
Multiply x by 200 and then add 50. Find m when
a $x = 5$ **b** $x = 10$

2 A rule is given as *divide the number x by 8 and then add 12.* Find the result when the number x is
a 40 **b** 72

Level 5

3 **a** Write these four temperatures (in °C) in order with the highest temperature first: 6 -3 14 -5
b Find the mean of these four temperatures.

4 **a** Draw and label both axes from -6 to 6.
Plot the points A(3, 4), B(-5, 4) and C(-5, -2).
b Find the coordinates of point D if the quadrilateral ABCD is a rectangle.
c Find the area of the rectangle ABCD.

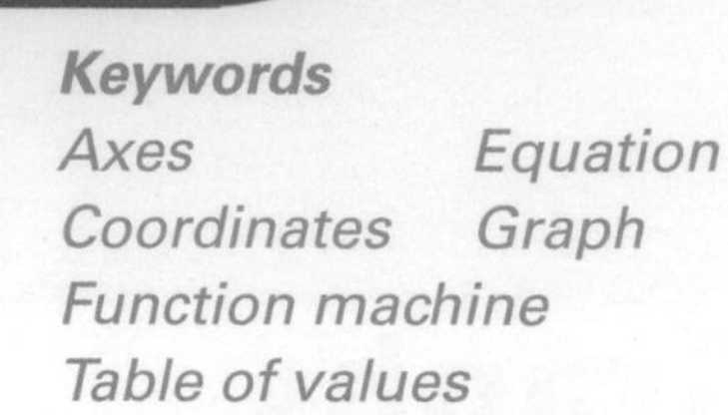

8a Tables of values

- Draw straight-line graphs using tables of values

Keywords
Axes *Equation*
Coordinates *Graph*
Function machine
Table of values

- You can use a **function machine** or an **equation** to complete a **table of values.**

This function machine shows the rule *'double x and add 1'*. You can write it as the equation $y = 2x + 1$.

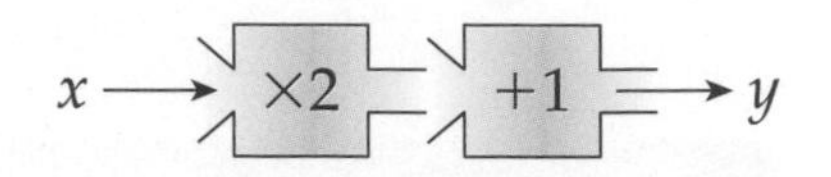

p. 10

When $x = 0,\ y = 2 \times 0 + 1 = 0 + 1 = 1$

$x = 1,\ y = 3$

$x = 2,\ y = 5$

$x = 3,\ y = 7$

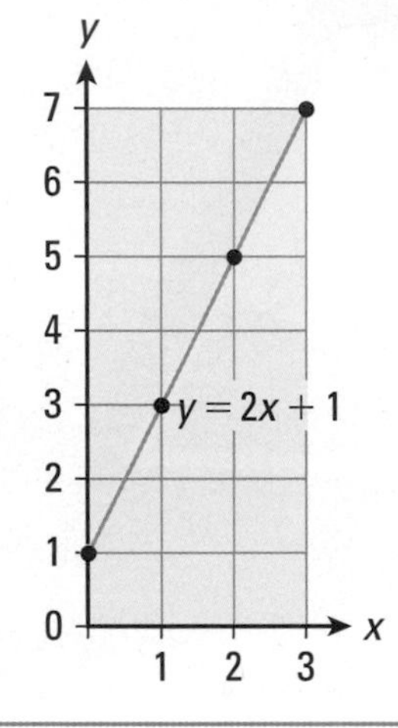

You can complete a table of values and write the **coordinates** of points.

x	0	1	2	3
y	1	3	5	7

The coordinates are (0, 1), (1, 3), (2, 5) and (3, 7).

You can plot the points on **axes** to draw a **graph**.

example

Draw the graph of $y = 12 - 2x$ by constructing a table of values with values of x as 0, 2, 4, 6.

When $x = 0, y = 12 - 2 \times 0 = 12 - 0 = 12$

$x = 2, y = 12 - 2 \times 2 = 12 - 4 = 8$

$x = 4, y = 12 - 8 = 4$

$x = 6, y = 12 - 12 = 0$

x	0	2	4	6
y	12	8	4	0

The coordinates are (0, 12), (2, 8), (4, 4) and (6, 0).

You can draw the graph on axes using these points.

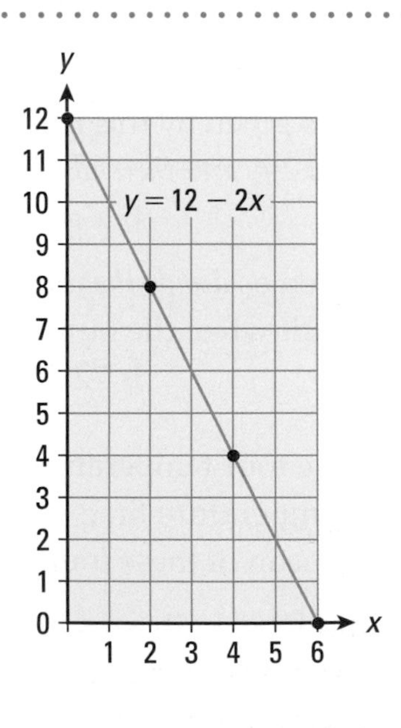

You need at least three points to draw a straight-line graph. Two points give you the line. The third point is a check.

Exercise 8a

1 Use the function machine to complete this table.

x	0	1	2	3
y				

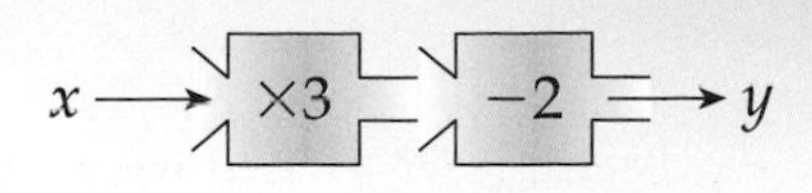

Plot points on appropriate axes.
Draw the straight-line graph and write its equation.

2 Copy and complete this table for each of the equations.

x	0	1	2	3	4
y					

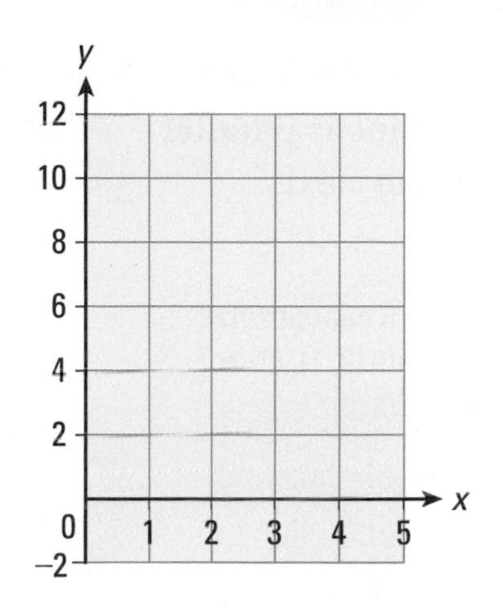

Draw the graph of each equation on a copy of these axes.

a $y = x + 2$ **b** $y = x - 2$ **c** $y = 2x + 3$
d $y = 2x - 2$ **e** $y = 10 - x$ **f** $y = 4 - x$

3 Decide whether each point is on the given line.
You do not need to draw any graphs.

a (2, 10) and $y = x + 8$ **b** (5, 17) and $y = 2x + 7$
c (3, 15) and $y = 3x - 6$ **d** (4, 2) and $y = 8 - 2x$

4 The graphs of $y = 2x$ and $y = 9 - x$ and the x axis are the three sides of a triangle.
. 96
Draw the triangle by drawing its sides on axes labelled from 0 to 9.
Find the height and the area of the triangle.

5 A youth club hires a hall for a disco.
The cost of electricity, £C, depends on the number of hours, x, that the hall is needed.
Copy and complete this table using the formula $C = 2x + 5$.
Draw the graph of C against x.
For how many hours does the club hire the hall if the charge for electricity is

x	1	2	3	4	5
C					

a £12 **b** £21?

challenge

Use a computer spreadsheet to create a table of values for the equations $y = 3x - 4$ and $y = 2x + 12$.
Extend the spreadsheet downwards to find the coordinates of the point where the graphs of these two equations intersect.

	A	B	C
1	x	y	y
2	0	=3*A2–4	=2*A2+12
3	=A2+1	=3*A3–4	=2*A3+12
4	=A3+1	=3*A4–4	=2*A4+12
5	=A4+1	=3*A5–4	=2*A5+12

Drawing straight-line graphs

- Recognise and draw different types of straight-line graphs

Keywords
Constant
Parallel
Equation
Slope

You can tell what a straight-line graph looks like from its **equation.**

If x is **constant,** the line is **parallel** to the y axis.

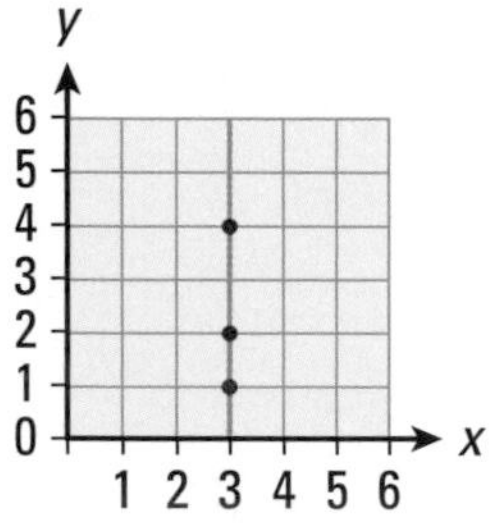

If y is **constant,** the line is **parallel** to the x axis.

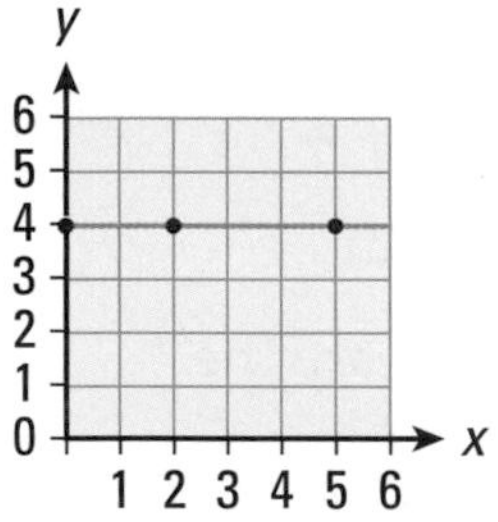

If both x and y are in the equation, the line **slopes** up or down.

$x = 3$ contains the points (3, 1), (3, 2), and (3, 4).

$y = 4$ contains the points (0, 4), (2, 4) and (5, 4).

$y = x + 1$ contains the points (2, 3), (3, 4) and (5, 6).

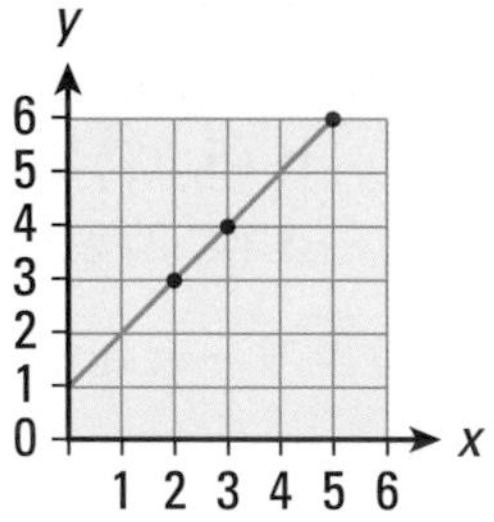

- You can describe shapes using equations of straight lines.

example

A triangle is enclosed by the straight lines $x = 6$, $y = 2$ and $y = \frac{1}{2}x + 1$.
Draw the triangle and find its area.

The line $x = 6$ has the points (6, 0), (6, 2), (6, 5), ... and is parallel to the y axis.

p. 96

The line $y = 2$ has the points (0, 2), (3, 2), (4, 2), ... and is parallel to the x axis.

The line $y = \frac{1}{2}x + 1$ has the points (0, 1), (4, 3), (6, 4) and slopes.

The triangle has a base of 4 units and a height of 2 units.
Its area is $\frac{1}{2} \times 4 \times 2 = 4$ square units.

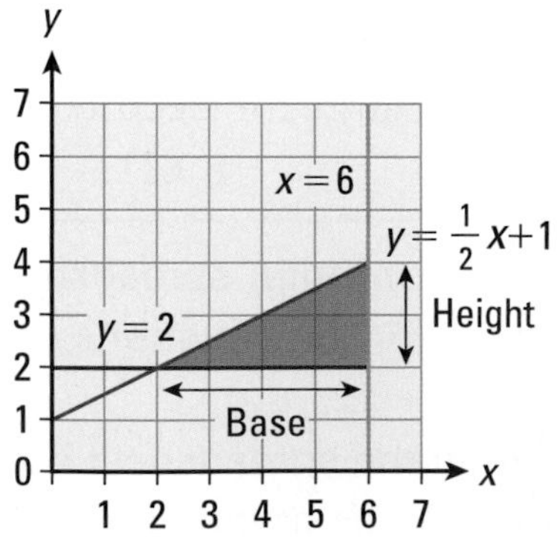

Exercise 8b

1 Match the equations in the box with the lettered lines in the diagram.

$y = x + 3$	$x = 2$	$x = 5$
$y = 2$	$y = 4$	

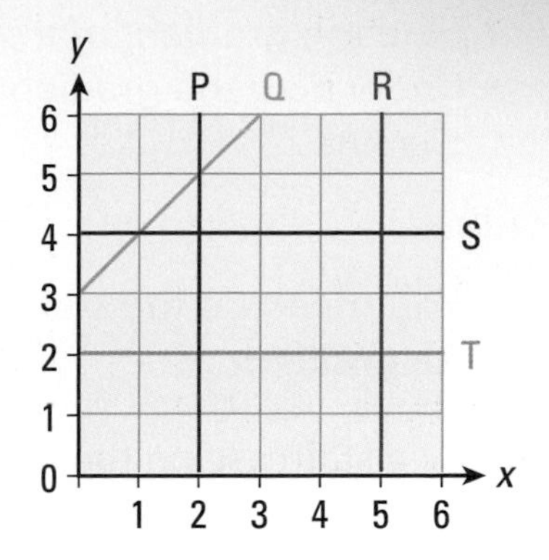

2 For each set of equations
i draw the four lines on axes from 0 to 7.
ii shade the rectangle that you make and find its area.
a $x = 3,\ x = 5,\ y = 4,\ y = 6$
b $x = 4,\ x = 5,\ y = 1,\ y = 4$
c $x = 1,\ x = 6,\ y = 3,\ y = 5$

3 Each of these sets of points are the corners of a square.
i On axes from -6 to 6, draw each square.
ii Find the equations of the diagonals of each square.
a (3, 2), (5, 4), (3, 6), (1, 4)
b (2, -2), (4, -4), (6, -2), (4, 0)
c (-5, -3), (-2, -6), (1, -3), (-2, 0)
d (-5, 3), (-4, 4), (-3, 3), (-4, 2)

4 For each pair of equations,
i copy and complete this table of values.

x	0	2	4	6
y				

ii draw the graphs of both lines on a copy of these axes.
iii find the coordinates of the point where the two lines intersect.
a $y = x + 2, y = 2x - 1$
b $y = x + 3, y = 3x - 1$
c $y = x + 1, y = \frac{1}{2}x + 3$
d $y = x - 1, y = 7 - x$
e $y = 4, y = 5 - x$
f $y = 8 - 2x, x = 2$

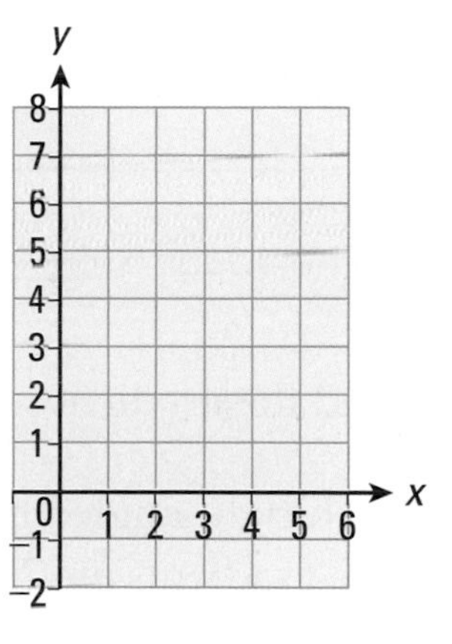

5 On axes from 0 to 8, draw triangles with sides given by the lines with these equations.
Find the area of each triangle.
a $y = 2, y = x + 2, y = 6 - x$
b $x = 2,\ y = 7 - x, y = x$
c $x = 6, y = 8 - x, y = \frac{1}{2}x + 2$

ICT
Use the graphical package on a computer to draw some of the graphs of the questions in this exercise and so check your answers.

Gradient of a straight-line graph

LEVEL 6

- Find the gradient of a straight-line graph
- Know how the gradient is linked with the equation of the line

Keywords
Falling *Sloping*
Gradient *Steepness*
Rising

- You measure the **steepness** of a **sloping** line by finding its **gradient**.

Draw a staircase on the line with horizontal steps of 1 square. The gradient is the number of squares that each step goes up or down.

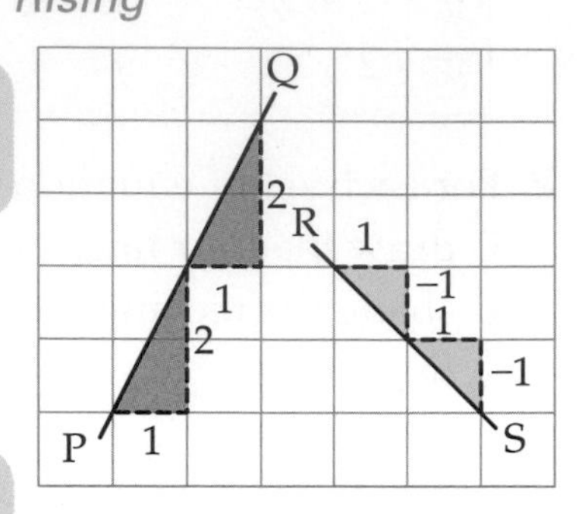

- A **rising** line has a positive gradient.
  A **falling** line has a negative gradient.

The gradient of line PQ is 2.
The gradient of line RS is -1.

example

Find the gradients of the lines $y = 2x$ and $y = \frac{1}{2}x$.

Each right-angled triangle is part of a staircase.
The gradients of the lines are 2 and $\frac{1}{2}$.

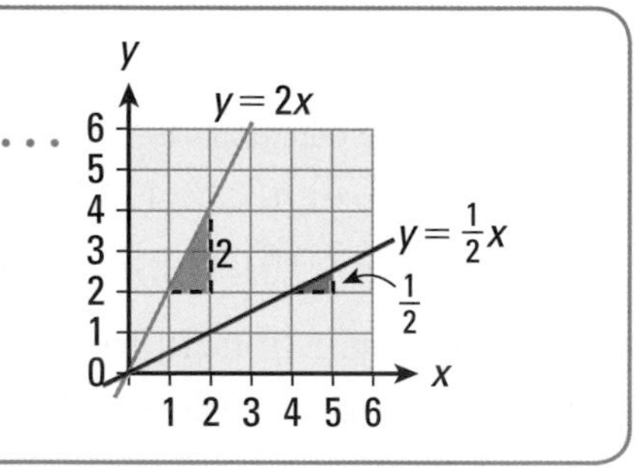

- The line $y = mx$ has a gradient of m.

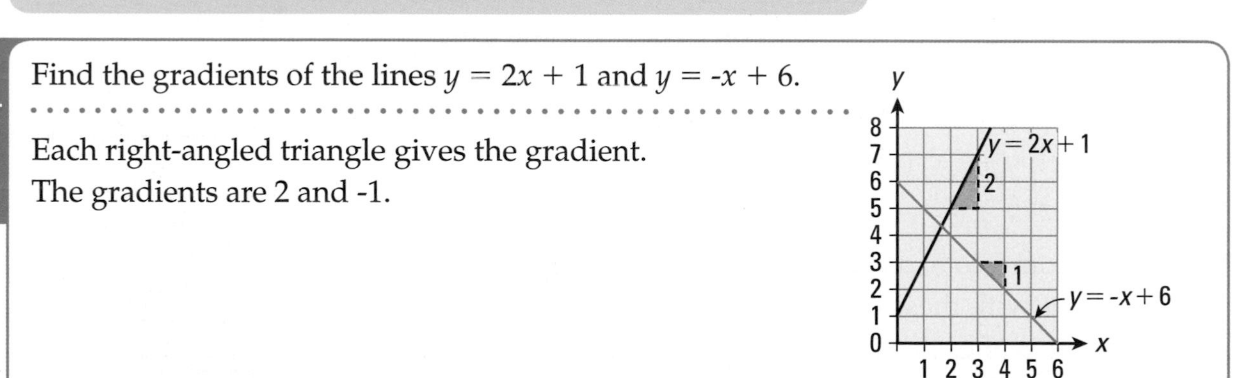

example

Find the gradients of the lines $y = 2x + 1$ and $y = -x + 6$.

Each right-angled triangle gives the gradient.
The gradients are 2 and -1.

- The line $y = mx + c$ has a gradient of m.

The line $y = 4x + 2$ has a gradient of 4.
It is a rising line.
The line $y = -3x + 5$ has a gradient of -3.
It is a falling line.

You can write $y = x + 4$ as $y = 1x + 4$, giving a gradient of 1.

Exercise 8c

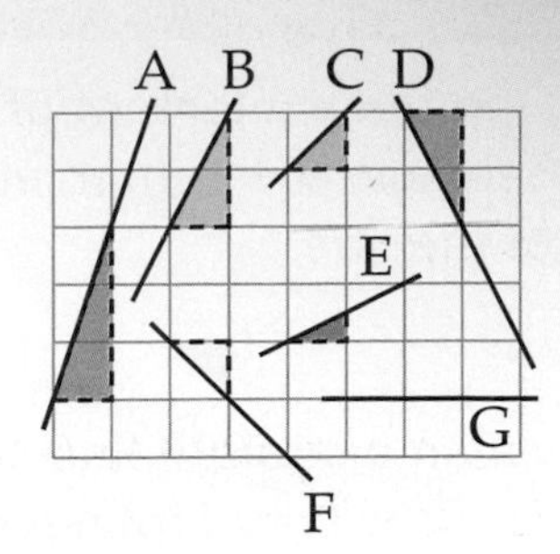

1 Find the gradients of the straight lines A to G.

2 Draw and label axes from 0 to 8.
Plot each pair of points and join them with a straight line.
Find the gradient of each line.

a (1, 4) and (3, 8) **b** (1, 4) and (2, 7)
c (1, 4) and (7, 7) **d** (1, 4) and (6, 4)
e (1, 4) and (5, 0) **f** (1, 4) and (3, 0)

3 Copy and complete this table of values for the equations $y = 2x - 1$ and $y = \frac{1}{2}x + 3$.

x	0	2	4	6
$y = 2x - 1$				
$y = \frac{1}{2}x + 3$				

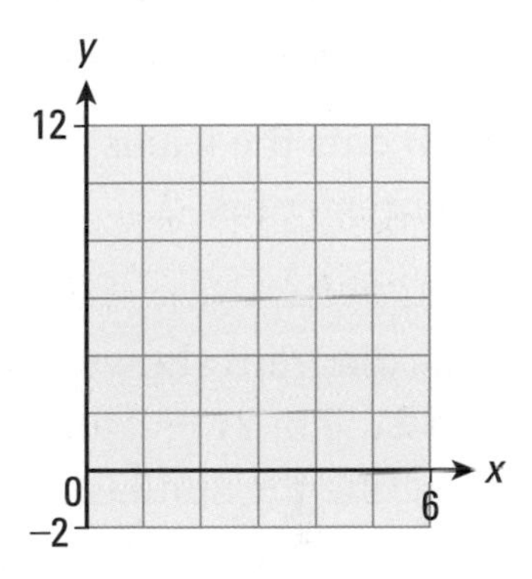

Draw their graphs on a copy of these axes.
Find the gradient of each line.

4 Find the gradient of the straight lines with these equations.
Do not draw any graphs.

a $y = 5x + 2$ **b** $y = 4x - 7$ **c** $y = x + 3$
d $y = \frac{1}{2}x + 6$ **e** $y = -6x + 4$ **f** $y = -3x + 1$

5 Find the gradient of the straight line with these equations.

a $y = 8x + 3$ **b** $y = -8x + 3$ **c** $y = 3 - 8x$
d $y = 2 - 4x$ **e** $y = 5 - x$ **f** $y = 1 - \frac{1}{2}x$

6 The temperature, T °C, in a science experiment rises over time x minutes so that $T = 3x + 2$.

Draw the graph of T for $x = 0$ to $x = 5$.

How fast is the temperature rising in °C per minute?

ICT challenge

Use the graphical package on a computer to draw the graphs of $y = mx + 3$ where m has

a whole-number values from 1 to 5
b whole-number values from -1 to -5
c the value 0
d any value greater than 100.

Explain your answers to parts **c** and **d**.

8d Intercept of a straight-line graph

LEVEL 6

- Find the y intercept of a straight-line graph
- See how the y intercept is linked with the equation of the line

Keywords
Intercept
Intersection

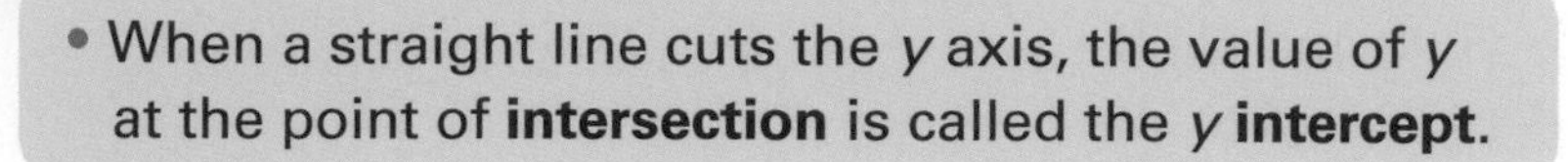

- When a straight line cuts the y axis, the value of y at the point of **intersection** is called the y **intercept**.

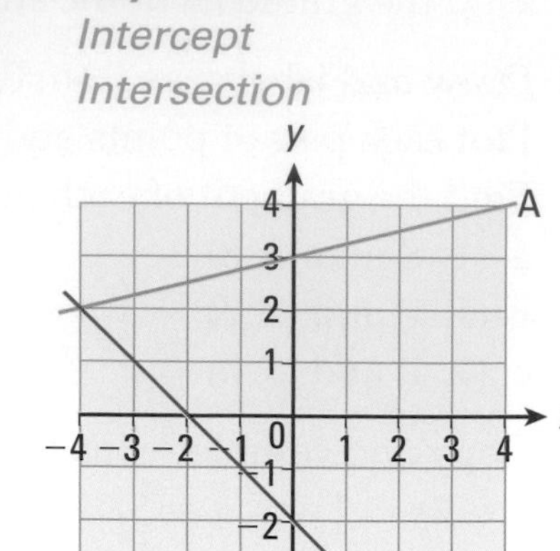

Line A cuts the y axis at the point (0, 3).
Its y intercept is 3.

Line B cuts the y axis at the point (0, -2).
Its y intercept is -2.

example

This diagram shows the graphs of $y = 2x + 3$, $y = 2x + 1$, $y = 2x$, $y = 2x - 2$ and $y = 2x - 4$.
Describe the similarities and differences of these lines.
Find the y intercept of each line.

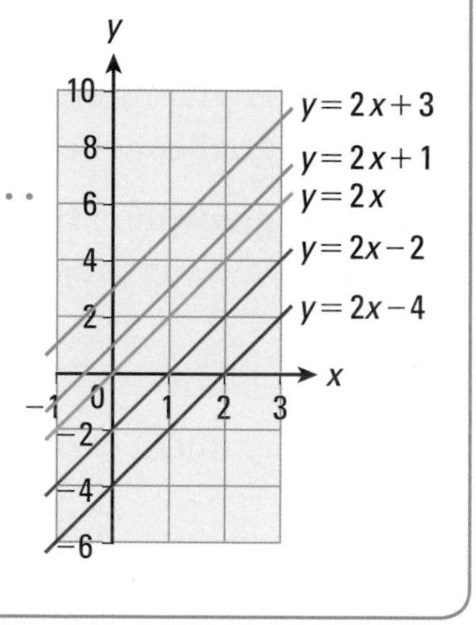

All the lines are parallel to each other because they all have a gradient of 2.
The lines cut the y axis at different points and so they all have different y intercepts.

Equation	y intercept
$y = 2x + 3$	3
$y = 2x + 1$	1
$y = 2x$	0
$y = 2x - 2$	-2
$y = 2x - 4$	-4

- The line $y = 2x + c$ has a y intercept of c. Its gradient is 2.
  The line $y = mx + c$ has a y intercept of c. Its gradient is m.

example

Without drawing any graphs, find the y intercept of these lines.

a $y = 4x$ **b** $y + 3 = 4x$

a Compare $y = mx + c$ with $y = 4x + 0$.
The y intercept is 0.

b Re-arrange $y + 3 = 4x$ by subtracting 3 from both sides to get $y = 4x - 3$.
Compare $y = mx + c$ with $y = 4x - 3$.
The y intercept is -3.

Check
On the y axis, $x = 0$.
Substitute into $y + 3 = 4x$.
$y + 3 = 0$ so $y =$ -3.
This is the y intercept. ✓

Exercise 8d

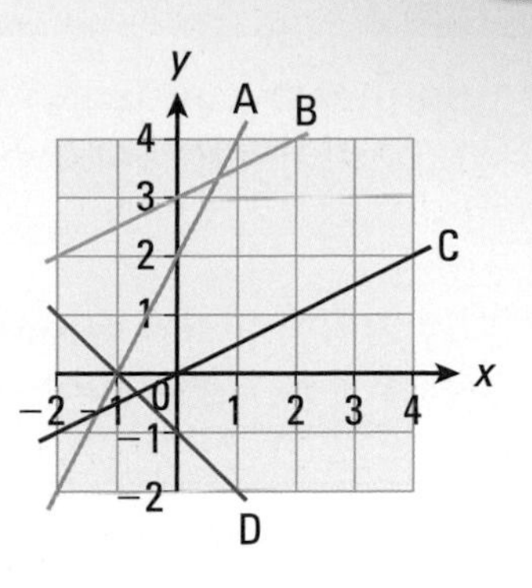

1 Find the y intercepts of the lines A to D.

2 Draw and label both axes from -5 to 5.
Plot each pair of points and join them with a straight line.
Find the y intercept of each line.

a (-2, 4) and (2, 2) **b** (-1, 1) and (2, 4)
c (-1, -2) and (4, -2) **d** (-4, -2) and (2, 1)
e (-2, -2) and (4, -5) **f** (-3, -4) and (3, -5)

3 Copy and complete this table of values for the equations $y = 2x - 3$ and $y = \frac{1}{2}x + 3$.

x	−2	0	2	4	6
$y = 2x - 3$					
$y = \frac{1}{2}x + 3$					

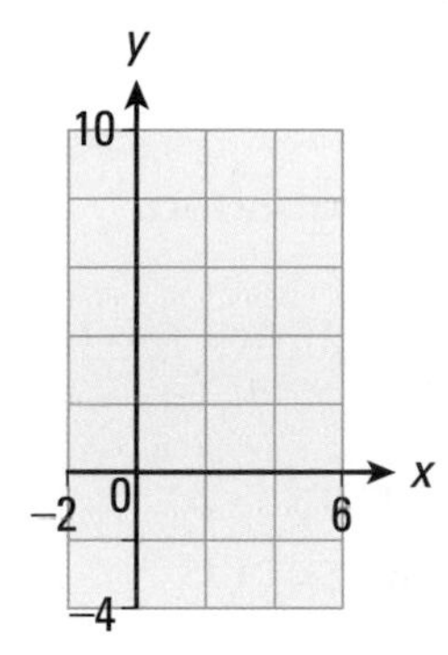

Draw their graphs on a copy of these axes.
Find the y intercept of each line.

4 Find the y intercept of the straight lines with these equations.
Do not draw any graphs.

a $y = 3x + 6$ **b** $y = 4x + 1$ **c** $y = 2x - 5$
d $y = \frac{1}{2}x - 2$ **e** $y = 6x$ **f** $y = x + 1$

5 Find the y intercept of the straight lines with these equations.

a $y = 8x + 5$ **b** $y = 3 + 2x$ **c** $y = 3 - 2x$
d $y = 6 - 2x$ **e** $y = 9 - 4x$ **f** $y = 8 + \frac{1}{2}x$

6 A resistor increases a voltage, V over a time x seconds using the equation $V = 4x + 2$.
Draw the graph of V for $x = 0$ to $x = 4$.
What is the initial voltage when $x = 0$?

ICT challenge

Use the graphical package on a computer to draw the graphs of $y = 2x + c$ where c has

a whole number values from 1 to 5
b whole-number values from -1 to -5
c the value 0.

If you repeat for the graphs of $y = 3x + c$, using the same values of c, what will be different about your graphs?

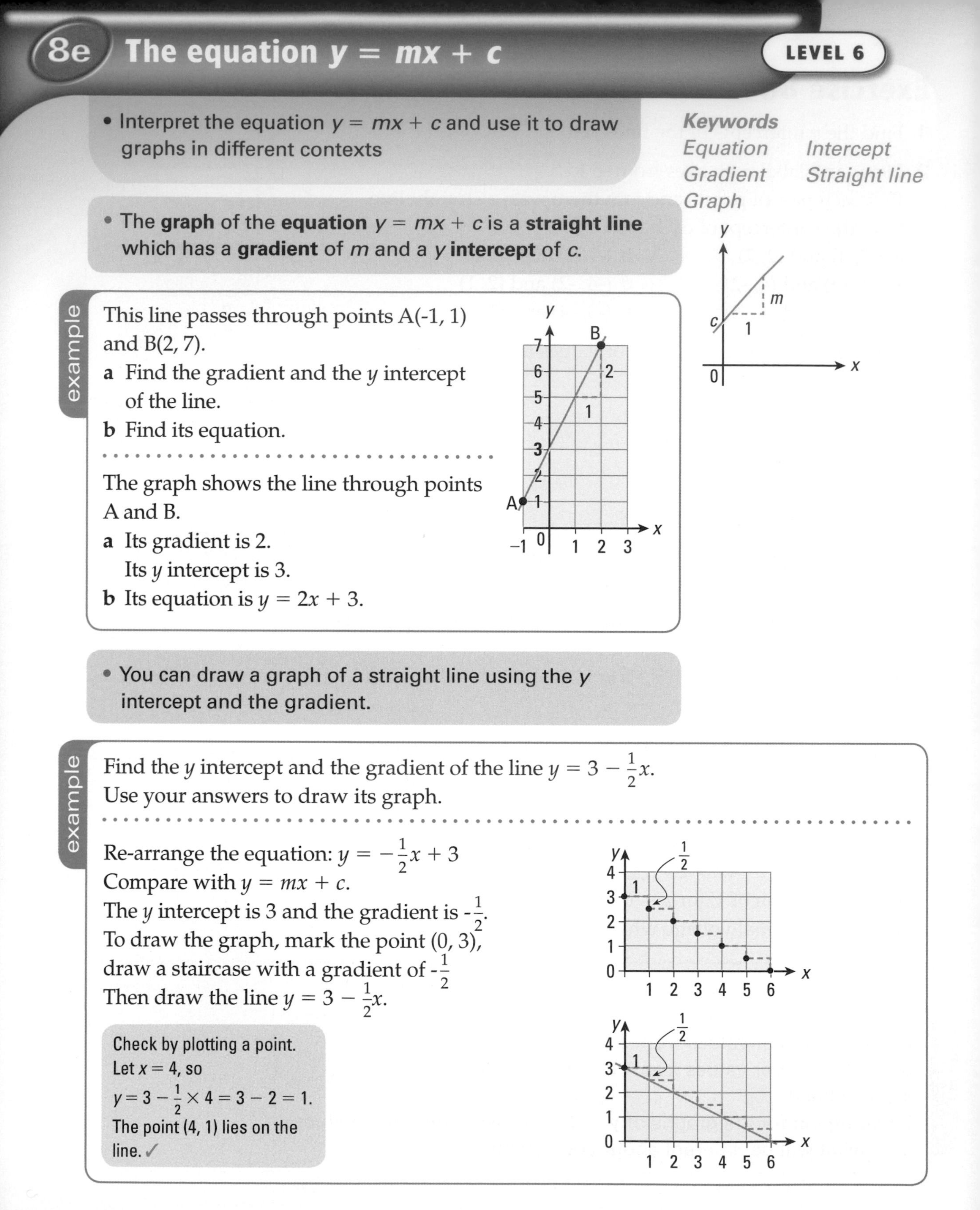

8e The equation $y = mx + c$

LEVEL 6

- Interpret the equation $y = mx + c$ and use it to draw graphs in different contexts

Keywords
Equation
Gradient
Graph
Intercept
Straight line

- The **graph** of the **equation** $y = mx + c$ is a **straight line** which has a **gradient** of m and a y **intercept** of c.

example

This line passes through points A(-1, 1) and B(2, 7).

a Find the gradient and the y intercept of the line.

b Find its equation.

The graph shows the line through points A and B.

a Its gradient is 2.
Its y intercept is 3.

b Its equation is $y = 2x + 3$.

- You can draw a graph of a straight line using the y intercept and the gradient.

example

Find the y intercept and the gradient of the line $y = 3 - \frac{1}{2}x$.
Use your answers to draw its graph.

Re-arrange the equation: $y = -\frac{1}{2}x + 3$
Compare with $y = mx + c$.
The y intercept is 3 and the gradient is $-\frac{1}{2}$.
To draw the graph, mark the point (0, 3), draw a staircase with a gradient of $-\frac{1}{2}$
Then draw the line $y = 3 - \frac{1}{2}x$.

Check by plotting a point.
Let $x = 4$, so
$y = 3 - \frac{1}{2} \times 4 = 3 - 2 = 1$.
The point (4, 1) lies on the line. ✓

Grade D

Exercise 8e

1 Copy and complete this table.

Equation	$y = 3x + 1$	$y = 4x - 5$	$y = \frac{1}{2}x + 2$	$y = 4 - 2x$
Gradient				
***y* intercept**				

2 For each of these straight lines A to E, find

a the gradient

b the y intercept

c the equation of the line.

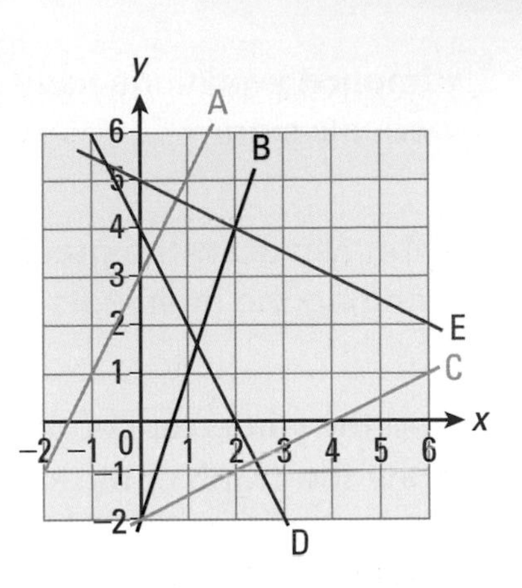

3 Draw and label axes from -6 to 6.
Plot each pair of points and join them with a straight line.
Find the gradient, the y intercept and the equation of each line.

a (-2, 1) and (2, 5) **b** (-2, -3) and (1, 3)

c (0, 5) and (4, 1) **d** (-1, -5) and (1, 1)

e (-2, 0) and (6, -4) **f** (-3, -4) and (3, -4)

4 Find the gradient and the y intercept of the straight lines with these equations. Do not draw any graphs.

a $y = 6x - 4$ **b** $y = 7x + 2$

c $y = 4x - 2$ **d** $y = 9 - 4x$

e $y = 7 - \frac{1}{2}x$ **f** $y = 3 - x$

5 A train travels 10 km from a station, then passes a signal box B.
It then travels 2 km each minute for the next 5 minutes.

a Copy these axes and plot (0, 10) to show B.

b Plot points to show the position of the train for each of the next 5 minutes.

c Draw a line to show the distance of the train from the station during this time and find its equation.

d What is the speed of the train, in km per minute?

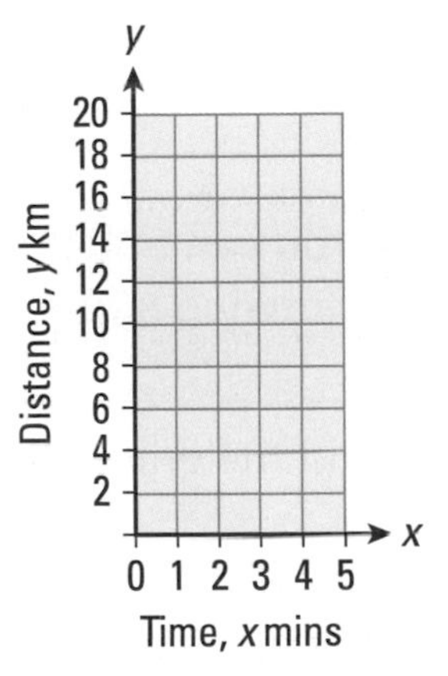

challenge

Here are the equations of five straight lines.
$y = 3x - 1$, $y = 2x + 1$, $y = 4 - 2x$, $y = 3x + 4$, $y = 1 - 2x$
By looking at the equations, find the lines which

a are parallel to each other

b have the same y intercept.

Check your answers using the graphical package on a computer.

8f Graphs of implicit equations

LEVEL 5/6

- Draw graphs of implicit equations and find their gradients and intercepts

Keywords
Directly
Implicit
Implied

- **Implicit** equations have x and y on the same side of the equals sign.

- You can draw the graph of the line $ax + by = c$ by finding the intercepts on both axes.

example

Find the y intercept of the straight line with the equation $3y + 4x = 12$.
Draw the graph of the straight line.

All points on the y axis have $x = 0$.
Substitute $x = 0$ into the equation. $3y + 4 \times 0 = 12$

$3y = 12$

Divide by 3 $\quad y = 4$

The point (0, 4) lies on the line, so the y intercept is 4.

All points on the x axis have $y = 0$.
Substitute $y = 0$ into the equation. $0 + 4x = 12$

$x = 3.$

The point (3, 0) lies on the line.
Draw the graph using the two points (0, 4) and (3, 0).

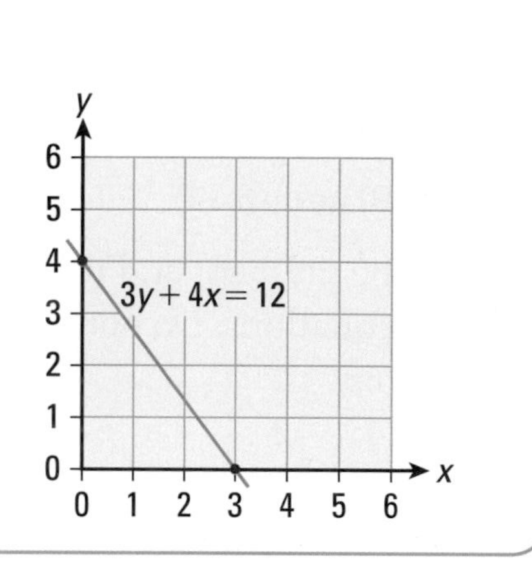

- You can find the gradient of the line $ax + by = c$ by drawing a graph.

example

Find the gradient of the straight line with the equation $2y - 3x = 12$.

Find the intercepts on the x and y axes.
When $y = 0$, $0 - 3x = 12$

$x = -4$

When $x = 0$, $2y - 0 = 12$

$y = 6$

The points (-4, 0) and (0, 6) lie on the line.
Use these two points to draw the line.

From the graph, the gradient of the line is $\frac{6}{4} = 1\frac{1}{2}$

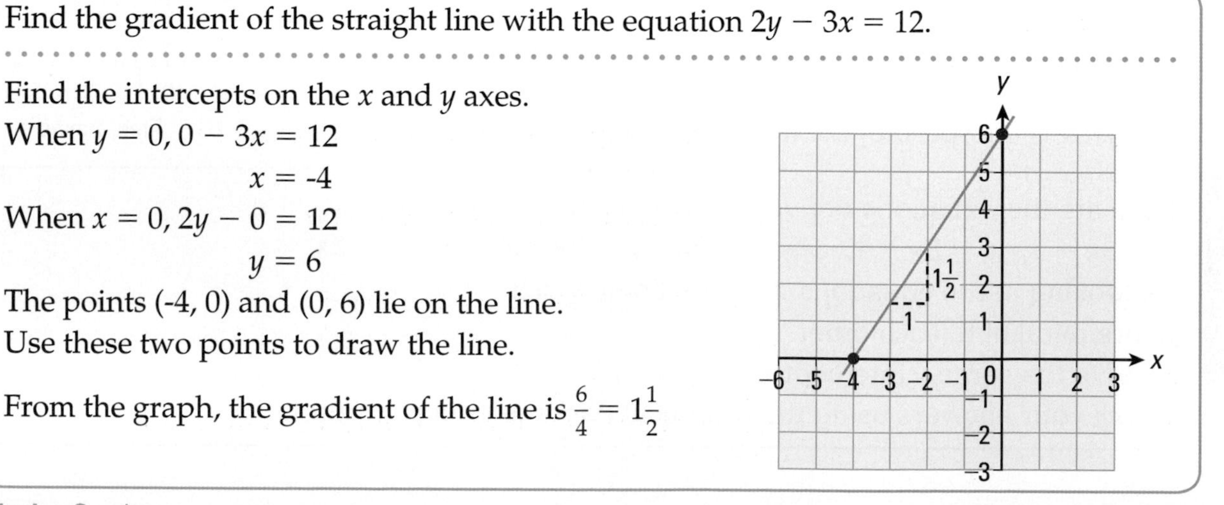

Exercise 8f

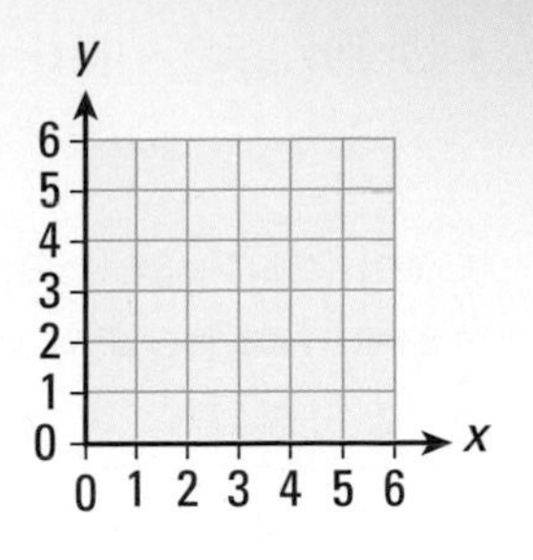

1 Find the intercepts on both axes for the lines with these equations. Draw the lines on a copy of these axes.

a $2x + 3y = 12$ b $5x + 2y = 10$
c $3x + 5y = 15$ d $4x + 3y = 12$
e $2x + 3y = 9$ f $x + 3y - 6 = 0$

2 Find the intercepts on both axes for the lines with these equations. Draw the lines on axes labelled from -6 to 6.

a $2x - 4y = 8$ b $6x - 5y = 30$
c $3x + 4y = -12$

3 Find the intercepts on both axes for the lines with these equations.
Draw the lines on axes labelled from 0 to 8.
Use your graphs to find the gradient of each line.

a $2x + y = 8$ b $3x + y = 6$
c $x + 2y = 4$

4 Draw axes labelled from -6 to 6.
On your axes, draw the graphs of the lines with these equations.
Find the gradient of each line from your graph.

a $3x - y = 3$ b $6x - 2y = 12$ c $x + 2y = -4$
d $x - y = 6$ e $x - 2y = 6$ f $2x + y = -2$

5 A shopkeeper buys x boxes of apples and y boxes of oranges for £24 where $2x + 4y = 24$.

a Draw the graph of $2x + 4y = 24$ on axes from 0 to 12.
b Use your graph to find the five different possible pairs of values for x and y. Remember that they must be whole numbers as she buys at least one box of each.
c If x and y are equal, how many of each does she buy?

investigation

A market gardener plants two kinds of apple tree. He plants x Coxes and y Bramleys.
Each Cox needs $4\,m^2$ of space and each Bramley needs $8\,m^2$. He plants a total area of $84\,m^2$.
Write an equation involving x and y for the total area that he uses.
Draw a graph of your equation.
Find all possible values of x and y from your graph.
He decides to plant equal numbers of Coxes and Bramleys. Find how many.

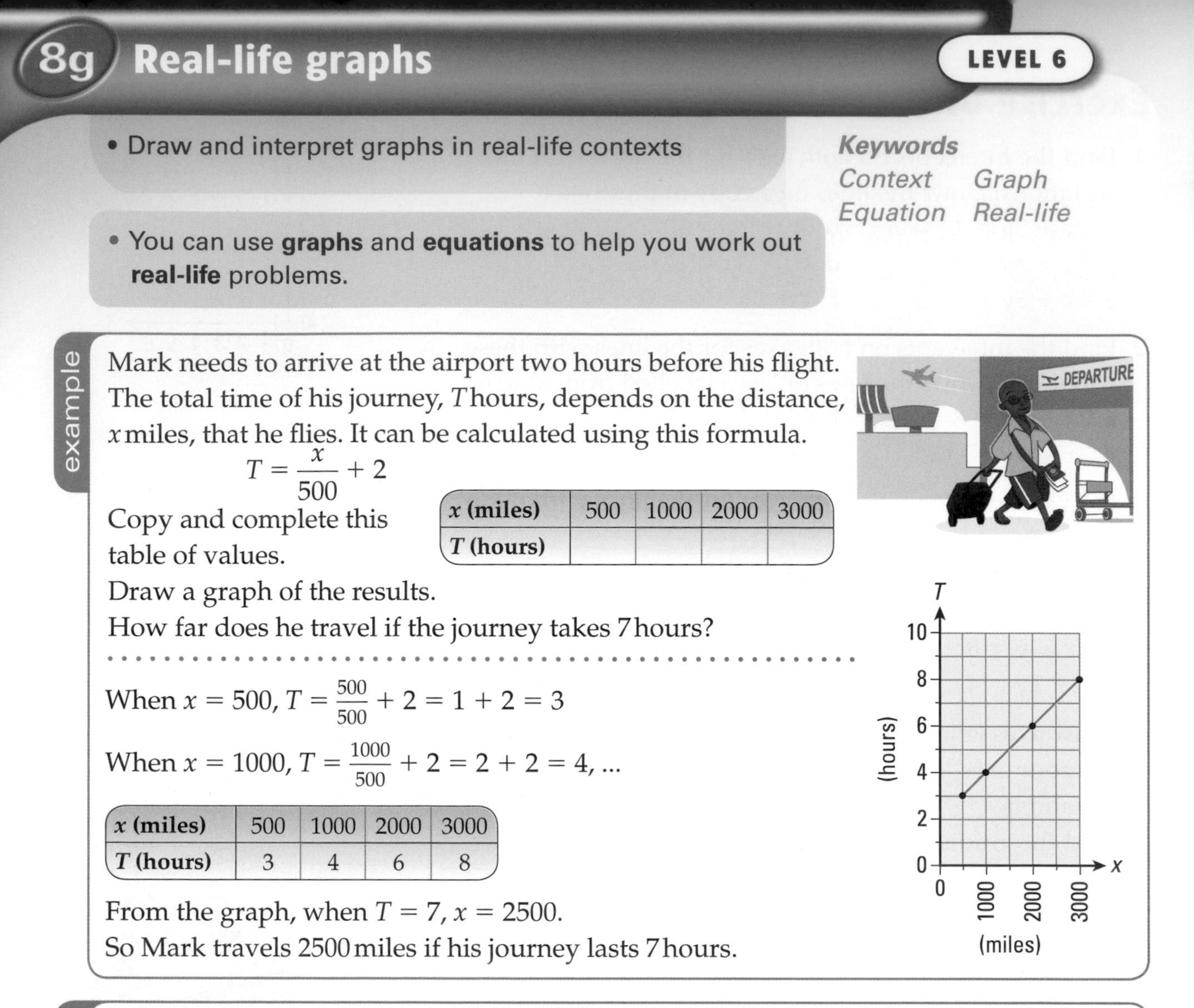

8g Real-life graphs

LEVEL 6

- Draw and interpret graphs in real-life contexts

Keywords
Context Graph
Equation Real-life

- You can use **graphs** and **equations** to help you work out **real-life** problems.

example

Mark needs to arrive at the airport two hours before his flight. The total time of his journey, T hours, depends on the distance, x miles, that he flies. It can be calculated using this formula.

$$T = \frac{x}{500} + 2$$

Copy and complete this table of values.

x (miles)	500	1000	2000	3000
T (hours)				

Draw a graph of the results.

How far does he travel if the journey takes 7 hours?

When $x = 500$, $T = \frac{500}{500} + 2 = 1 + 2 = 3$

When $x = 1000$, $T = \frac{1000}{500} + 2 = 2 + 2 = 4, \ldots$

x (miles)	500	1000	2000	3000
T (hours)	3	4	6	8

From the graph, when $T = 7$, $x = 2500$.

So Mark travels 2500 miles if his journey lasts 7 hours.

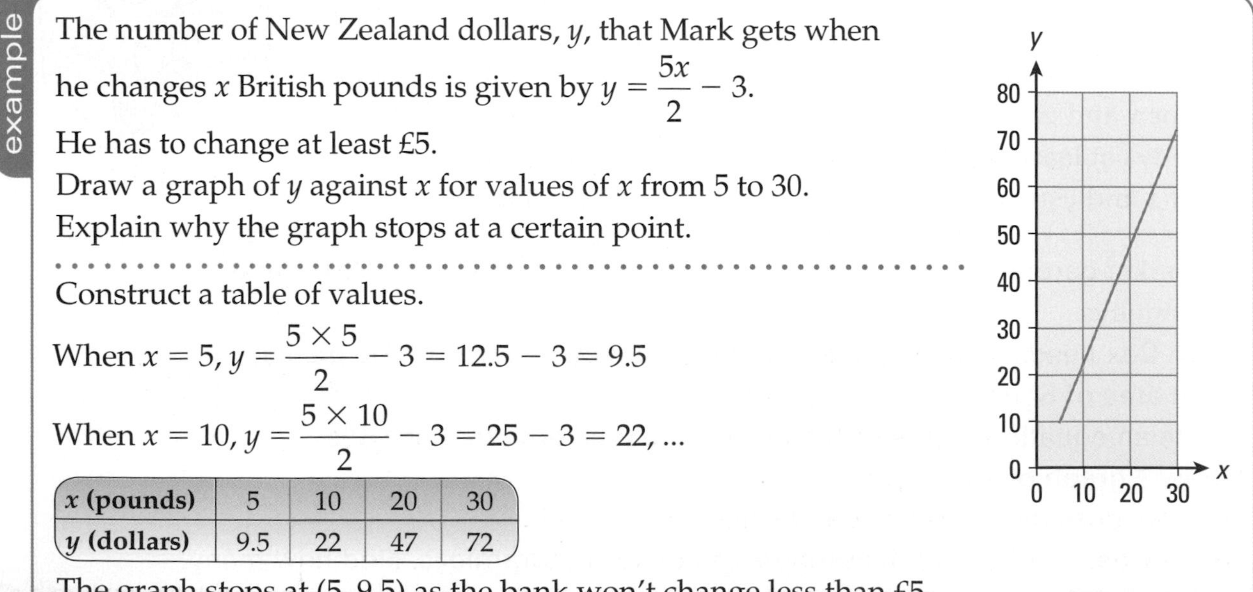

example

The number of New Zealand dollars, y, that Mark gets when he changes x British pounds is given by $y = \frac{5x}{2} - 3$.

He has to change at least £5.

Draw a graph of y against x for values of x from 5 to 30.

Explain why the graph stops at a certain point.

Construct a table of values.

When $x = 5$, $y = \frac{5 \times 5}{2} - 3 = 12.5 - 3 = 9.5$

When $x = 10$, $y = \frac{5 \times 10}{2} - 3 = 25 - 3 = 22, \ldots$

x (pounds)	5	10	20	30
y (dollars)	9.5	22	47	72

The graph stops at (5, 9.5) as the bank won't change less than £5.

Exercise 8g

p. 38

1 Triangle ABC is isosceles.

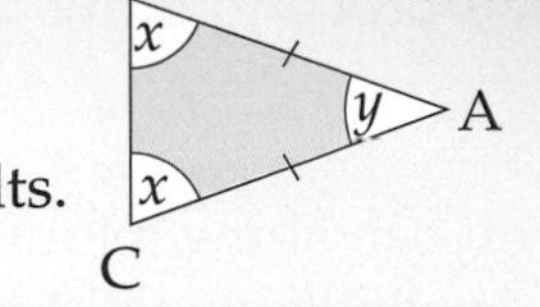

a Calculate y for different values of x.
Copy and complete this table and draw a graph of your results.

b What is special about the triangle when
i $x = 45°$ **ii** $x = 90°$?

x	10	20	30	40	60	80	90
y							

2 A hire company charges £20 plus 2 pence for every mile you travel in their van.
If you travel x miles the cost, £C, is given by $C = \frac{2x}{100} + 20$.

a Copy and complete this table and draw a graph of your results on a copy of these axes.

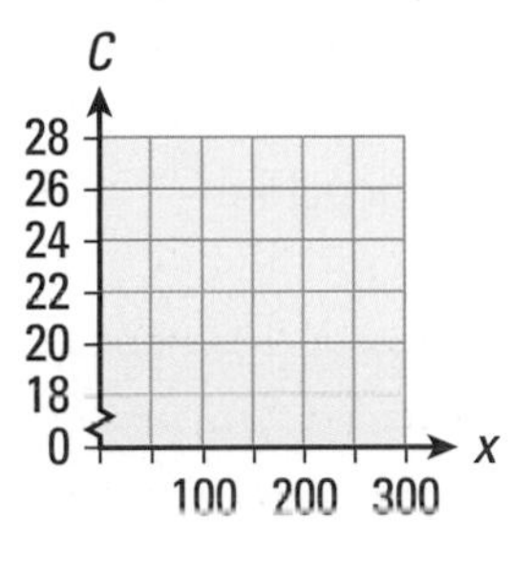

x (miles)	50	100	200	300
C (£)				

b If you use the van for 250 miles, how much are you charged?

3 A car starts its journey with a full tank of petrol.
After travelling x km it has y litres of petrol left in the tank, where $y = 40 - \frac{x}{20}$.

a Copy and complete this table and draw a graph of your results.

x (km)	0	100	200	400	600	800
y (litres)						

b How many litres are in the full tank?

c How far can the car travel before running out of petrol?

4 You drop a stone from a tall building.
It falls a distance x metres in a time t seconds where $x = 5 \times t^2$.

a Copy and complete this table and draw a graph of your results.

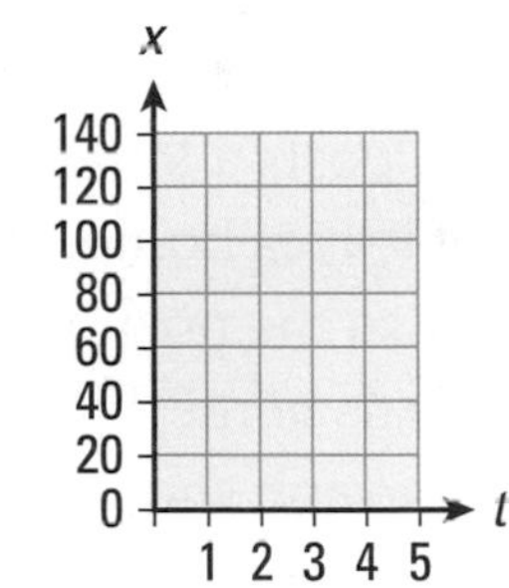

t (secs)	1	2	3	4	5
x (metres)					

b What symbol in the equation tells you that the graph will not be a straight line?

c If the stone hits the ground after 4.5 seconds, estimate the height of the building.

investigation

A farmer makes a rectangular pen for his sheep so that it always has a perimeter of 24 metres.

a Construct a table of possible values of x and y and draw a graph of your results.

b Find the equation which links x and y.

c Which values of x and y give the maximum possible value of the area of the sheep-pen? What kind of rectangle is it in this case?

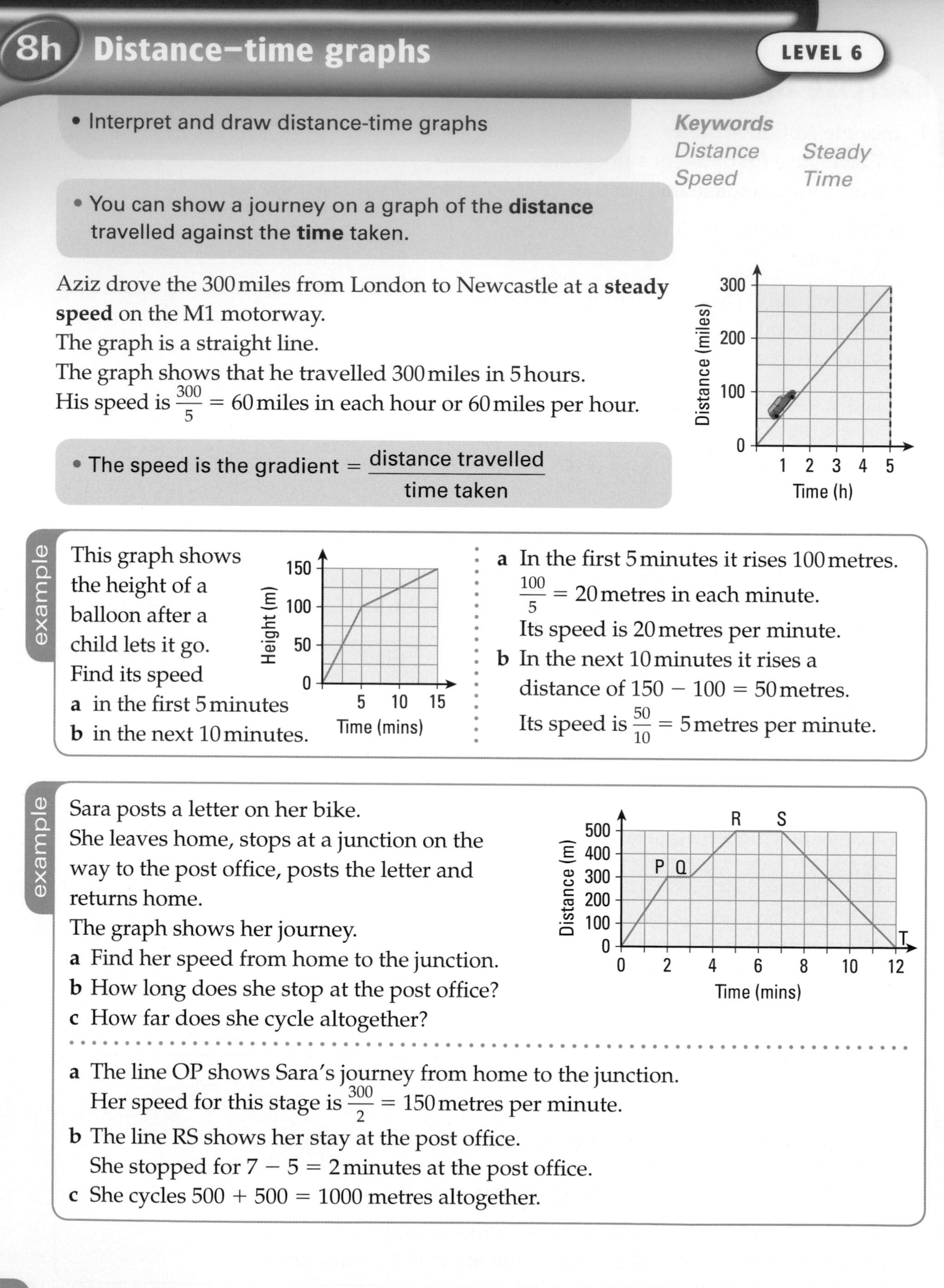

8h Distance–time graphs

LEVEL 6

- Interpret and draw distance-time graphs

Keywords
Distance
Speed
Steady
Time

- You can show a journey on a graph of the **distance** travelled against the **time** taken.

Aziz drove the 300 miles from London to Newcastle at a **steady speed** on the M1 motorway.
The graph is a straight line.
The graph shows that he travelled 300 miles in 5 hours.
His speed is $\frac{300}{5} = 60$ miles in each hour or 60 miles per hour.

- The speed is the gradient $= \dfrac{\text{distance travelled}}{\text{time taken}}$

example

This graph shows the height of a balloon after a child lets it go.
Find its speed
a in the first 5 minutes
b in the next 10 minutes.

a In the first 5 minutes it rises 100 metres.
$\frac{100}{5} = 20$ metres in each minute.
Its speed is 20 metres per minute.

b In the next 10 minutes it rises a distance of $150 - 100 = 50$ metres.
Its speed is $\frac{50}{10} = 5$ metres per minute.

example

Sara posts a letter on her bike.
She leaves home, stops at a junction on the way to the post office, posts the letter and returns home.
The graph shows her journey.
a Find her speed from home to the junction.
b How long does she stop at the post office?
c How far does she cycle altogether?

a The line OP shows Sara's journey from home to the junction.
Her speed for this stage is $\frac{300}{2} = 150$ metres per minute.

b The line RS shows her stay at the post office.
She stopped for $7 - 5 = 2$ minutes at the post office.

c She cycles $500 + 500 = 1000$ metres altogether.

Exercise 8h

1 This graph shows Harry taking his dog for a walk.
- **a** What is their furthest distance from home?
- **b** How long does it take to get this far?
- **c** For how long do they stop on the way back?
- **d** How far from home are they when they stop?
- **e** How long in total do they take to get back home?
- **f** How long does the whole walk take?

2 You are waiting at a bus stop and you see your bus 800 m away. This graph shows its journey.
- **a** How many times does the bus stop before it reaches you?
- **b** How long does it take to reach its first stop?
- **c** How far apart are the first and second stops?
- **d** How long does it spend at its second stop?

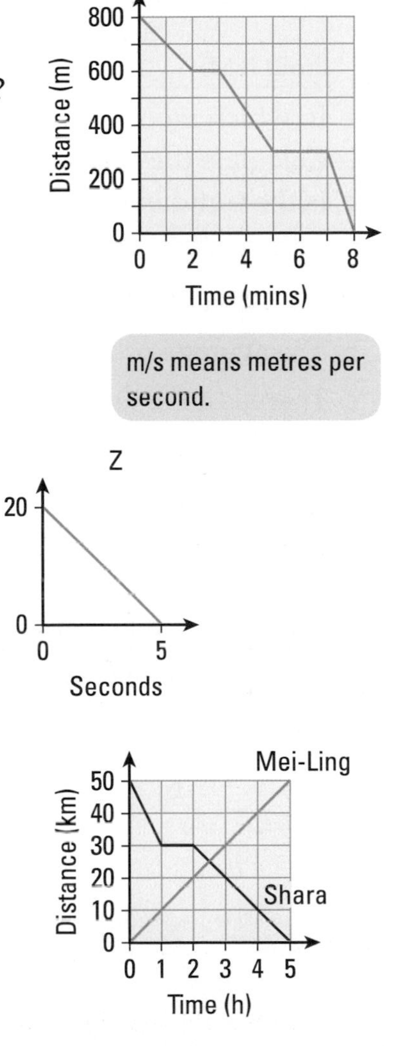

3 Match the graphs with the descriptions of a car.
- **a** Moving away from you at a speed of 4 m/s.
- **b** Moving towards you at a speed of 4 m/s.
- **c** Stopped at a distance of 20 m from you.

m/s means metres per second.

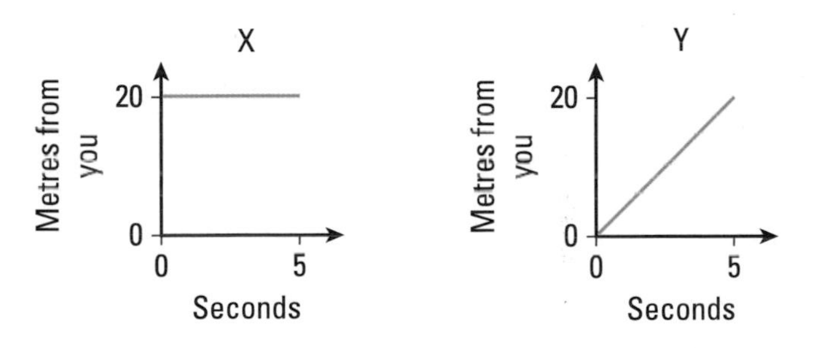

4 Mei-Ling and Shara cycle on the same road in opposite directions, as shown on this graph.
- **a** Who has a rest on the way? How long is the rest?
- **b** How long is it before they pass each other?
- **c** How far does Mei-Ling cycle and what is her speed?
- **d** What is Shara's speed after she has rested?

challenge

Draw a graph for your journey to school in a morning.
Include any times when you stop, such as when you are waiting for a bus.
Show how far you travel and how long each part of your journey takes.

8i Times series

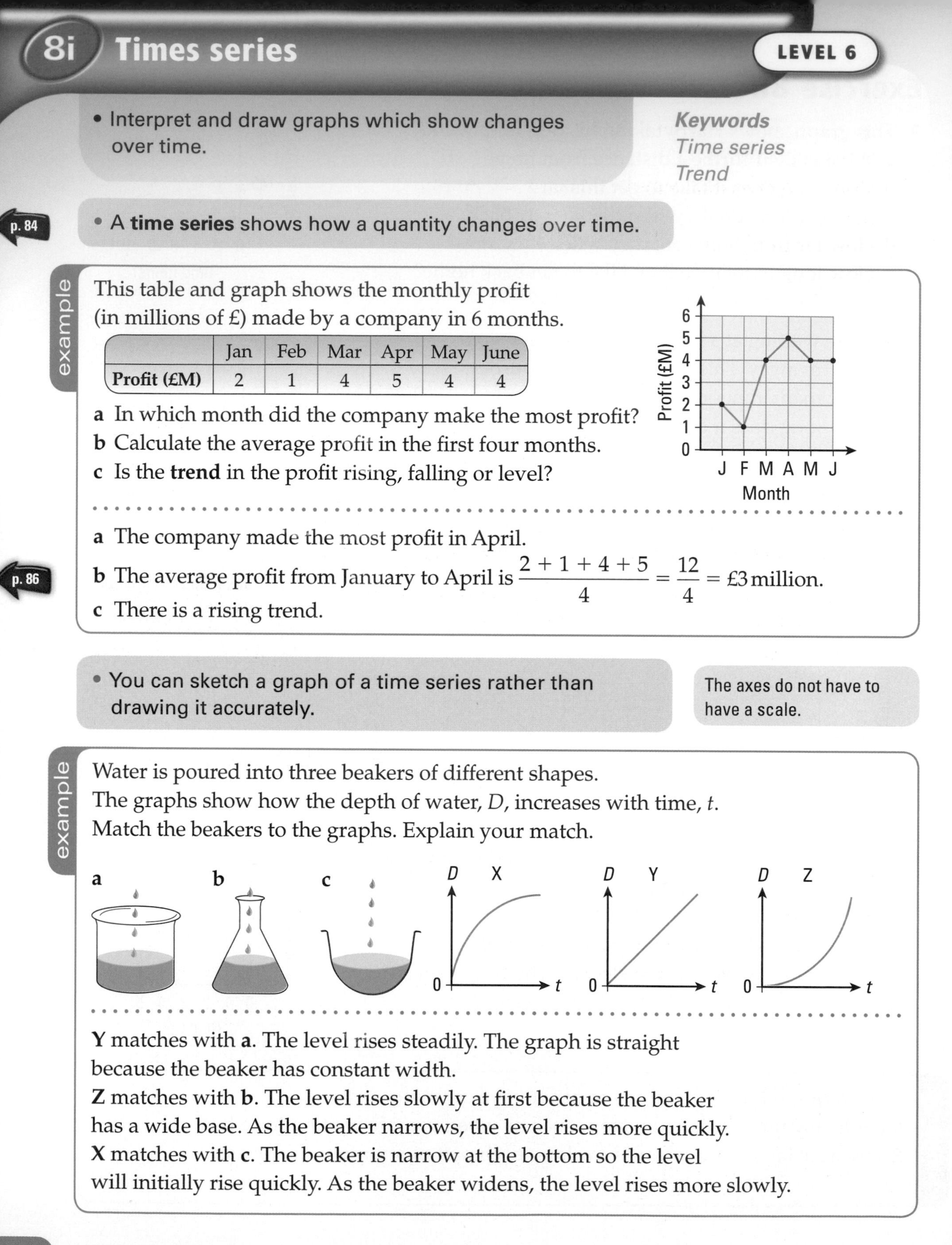

- Interpret and draw graphs which show changes over time.

Keywords
Time series
Trend

p. 84

- A **time series** shows how a quantity changes over time.

example

This table and graph shows the monthly profit (in millions of £) made by a company in 6 months.

	Jan	Feb	Mar	Apr	May	June
Profit (£M)	2	1	4	5	4	4

a In which month did the company make the most profit?
b Calculate the average profit in the first four months.
c Is the **trend** in the profit rising, falling or level?

a The company made the most profit in April.

p. 86

b The average profit from January to April is $\frac{2+1+4+5}{4} = \frac{12}{4} = £3$ million.

c There is a rising trend.

- You can sketch a graph of a time series rather than drawing it accurately.

The axes do not have to have a scale.

example

Water is poured into three beakers of different shapes.
The graphs show how the depth of water, D, increases with time, t.
Match the beakers to the graphs. Explain your match.

Y matches with **a**. The level rises steadily. The graph is straight because the beaker has constant width.
Z matches with **b**. The level rises slowly at first because the beaker has a wide base. As the beaker narrows, the level rises more quickly.
X matches with **c**. The beaker is narrow at the bottom so the level will initially rise quickly. As the beaker widens, the level rises more slowly.

Exercise 8i

1 This graph shows the number of births in a hospital over a period of five weeks.

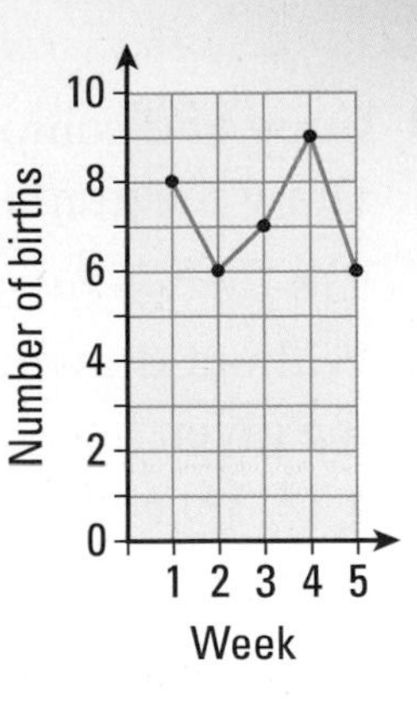

a Copy this table and complete it using the graph.

Week	1	2	3	4	5
No. of births					

b In which weeks were there fewest births?

c Calculate the mean number of births in the first three weeks.

d Is the trend in the number of births rising, falling or level?

2 This table show the number of accidents at a road junction over a period of six months.

Month	Jan	Feb	March	April	May	June
No. of accidents	16	14	15	10	8	9

a Draw a time-series graph for this data.

b What is the largest monthly fall in the number of accidents?

c Calculate the mean number of accidents over the 6 months.

d Is the trend in the number of accidents rising, falling or level?

3 The volume of tea in a cup depends on how you drink it. Match the descriptions **a** to **d** with the graphs.

a The tea is drunk all at one go.

b The tea is drunk in two gulps, half a cup each time.

c The tea is drunk sip by sip.

d The tea is not drunk at all.

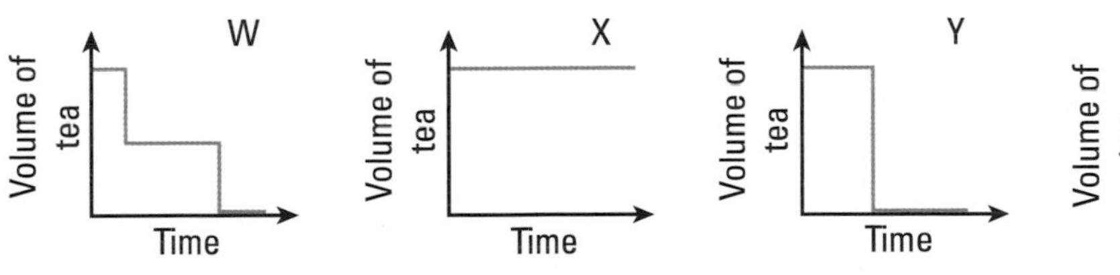

4 A cook uses olive oil from a 1 litre bottle.
This graph shows the amount of oil in the bottle over a week.
Give an explanation for the shape of the graph.

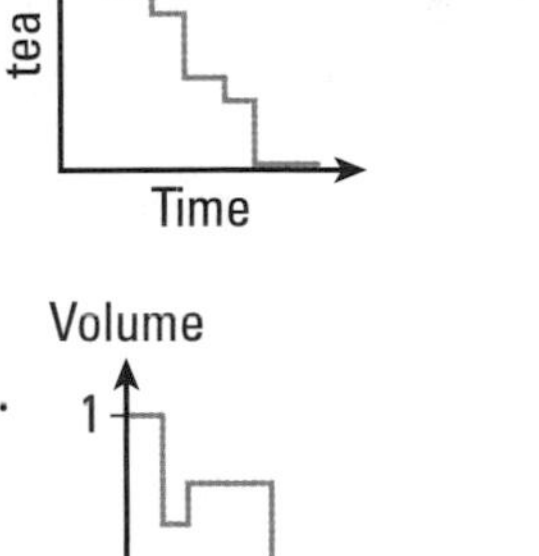

challenge

Sketch graphs to illustrate these situations.

a The selling price of a car, bought new, over its lifetime

b The annual repair costs of a car, bought new, until it is scrapped

c The annual mileage of a car with several different owners over its lifetime.

Explain why the graphs have their shapes and describe any trends.

8 Consolidation

8a

1 Copy and complete this table for each of the equations. Draw the graph of each equation on appropriate axes.

x	0	2	4	6
y				

a $y = 2x - 3$ **b** $y = 9 - x$ **c** $y = 10 - 2x$

2 Without drawing any graphs, decide whether each point is on the given line.

a (2, 14) and $y = 3x + 8$ **b** (5, 15) and $y = 2x - 5$

8b

3 Match the equations in the box with lines A, B, C or D.

$y = x + 6$	$y = 6 - x$	$x = 3$	$y = 3$

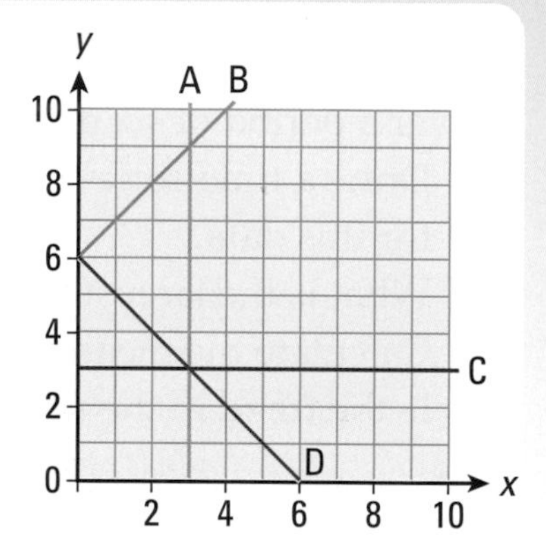

8c

4 Draw and label axes from 0 to 6. Plot each pair of points and join them with a straight line. Find the gradients of each line.

a (1, 2) and (3, 6) **b** (3, 5) and (6, 2) **c** (0, 1) and (4, 3)

8d

5 Find the y intercepts of the lines A to C in the graph on the right.

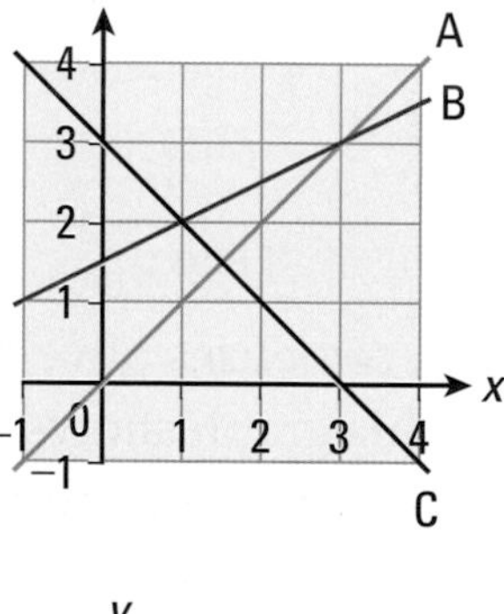

6 Copy and complete this table of values for the equations $y = 2x + 1$ and $y = 3x - 1$.

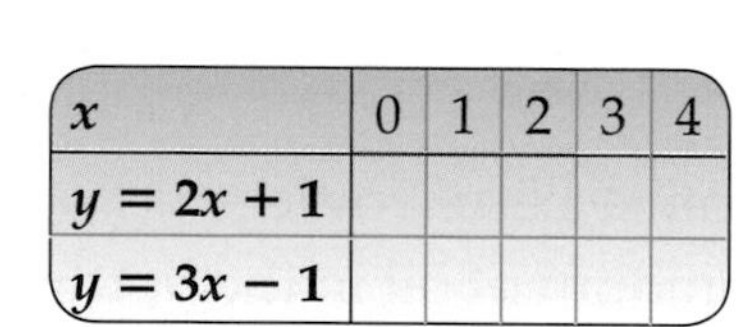

x	0	1	2	3	4
$y = 2x + 1$					
$y = 3x - 1$					

Draw their graphs and find the y intercept of each line.

8e

7 Find the gradient and the y intercept of the straight lines with these equations. Do not draw any graphs.

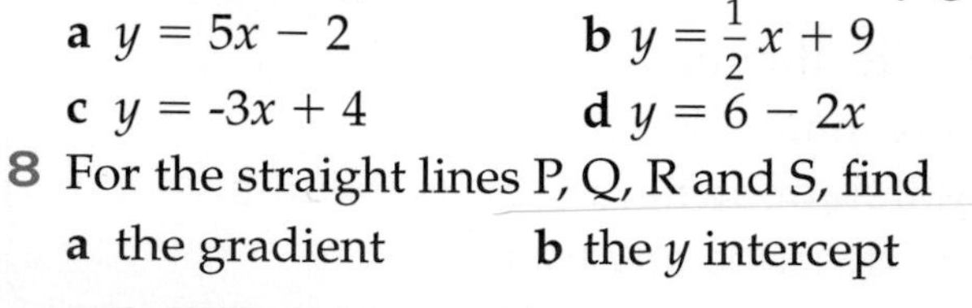

a $y = 5x - 2$ **b** $y = \frac{1}{2}x + 9$

c $y = -3x + 4$ **d** $y = 6 - 2x$

8 For the straight lines P, Q, R and S, find

a the gradient **b** the y intercept **c** the equation.

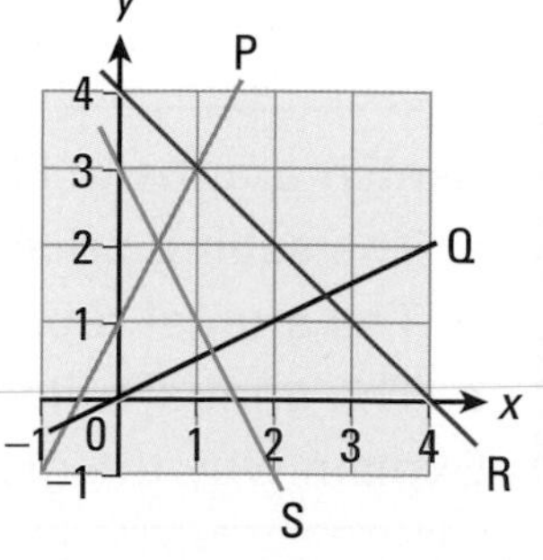

9 Find the points where these lines cut the x-axis and y-axis.
Draw their graphs on axes labelled from -6 to 6.
Use your graphs to find the gradient of each line.

a $2x + y = 6$ **b** $2x + 4y = 12$ **c** $2x - 2y = 9$

10 A car has a full tank of petrol. It uses p litres. It can now travel a further distance of d km before it needs more petrol.

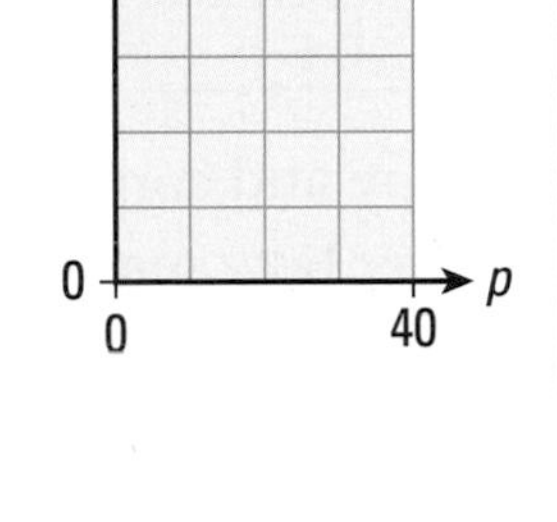

a If $d = 800 - 20p$, copy and complete this table and draw a graph of your results on a copy of these axes.

p	0	10	20	30	40
d					

b What is the furthest distance the car can go on a full tank?

c How many litres does a full tank hold?

d What is the gradient of the graph?
What does the gradient tell you about the fuel consumption?

11 The graph shows the distance travelled by a railway truck over a period of 40 seconds.
Find its speed during

a the first 10 seconds

b the next 10 seconds

c the last stage of its journey.

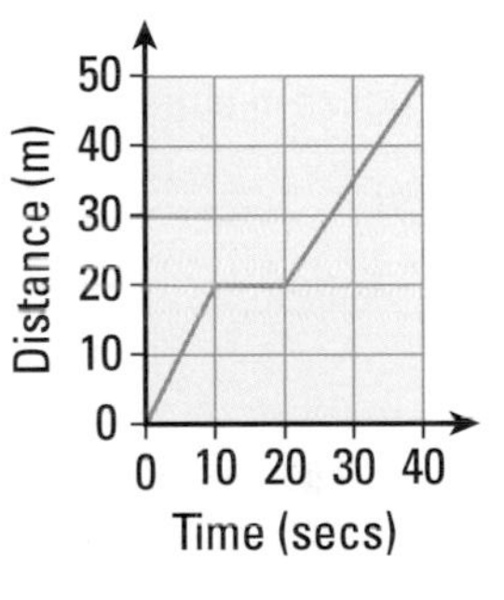

12 These four graphs show changes over time t.
Match the graphs to these descriptions of the variable, y.

a The distance travelled by a train moving at a steady speed.

b The temperature of a cup of coffee left undrunk.

c The outdoor temperature on a cloudy day.

d The amount of pocket money still to be spent during a holiday.

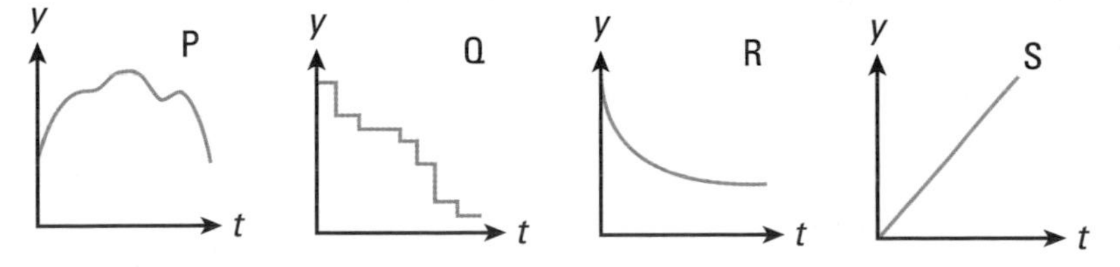

8 Summary

Assessment criteria

- Plot the graphs of linear functions **Level 6**
- Plot and interpret graphs arising from real situations **Level 6**

Level 6

1 There is an oil leak from the engine of Sally's car.
The volume of the oil left in the engine is v, where
$v = 10 - \frac{d}{2}$ and d is the number of days.

d (day)	0	5	10	15
m (litres)				

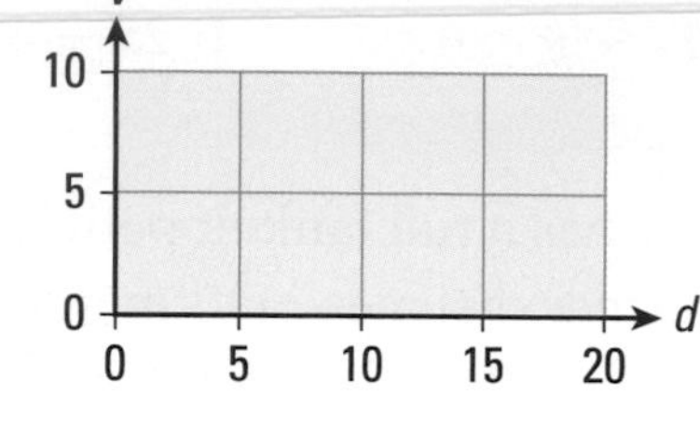

a Copy and complete the table and draw a graph of $v = 10 - \frac{d}{2}$

b After how many days does all the oil run out?

Riaja's answer ✔

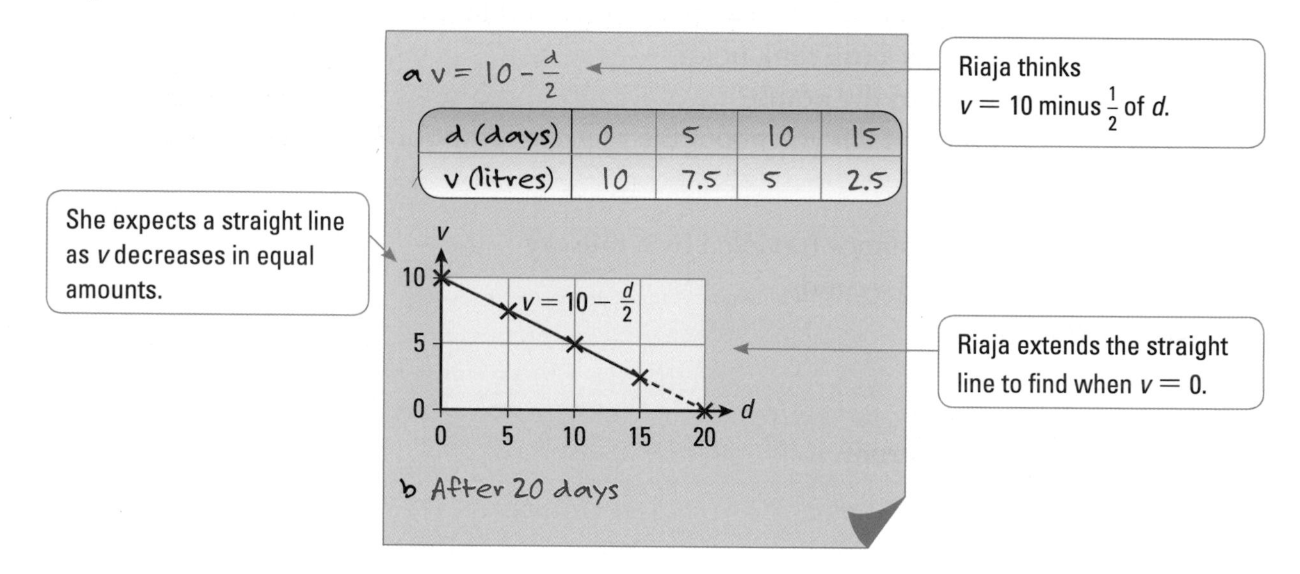

Level 7

2 **a** A straight line goes through the points (0, 1), (2, 5) and (4, 9)
The equation of the line is $y = 2x + 1$
Is the point (7, 12) on this straight line?
Explain your answer.

b A different straight line goes through the points (0, 1), (2, 7) and (4, 13)
Write down the equation of this straight line.

Key Stage 3 2008 5–7 Paper 1

9 Statistics

Probability

Many people buy lottery tickets and scratchcards once they are over 16. In a typical lottery, 6 numbers are picked from 49 balls, The probability of winning the jackpot is 1 in 14 million (quite low!). A scratchcard will often have a probability of winning of 1 in 5 (much better) but the amount to be won will be less.

What's the point? An understanding of probability can help you predict outcomes and judge risk in everyday situations. It can also help people decide if its worth buying a lottery ticket!

Check in

Level 5

1 Draw a probability scale from 0 to 1.
Mark divisions on the scale and label them with decimals.
Show where you might put events that could be described with these words.

a Impossible **b** Certain
c An even chance **d** Very unlikely

2 An ordinary dice is rolled. What is the probability of the score being a prime number?
Show all of your working.

3 Convert each of these fraction and percentages to decimals.

p. 110

a $\frac{3}{5}$ **b** $\frac{5}{8}$ **c** $\frac{9}{20}$
d 15% **e** 27% **f** 3.7%

Prediction and uncertainty

LEVEL 5

- Think about ideas of uncertainty and prediction

Keywords
Certain
Experiment
Impossible
Unpredictable
Variation

- You can describe probability in words. For example,
  - you can know for **certain** that something will happen
    The day after next Tuesday will be a Wednesday.
  - you can know that an outcome is **impossible.**
    A person chosen from your class will be 200 years old.

- You can use probabilities to explain what you expect to happen in an **experiment.**
  An experiment is a series of trials.

The exact results of a particular experiment are usually **unpredictable**. You might get different results when the experiment is repeated.

example

In an experiment, a teacher asked students to roll an ordinary dice 60 times.
David produced this set of results.
Should his teacher be suspicious?

Score	1	2	3	4	5	6
Frequency	10	10	10	10	10	10

It is possible that David actually got these results, but his teacher might think he made them up from what he thought the results should be. Real results for this experiment would show a lot of **variation.**

Unpredictability is all around us.

- A weather forecast is only a prediction and might be wrong.

  A forecast might say, 'a 30% chance of rain by midday'.

- People sometimes feel that they are having 'a run of bad luck' when they lose their keys or miss the bus. This is often simple coincidence.
- Part of the fun of watching a sporting event is that you can't be certain of the result.

Some sports and games involve more chance than others.

Exercise 9a

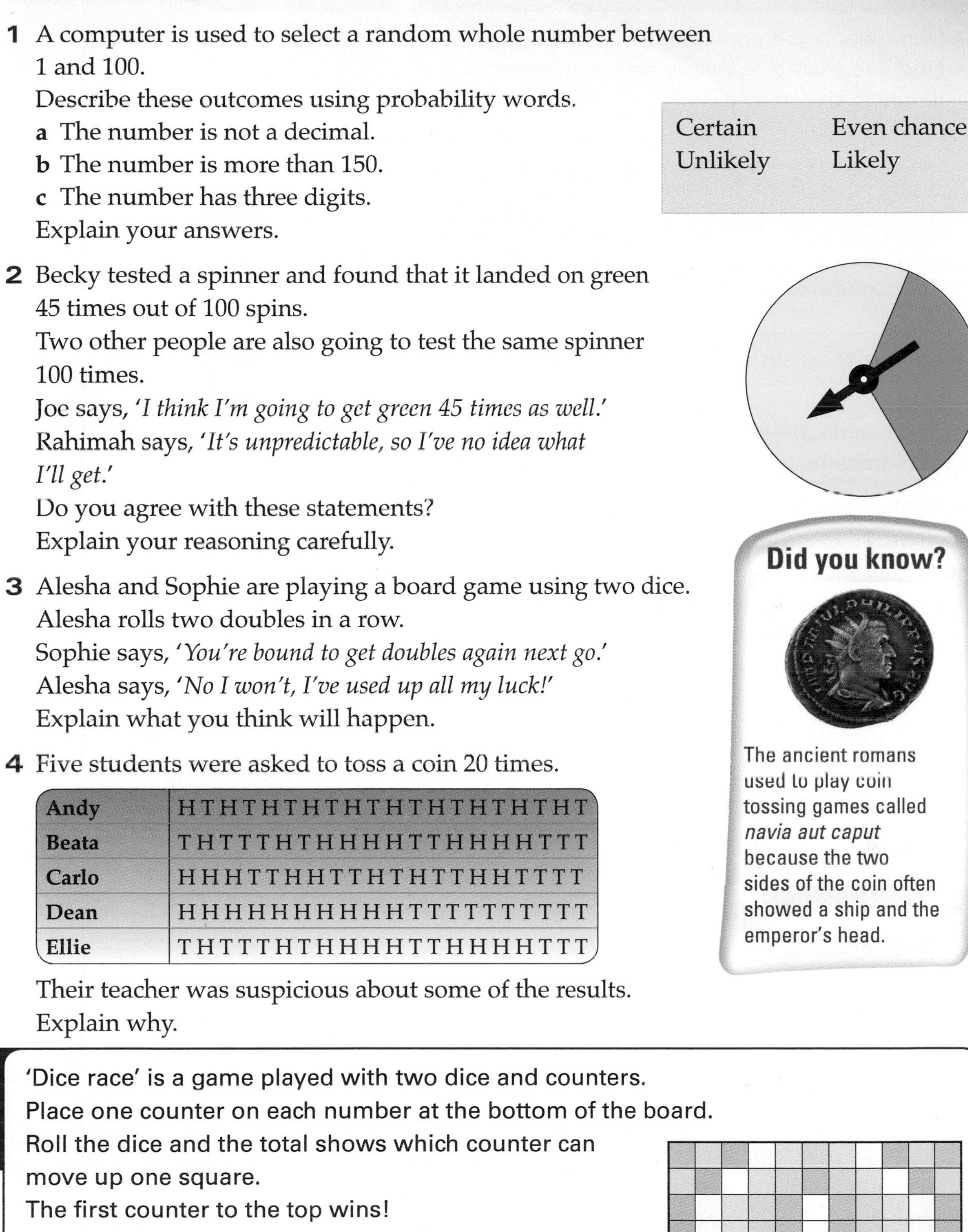

1 A computer is used to select a random whole number between 1 and 100.
Describe these outcomes using probability words.
a The number is not a decimal.
b The number is more than 150.
c The number has three digits.
Explain your answers.

Certain	Even chance
Unlikely	Likely

2 Becky tested a spinner and found that it landed on green 45 times out of 100 spins.
Two other people are also going to test the same spinner 100 times.
Joe says, '*I think I'm going to get green 45 times as well.*'
Rahimah says, '*It's unpredictable, so I've no idea what I'll get.*'
Do you agree with these statements?
Explain your reasoning carefully.

3 Alesha and Sophie are playing a board game using two dice.
Alesha rolls two doubles in a row.
Sophie says, '*You're bound to get doubles again next go.*'
Alesha says, '*No I won't, I've used up all my luck!*'
Explain what you think will happen.

4 Five students were asked to toss a coin 20 times.

Andy	H T H T H T H T H T H T H T H T H T H T
Beata	T H T T T H T H H H H T T H H H H T T T
Carlo	H H H T T H H T T H T H T T H H T T T T
Dean	H H H H H H H H H H T T T T T T T T T T
Ellie	T H T T T H T H H H H T T H H H H T T T

Their teacher was suspicious about some of the results.
Explain why.

Did you know?

The ancient romans used to play coin tossing games called *navia aut caput* because the two sides of the coin often showed a ship and the emperor's head.

puzzle

'Dice race' is a game played with two dice and counters.
Place one counter on each number at the bottom of the board.
Roll the dice and the total shows which counter can move up one square.
The first counter to the top wins!
Does the same counter always win?
What happens if you change the number of moves needed to win?

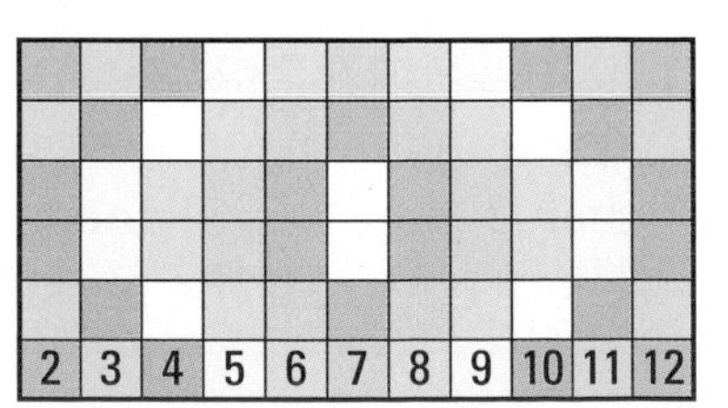

9b Mutually exclusive events

LEVEL 6

- Understand the vocabulary of probability
- Find and record mutually exclusive events for a single trial

Keywords
Event *Outcome*
Experiment *Trial*
Collectively exhaustive
Mutually exclusive

- A **trial** is anything that we can find the result of. A series of one or more trials is an **experiment**.

Rolling a dice is a trial.

- The **outcomes** of a trial are the possible results.

Spinning a coin ten times is an experiment

- An **event** is a set of outcomes.

- Two events are **mutually exclusive** if they have no outcomes in common. They cannot both happen.

example

Keira rolls an ordinary dice.

a List all the outcomes.

b Explain whether these pairs of events are mutually exclusive.

i An even score and a multiple of 3.

ii A score less than 4 and a score more than 3.

a The possible outcomes are 1, 2, 3, 4, 5 and 6.

b i Outcomes for 'an even score' are {2, 4, 6}.
Outcomes for 'a multiple of 3' are {3, 6}.
The outcome 6 is common to both events.
They are not mutually exclusive.

ii Outcomes for 'a score less than 4' are {1, 2, 3}.
Outcomes for 'a score more than 3' are {4, 5, 6}.
No outcome is common to both sets.
The events are mutually exclusive.

- Outcomes are **exhaustive** if between them they include all the possible outcomes of an event.

Events that are exhaustive could also be mutually exclusive.

example

Keira rolls a dice again. Explain whether each pair of events in **b** are exhaustive.

i The outcomes for 'an even score' and 'a multiple of 3' are {2, 4, 6} and {6}. They do not cover all the possible outcomes so they are not exhaustive.

ii The outcomes for 'a score less than 4' and 'a score more than 3' are {1, 2, 3} and {4, 5, 6}.
These cover all the possible outcomes, so are exhaustive.

Exercise 9b

1 Alfie rolls an ordinary dice.
X is the event 'the score is even'.
Y is the event 'the score is odd'.

a List all of the outcomes that belong to

i event X **ii** event Y.

b Are these events mutually exclusive? Explain your answer.

2 A football team's result in their next game will be a win, lose or draw.
Explain why

a these three results are mutually exclusive

b these three results are exhaustive.

3 This set of cards is placed in a bag, and a card is picked at random.

a List all the possible outcomes for this experiment.

b The event A is 'the chosen letter is a vowel'.
List the outcomes that belong to event A.

c The event B is 'the chosen letter is a consonant.'
List the outcomes that belong to event B.

d Are events A and B mutually exclusive?
Explain your answer.

e Are events A and B exhaustive?
Explain your answer.

4 Kyle's teacher places this set of cards in a bag and picks a card at random.

1 2 3 4 5 6 7 8 9 10

a List the outcomes that belong to each of these events.

A = 'A prime number' B = 'An odd number'
C = 'An even number' D = 'A factor of 12'

b Explain whether each of these statements are true or false.

i Events B and C are mutually exclusive.

ii Events B and C are exhaustive.

iii Events A and C are mutually exclusive.

iv Events C and D are exhaustive.

discussion

Freya says 'If events A and B are both mutually exclusive and exhaustive, then

a either event A will happen or event B will happen

b events A and B cannot both happen.'

Do you agree with her?

Calculating probabilities

LEVEL 6

- Calculate probabilities using equally likely outcomes
- Know that the sum of all mutually exclusive outcomes is 1, and use this when solving problems.

Keywords
Equally likely
Probability scale
Theoretical probability

- Probabilities can be shown on a probability **scale** from 0 (impossible) to 1 (certain).

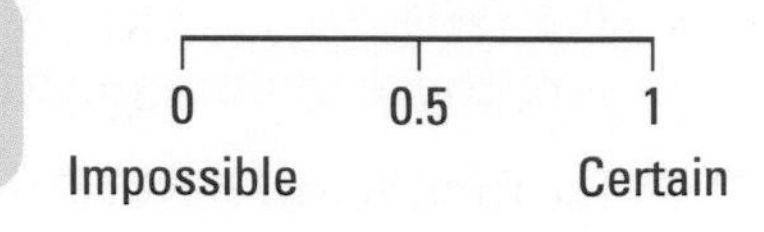

- You can find a **theoretical probability** of an event when all the outcomes are equally likely.

  Probability of an event =

$$\frac{\text{Number of outcomes belonging to the event}}{\text{Total number of equally likely outcomes}}$$

They can be written as fractions, decimals or percentages.

example

Sam has a multipack of 24 packets of crisps.
Six are ready salted, six are cheese and onion, six are salt and vinegar and six are barbeque.
Find the probability that he picks a packet of salt and vinegar crisps.

p. 110

There are 24 **equally likely** outcomes and six of them are salt and vinegar.

P(salt and vinegar) $= \frac{6}{24} = 0.25 = 25\%$

You use the notation P(A) to mean 'the probability of event A'.

- If mutually exclusive events are also exhaustive then the total of their probabilities is 1.
  The probability that event A does **not** occur is 1 − P(A).

example

Find the probability that Sam picks a packet of crisps that are **not** salt and vinegar.

P(salt and vinegar) $= \frac{6}{24} = \frac{1}{4} = 25\%$

P(not salt and vinegar) = 1 − P(salt and vinegar)

$= 1 - \frac{1}{4} = \frac{3}{4} = 0.75 = 75\%$

LEVEL 6

Grade D

Exercise 9c

1 Julie rolls an ordinary dice.
Use the formula for theoretical probability to find
a P(2) **b** P(3 or 4) **c** P(a prime number).
Give each answer as a fraction, a decimal and a percentage.

2 Use your answers to question 1 to work out
a P(not 2) **b** P(neither 3 nor 4) **c** P(not a prime number)
Give each answer as a fraction, a decimal and a percentage.

3 Here are the percentages for three events.
$P(A) = \frac{3}{16}$ $P(B) = 0.92$ $P(C) = 12.5\%$
Find the probability of each of these events **not** occurring.

4 A card is chosen at random from an ordinary pack.
Find the probability of each of these events.
a P(Jack) **b** P(red 9) **c** P(2, 4, 6, 8 or 10)
Give each answer as a fraction, a decimal and a percentage.

An ordinary pack contains 52 cards: 26 red (diamonds and hearts) and 26 black (clubs and spades).

5 Use your answers to question **4** to find the probability of each of the events **not** occurring.

6 A computer is used to choose a random whole number from 1 to 100 inclusive.
Find the probability that the chosen number is
a 37 **b** An even number
c A prime number **d** Not prime
e Less than 8 **f** More than 8.

There are 25 prime numbers between 1 and 100.

7 Dave chooses a letter of the alphabet at random.
Find the probability that the chosen letter is
a a vowel **b** not a vowel **c** after T in the alphabet
d not included in the letters of the word 'dog'.
Give each answer as a fraction, a decimal and a percentage.

discussion

Carmen's team are taking part in a baseball tournament.
She says, 'There are three possible outcomes:
win, lose or draw. So, the probability that we will win
the tournament is $\frac{1}{3}$.'
Do you agree?

9d The outcomes of two trials

LEVEL 6

- Find and record the outcomes for two trials

Keywords
Sample-space diagram
Tree diagram
Trials
Two-way table

- **Sample-space diagrams** can be used to record all the possible outcomes of two **trials**.
  These can be **two-way tables** or **tree diagrams**.

example

Sun tosses a coin twice.
Record all the possible outcomes using
a a two-way table **b** a tree diagram.

The set of all the outcomes is called the sample space.

a

p. 80

	H	T
H	(H, H)	(H, T)
T	(T, H)	(T, T)

The possible outcomes are
{(H, H), (H, T), (T, H), (T, T)}.

b

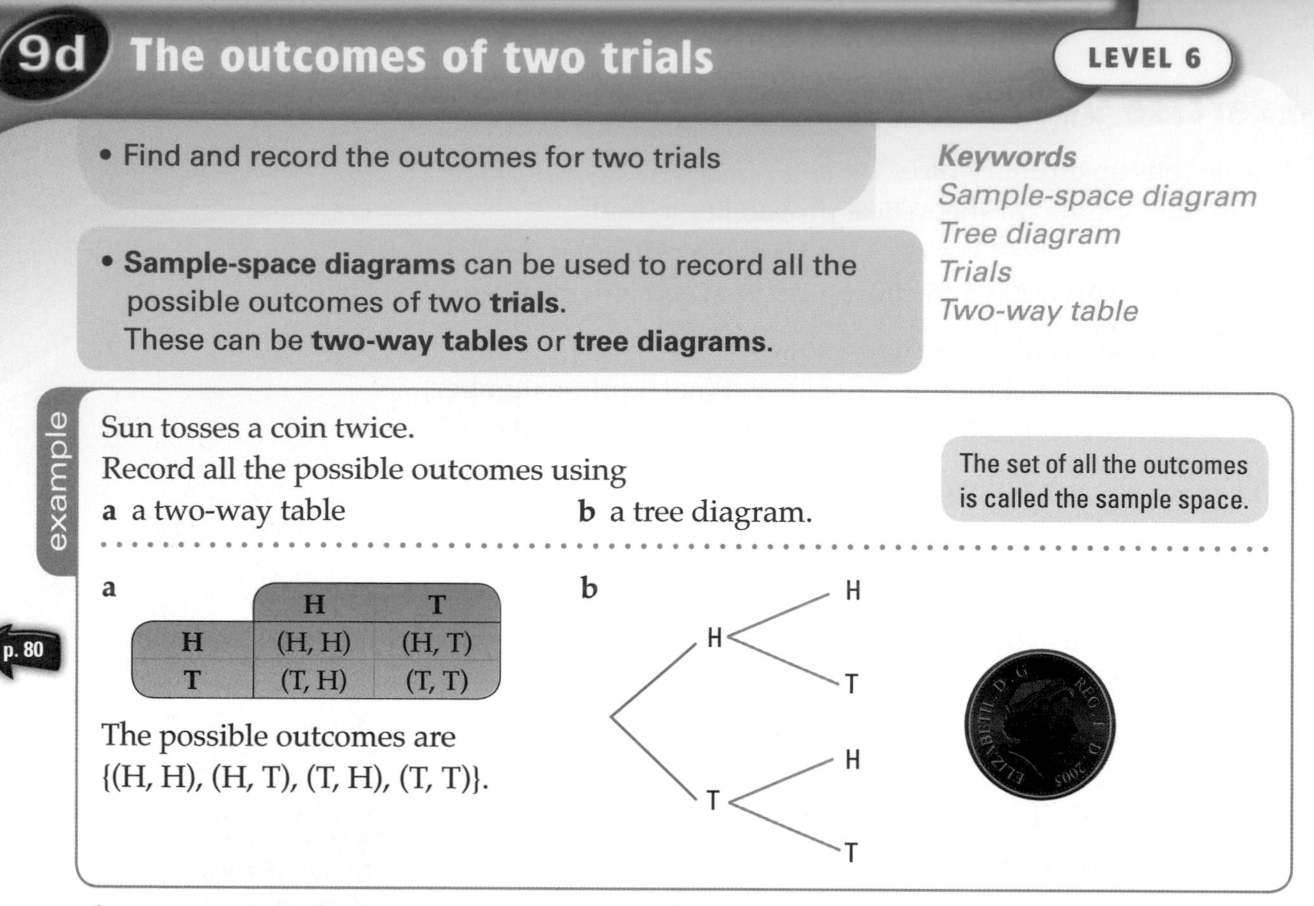

There are exactly four possible outcomes to this experiment on each diagram. However, you can match the outcomes to events in different ways.
These are some of the possible events.

Event A = 'at least one head'	Event B = 'same result on both coins'
Event C = 'first result is tails'	Event D = 'exactly one head'

example

Marie rolls two dice and calculates the total score.
Show the possible outcomes on a sample-space diagram.

	1	2	3	4	5	6
1	2	3	4	5	6	7
2	3	4	5	6	7	8
3	4	5	6	7	8	9
4	5	6	7	8	9	10
5	6	7	8	9	10	11
6	7	8	9	10	11	12

There are 36 separate outcomes.
There are many possible events, for example 'doubles', 'a score of 7', or 'a score greater than 4'.

A two-way table is much easier than a tree diagram in this example.

Exercise 9d

1 Martina plays two games of tennis.
She either wins or loses each game.
a Show the possible outcomes for the two games on a tree diagram.
b Draw a two-way table to show the same information.
c Copy and complete this list of the possible outcomes for the two games: {(win, win), (win, lose), ... }.

There are four outcomes in total.

2 Zaina's mother drives her to school each day.
On their route they pass two sets of traffic lights.
Each set is either red, amber or green when they reach it.
a Show the possible settings of both sets of lights in a two-way table.
b Draw a tree diagram to show the same information.
c List the possible outcomes.

3 A technician checks a computer by carrying out two tests.
First she tests the monitor and then the hard drive.
The computer either passes or fails each test.
a Draw a tree diagram to show the possible outcomes of this two-stage check.
b List the possible outcomes.

4 In an experiment, a coin is tossed and a random whole number between 1 and 10 is chosen by a computer.
Which sort of diagram would be best to show all the outcomes for this experiment, a two-way table or a tree diagram?
Explain your answer and draw your chosen diagram.

5 A music exam has two parts: a theory test followed by a performance test.
The possible outcomes are {(pass, credit), (pass, pass), (pass, fail), (fail, credit), (fail, pass), (fail, fail)}.
a Draw a tree diagram to show the possible outcomes.
b Show the same information in a two-way table.
c Give an example of an event which includes exactly three of the outcomes given.

challenge

Draw a suitable sample-space diagram for each of these experiments.
a Two ordinary dice are rolled and the product of the scores is calculated.
b A coin is tossed four times, and the result is recorded each time.
Justify your choice of diagram in each case.

9e Experimental probability

LEVEL 7

- Calculate estimates of experimental probability

Keywords
Estimate
Experiment
Relative frequency

- You can calculate theoretical probabilities when you know all the possible outcomes of a trial and that all the outcomes are equally likely.

Sometimes you might not know what all the possible outcomes are.

The next bird you see from your window will be a robin.

There may be many possible outcomes.

Or you may not be sure that they are all equally likely.

The next game played by a football team will end in a draw

There are exactly three possible outcomes: win, lose or draw, but they might not be equally likely.

- In an experiment you use the **relative frequency** of an event as an **estimate** of its probability.

$$\text{Relative frequency} = \frac{\text{Number of successful trials}}{\text{Total number of trials}}$$

example

Afzal and Barry tested this spinner.
Here are their results.

	Afzal	Barry
Red	42	18
Blue	58	32

Use the data to estimate the probability of the spinner landing on red.
Comment on your answers.

In Afzal's experiment there were 42 successful trials out of 100.

$P(\text{red}) = \frac{42}{100} = 0.42$

In Barry's experiment there were 18 successful trials out of 50.

$P(\text{red}) = \frac{18}{50} = 0.36$

Afzal's results should be more reliable as there are a larger number of trials.

You could also combine both sets of data to get a more reliable estimate.
There were 60 successful trials out of 150.
$P(\text{red}) = \frac{60}{150} = 0.4$

- Increasing the number of trials makes the estimated probability more reliable but means that the **experiment** will take longer.

Exercise 9e

1 Tim practised darts by aiming at the bulls eye.
He hit the bulls eye 13 times and missed 47 times.

a How many trials were there in this experiment?

b How many of the trials were successful?

c Estimate the probability of Tim hitting the bulls eye with a single dart. Show your working.

2 In an experiment, three students threw a drawing pin and recorded the number of times it landed 'point up' and 'point down'.

	Up	Down
Dan	63	37
Caz	34	16
Charlie	135	65

a Find the estimated value of P(down) for each student.

b Whose value of P(down) should be most reliable? Explain your answer.

c Combine all three sets of data to calculate a better estimate of the experimental probability.
Show all your working.

3 Jenny wrote the letters of the word MATHS on five pieces of paper of various shapes and sizes.
She put the pieces in a bag, picked one without looking, recorded the letter and put the paper back.
Jenny's experiment had 50 trials. These are her results.

H M S H H S M M M H A H A T H M H
H T H H S M H M H T H H S M S H H
M S M S H H T M H M H H S H H S

a Explain why the five possible outcomes for each trial are not equally likely.

b Estimate the experimental probability of each outcome.

discussion

The coach of a hockey team is preparing for the first match of the new season.
She looks at the results of their matches last season.
There were 12 wins, 8 losses, and 2 draws.
She says, 'We won 12 out of 22 games, so there's a better than even chance that we'll win our first game of the new season.'
Do you think this statement is reasonable? Explain your answer.

9f Comparing theoretical and experimental probabilities

LEVEL 7

- Compare experimental and theoretical probabilities in a range of contexts

Keywords
Biased
Experimental
Theoretical

- You can compare **theoretical** probabilities with estimated **experimental** probabilities.

example

A fairground game uses a four-sided spinner.
In one evening the game is played 150 times.
Calculate the experimental probability from the results in the table and compare these to the theoretical probabilities.
Comment on your results.

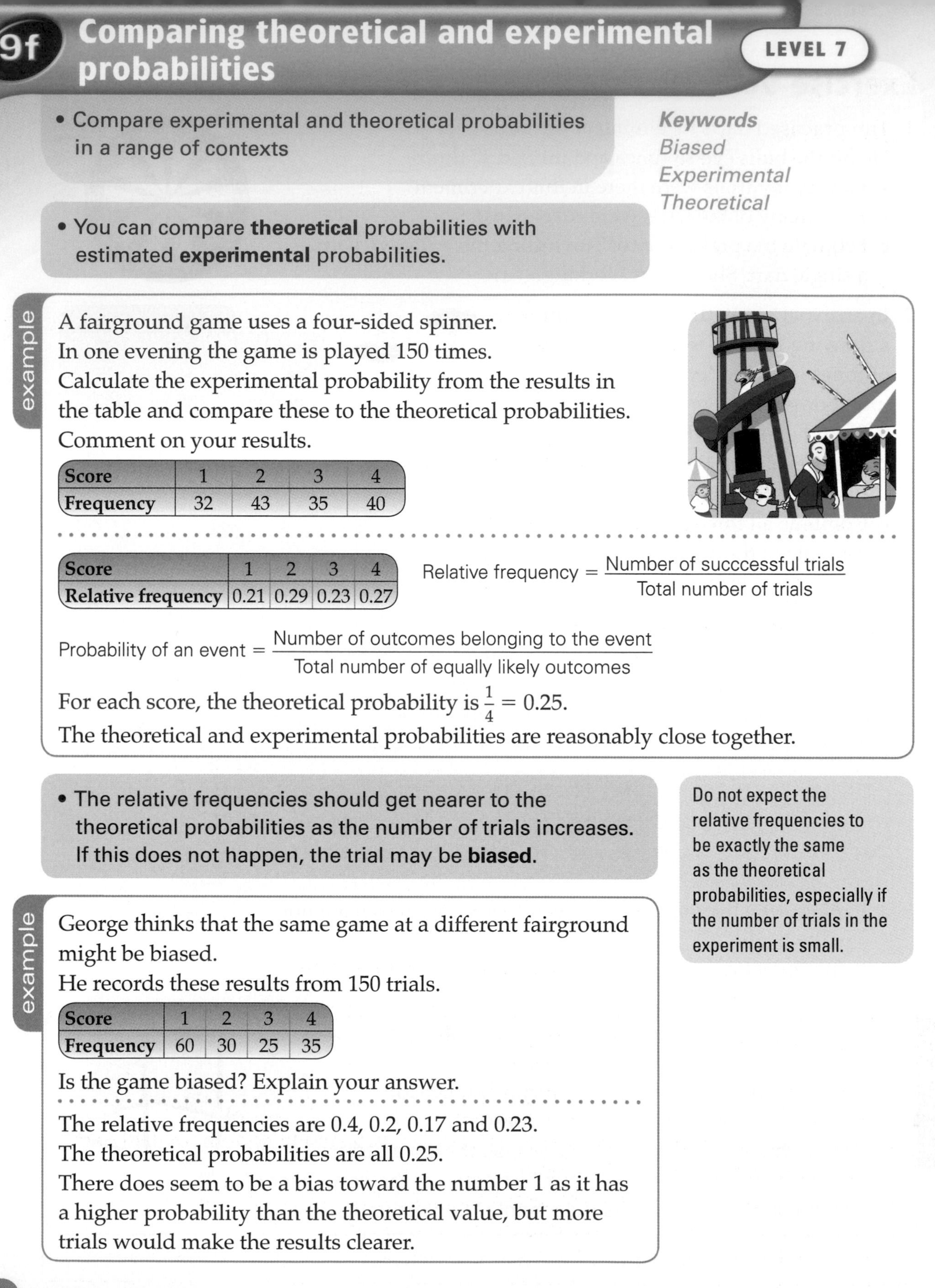

Score	1	2	3	4
Frequency	32	43	35	40

Score	1	2	3	4
Relative frequency	0.21	0.29	0.23	0.27

Relative frequency = $\frac{\text{Number of succcessful trials}}{\text{Total number of trials}}$

Probability of an event = $\frac{\text{Number of outcomes belonging to the event}}{\text{Total number of equally likely outcomes}}$

For each score, the theoretical probability is $\frac{1}{4} = 0.25$.
The theoretical and experimental probabilities are reasonably close together.

- The relative frequencies should get nearer to the theoretical probabilities as the number of trials increases. If this does not happen, the trial may be **biased**.

Do not expect the relative frequencies to be exactly the same as the theoretical probabilities, especially if the number of trials in the experiment is small.

example

George thinks that the same game at a different fairground might be biased.
He records these results from 150 trials.

Score	1	2	3	4
Frequency	60	30	25	35

Is the game biased? Explain your answer.

The relative frequencies are 0.4, 0.2, 0.17 and 0.23.
The theoretical probabilities are all 0.25.
There does seem to be a bias toward the number 1 as it has a higher probability than the theoretical value, but more trials would make the results clearer.

Exercise 9f

1 Jake tested a coin by tossing it.
There were 38 heads and 27 tails.
a Use the relative frequencies of heads and tails to estimate the experimental probability of each result.
b Compare the experimental and theoretical probabilities for each result. Is the coin fair? Explain your answer.

2 Kathryn tested a dice by counting the number of sixes after 10, 50, 100 and 200 rolls.

Number of rolls	10	50	100	200
Number of sixes	1	6	14	32

a Calculate the relative frequency of a score of six after 10, 50, 100 and 200 rolls.
Give your answers to 2 decimal places.
b Calculate the theoretical probability of getting a score of 6 with a roll of the dice.
c Compare your answers to parts **a** and **b**.

3 In an experiment, Petra shuffles a pack of playing cards and picks one at random. She records the card, then returns it to the pack before shuffling and dealing again.
She picks 60 cards altogether.

7♣	K♦	8♣	A♥	6♠	5♠	9♥	8♥	5♠	5♥
3♣	4♠	4♦	4♦	7♥	9♦	2♥	Q♥	4♥	8♣
K♠	7♠	9♦	10♣	5♣	Q♣	A♥	K♥	Q♠	K♦
5♣	6♣	A♥	10♠	K♣	J♦	Q♣	2♥	3♠	4♥
5♠	Q♥	2♣	10♥	A♥	J♥	3♣	A♦	3♠	J♥
7♦	K♣	7♦	5♣	6♦	6♠	K♣	10♠	5♠	A♦

a Estimate the experimental probability of picking
i a Club (♣) **ii** a red card (♥ or ♦) **iii** a 2, 3 or 4.
b Compare your answers to the theoretical probabilities and comment on your answers.

challenge

Darren rolled two ordinary dice and recorded the total 100 times.

Total	2	3	4	5	6	7	8	9	10	11	12
Frequency	1	6	7	17	13	21	9	7	8	8	3

a Draw a sample-space diagram and calculate the probability of each total, giving your answers to 2 decimal places.
b Use the experimental results to calculate the relative frequency of each score.
c Compare the theoretical and experimental probabilities.
Do you think the dice are fair? Explain your answer.

9 Consolidation

9a

1 Kate puts cards marked with each whole number from 1 to 100 into a box and then picks a card at random.
Give an example of an outcome that is

a Certain **b** Impossible
c Very unlikely **d** An even chance.

9b

2 A computer is used to choose a number between 1 and 1000.
Give examples of

a a set of three events that are exhaustive
b a set of four events that are mutually exclusive.

3 Peter rolls a red dice and a blue dice.
The event X is 'The product of the scores on the two dice is odd'.
The event Y is 'The score on the red dice is 4'.

a Explain why the events X and Y are mutually exclusive.
b Explain why the events X and Y are not exhaustive.

9c

4 Two Jokers are added to an ordinary pack of 52 playing cards.
A card is picked at random.

a Find the probability that the card chosen is a Joker.
Give your answer as a fraction in its simplest terms, a decimal and a percentage.

b Use your answers to part **a** to find the probability that the chosen card is not a Joker.
Give your answer in all three forms.

5 James deals these four cards from an ordinary pack of 52 cards.

What is the probability that the next card dealt from the remaining pack is another Queen?
Give your answer as a percentage.

9d

6 A brown bag contains three cards marked A, B and C.
A white bag contains two cards marked X and Y.
Shayla picks a card at random from each bag.
Show all the possible outcomes using
a a two-way table **b** a tree diagram.

7 This two-way table shows the possible outcomes when Ben chooses cards from two boxes.

	1	2	3
A	(A, 1)	(A, 2)	(A, 3)
B	(B, 1)	(B, 2)	(B, 3)

Draw a tree diagram to show this set of outcomes.

9e

8 Steve was practising his basketball shooting and scored 9 times out of 32 attempts.
Estimate the probability of Steve scoring with his next shot.

9 A radio show played 24 songs one morning.
Nine of these songs were by solo female artists.
Use this information to estimate the probability of the first song played in the next day's programme being by a female solo artist.

10 A technician checked the maintenance records for a computer network.
He found that the server had crashed on 43 days over the past year.
a Use this data to estimate the probability that the server crashes on any day chosen at random.
b He was not told whether the data was for a leap year.
Explain why this does not make much difference.

9f

11 Carol tested a dice and got three 6s out of six rolls.
a Is there enough evidence to suggest that the dice is biased?
Explain your answer.
b Carol carried on testing the dice and ended up with 18 sixes in 60 rolls.
Is there now enough evidence to suggest that the dice is biased?
Explain your answer.

9 Summary

Assessment criteria

- Know that the sum of mutually exclusive outcomes is 1 **Level 6**
- Understand relative frequency as an estimate of probability **Level 7**
- Select methods based on equally likely outcomes **Level 6**

Level 6

1 The spinner is numbered 1 to 5.
The probability of spinning each number is shown in the table.

Number	1	2	3	4	5
Probability	0.1	p	0.3	0.3	p

Calculate the value of p.

Nick's answer ✔

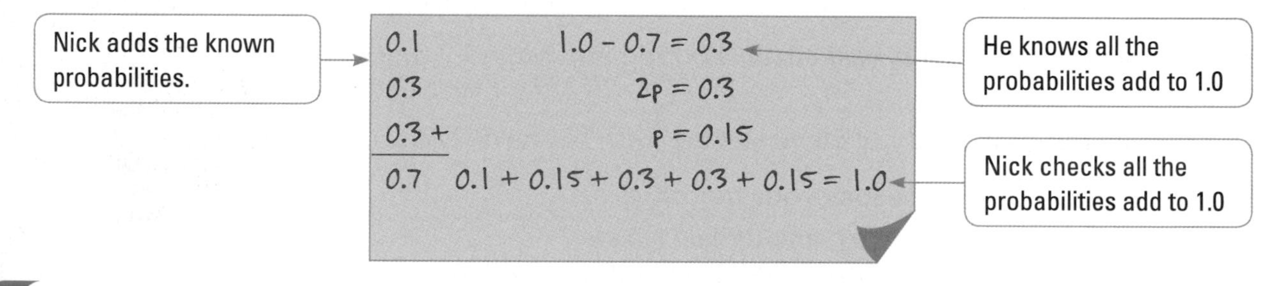

Level 7

2 Meg and Ravi buy sweet pea seeds and grow them in identical conditions.
Meg's results:

Number of packets	Number of seeds in each packet
5	20

Number of seeds that germinate from each packet
18, 17, 17, 18, 19

Ravi's results:

Number of packets	Number of seeds in each packet
10	20

Total number of seeds that germinate
170

a Using Meg's results and Ravi's results, calculate two different estimates of the probability that a sweet pea seed will germinate.

b Whose results are likely to give the better estimate of the probability?
Explain why.

Key Stage 3 2005 5–7 Paper 1

10 Geometry

Transformations and scale

In Scotland in the 1740s it was against the law to support Prince Charles Edward Stuart. There were extreme penalties, including death, for supporters who pledged their loyalty to the Prince.
The painting on the square base looks completely random. However, when the cylinder is placed in the correct spot, the paint is reflected to form an image of 'Bonnie Prince Charlie'.

The Secret Portrait can be found at the West Highland Museum, Fort William, Scotland.

What's the point? Reflection is one of the transformations that can be used to create images and patterns.

Check in

Level 5

1 Copy this diagram. Draw the flag after a translation of 4 units to the right and 2 units down.

2 Draw the enlargement of this kite with a scale factor of 3 on squared paper.

p. 92

3 Convert these metric measurements to the units in brackets.

a 230 cm (m) **b** 400 000 cm (km)
c 5.5 km (m) **d** 4.5 km (cm)

4 Use a protractor to measure the marked angles.

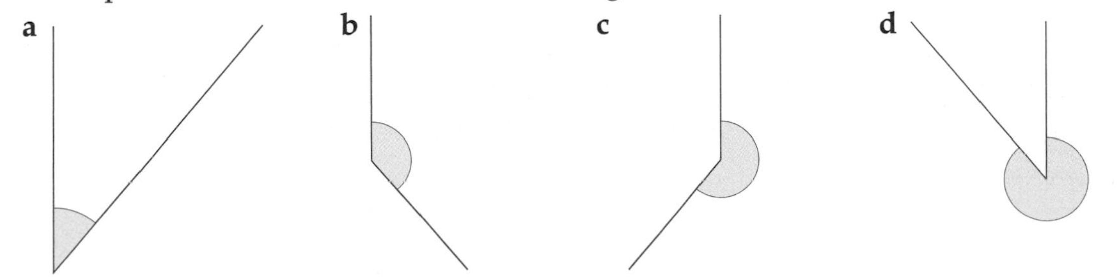

Transformations

LEVEL 6

- Reflect, rotate and translate 2-D shapes

Keywords
Congruent *Reflection*
Image *Rotation*
Map *Transformation*
Object *Translation*

- A **transformation maps** the **object** to the **image**.

A **reflection** flips the object over a mirror line.
You describe a reflection by giving the mirror line.

A reflection in the line $x = 2$

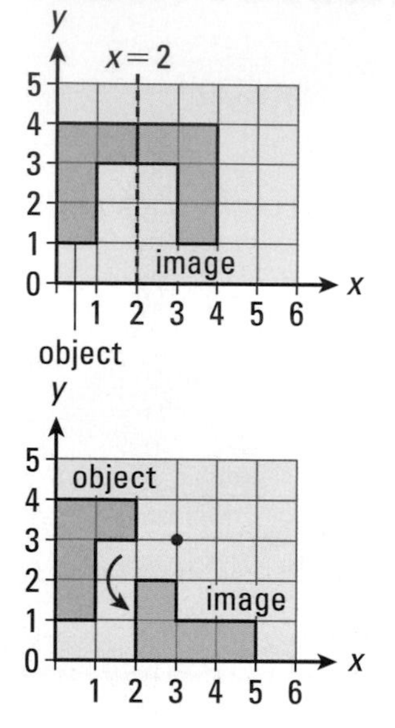

A **rotation** turns the object about a point, called the centre of rotation.
You describe a rotation by giving
- the centre of rotation
- the angle of rotation
- the direction of turn (clockwise or anticlockwise)

An anticlockwise rotation of 90° about (3, 3)

A **translation** slides the object.
You describe a translation by giving
- the distance moved right or left
- the distance moved up or down.

A translation of 2 right 1 down $\begin{pmatrix}2\\1\end{pmatrix}$

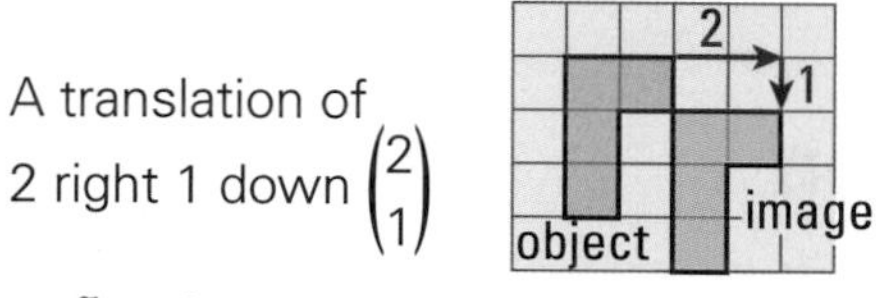

p. 46

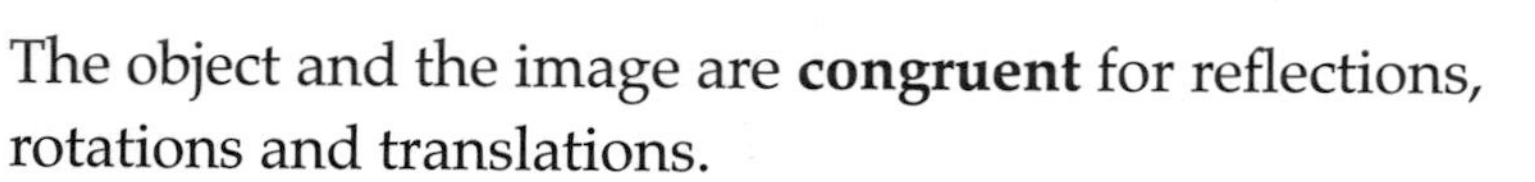

The object and the image are **congruent** for reflections, rotations and translations.

Congruent shapes are the same shape and the same size.

example

The blue hexagon is mapped to the green hexagon.

Find the centre of rotation and the angle of rotation.

Use trial and improvement to find the centre of rotation and the angle of rotation.

The transformation is a clockwise rotation of 90° about the point (-1, 2).

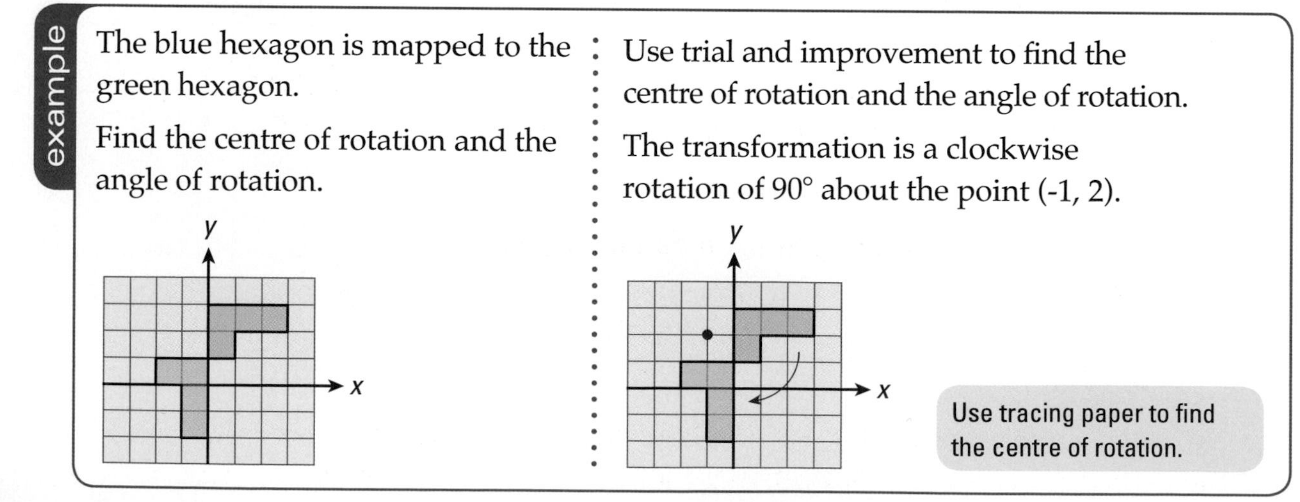

Use tracing paper to find the centre of rotation.

LEVEL 6

Exercise 10a

1 Rotate each triangle through 180° about the dot.
Write the mathematical name of the quadrilateral formed by the object and the image and explain your reasoning.

a **b** **c** **d** **e**

2 Describe the translation on this grid that maps

a shape A to shape B

b shape B to shape C

c shape A to shape C.

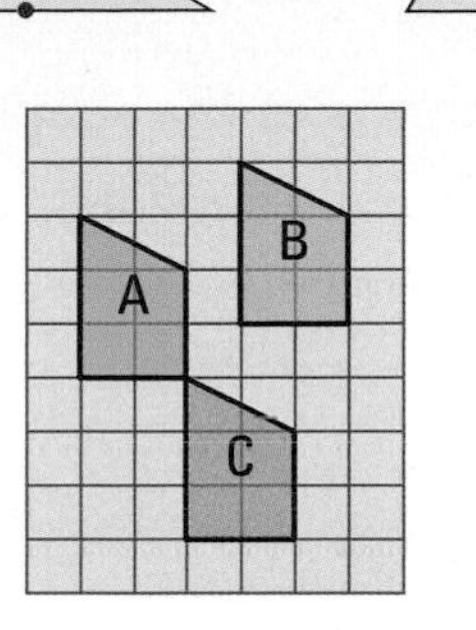

3 **a** Draw the blue triangle and its reflection in the y-axis.

b Reflect both triangles in the x-axis.

c What is the mathematical name of the shape formed by the blue triangle and its images? Explain your reasoning.

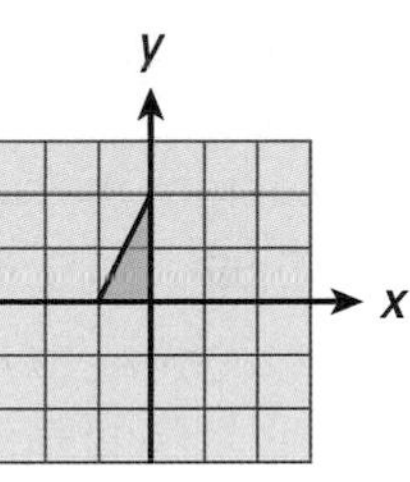

4 **a** Draw the quadrilateral ABCD on square grid paper and reflect it in the x axis. Mark the equal angles and the equal sides on your diagram.

b Repeat part **a** but this time reflect the quadrilateral in the y axis.

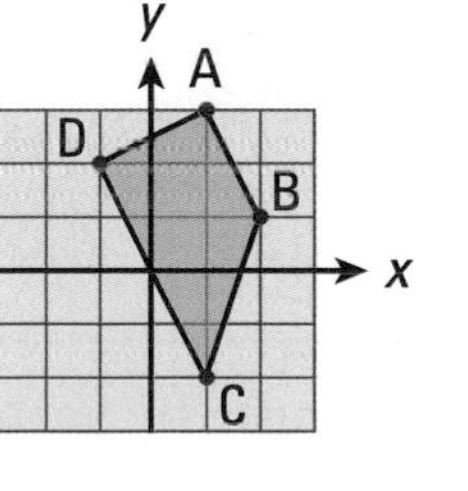

5 **a** On square grid paper, draw a triangle with vertices (0, 0), (0, 2), (1, 2).

b After a rotation the coordinates of the vertices of the image are (1, -1), (-1, -1), (-1, 0).

c Find the centre of rotation and the angle of rotation.

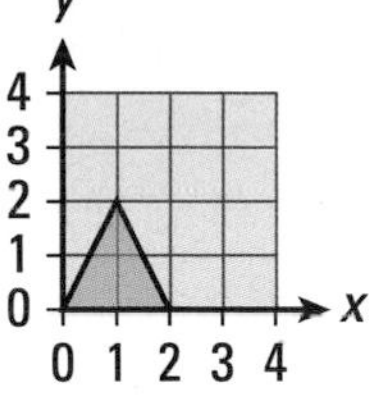

activity

Transform the tile to create three different patterns.

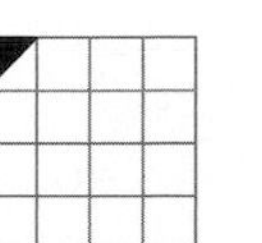

Translations by either one square across or down.

Reflections in a horizontal or a vertical line.

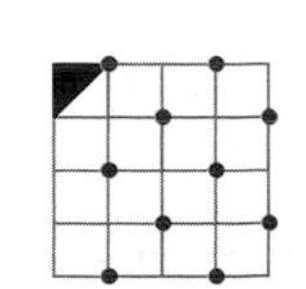

Anticlockwise rotations of 90° about the dots.

10b Enlargements

LEVEL 6

- Enlarge a 2-D shape using a centre of enlargement and a positive scale factor

Keywords
Centre of enlargement
Enlargement
Object
Image
Similar
Scale factor

- An **enlargement** is a type of transformation that alters the size of the shape.

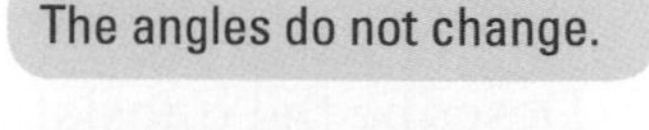

The angles do not change.

You multiply the lengths of the shape by the **scale factor**.

The **object** and the **image** are **similar** as they are the same shape but a different size.

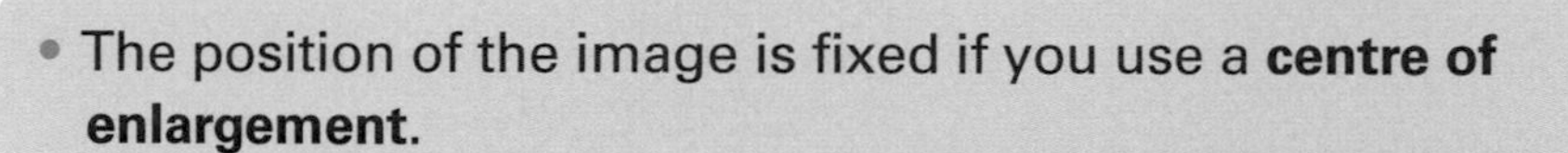

- The position of the image is fixed if you use a **centre of enlargement.**

Draw lines from the centre of enlargement through the vertices of the object.

The distance from the centre of enlargement to each vertex is multiplied by the scale factor to give the corresponding distance from the centre of enlargement to each vertex of the image.

Measure the lengths of the image and the object to check the scale factor: $6 \div 3 = 2$.

The enlargement is scale factor 2.

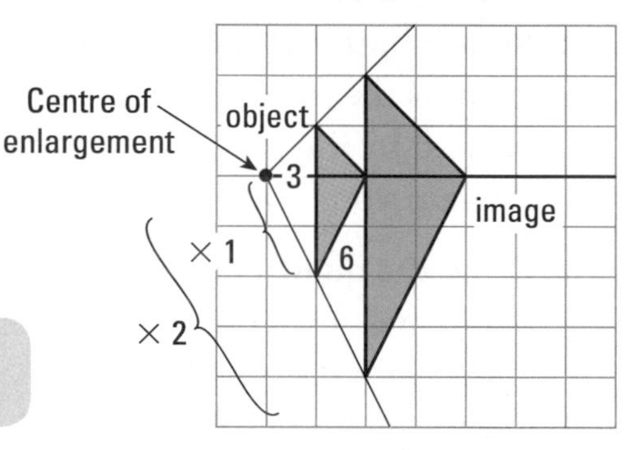

example

Enlarge the pink rectangle by scale factor 2 using (0, 1) as the centre of enlargement.

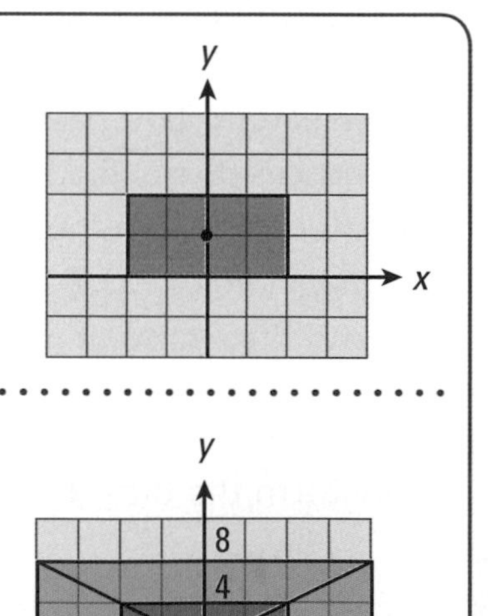

Draw lines from (0, 1) through the vertices of the rectangle.
Multiply the distances from (0, 1) to the vertices by 2 to find the vertices of the image.
The image and the pink rectangle are similar.

The lengths of the rectangle have been multiplied by 2.
$2 \times 2 = 4$ and $4 \times 2 = 8$

LEVEL 6

Grade D

Exercise 10b

1 Each blue shape is an enlargement of the pink shape.
Copy each diagram onto square grid paper.
Calculate the scale factor and find the coordinates of the centre of enlargement.

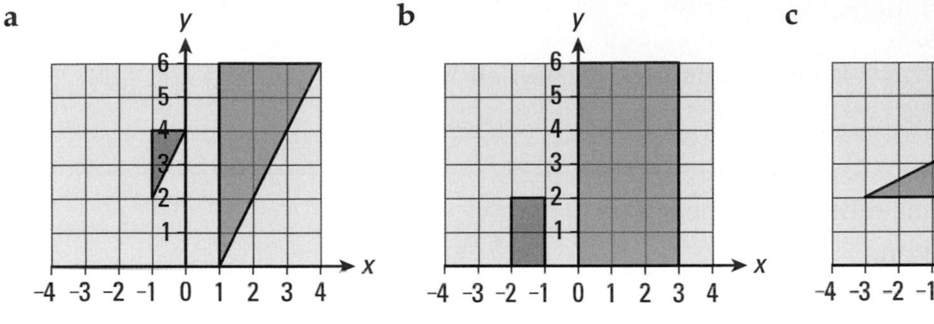

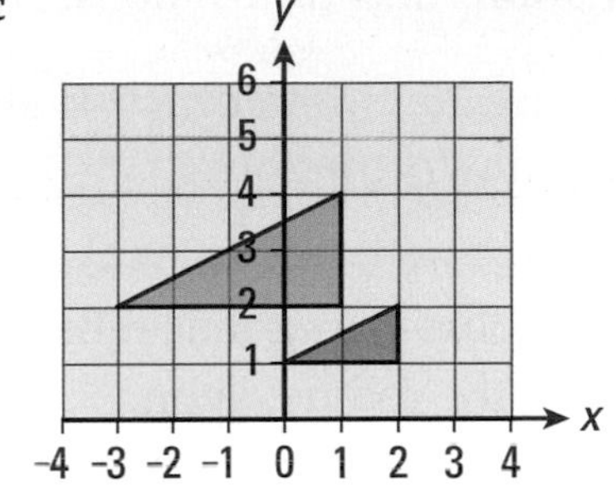

2 Copy each shape onto square grid paper.
Draw the enlargement of the shape using the dot as the centre of enlargement and the scale factor given.

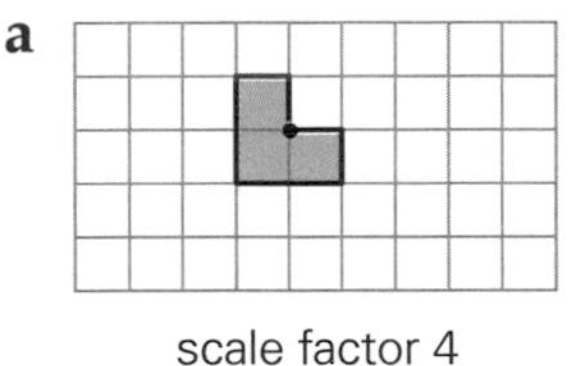

scale factor 4

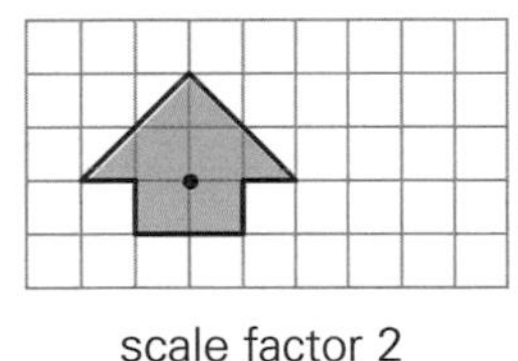

scale factor 2

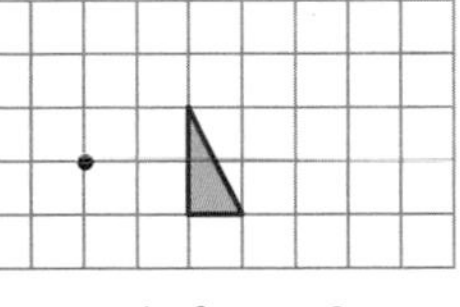

scale factor 3

3 **a** Draw triangle ABC on a coordinate grid.
b Enlarge the triangle by scale factor 2 using (0, 0) as the centre of enlargement.
c What are the coordinates of the vertices of the enlarged triangle?
d What do you notice about the coordinates of the object and the image?

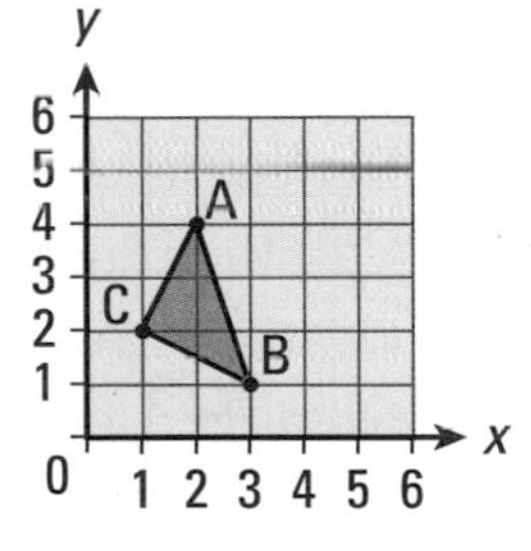

4 The green rectangle is an enlargement of the blue rectangle.
The blue rectangle measures 3 cm by 2 cm.
One side of the green rectangle measures 12 cm.
a What are the two possible scale factors of the enlargement?
b Calculate the unknown length of the green rectangle in each case.

activity

a Enlarge the shape by scale factor 2.
b Divide the enlargement into four congruent shapes.

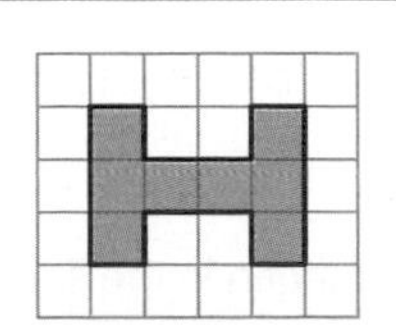

Congruent shapes are exactly the same size and the same shape.

10c Combinations of transformations

LEVEL 6

- Explore and compare combinations of transformations of 2-D shapes

Keywords
Congruent
Transformation

The object and the image are **congruent** for reflections, rotations and translations.

- You can transform 2-D shapes using a combination of transformations.

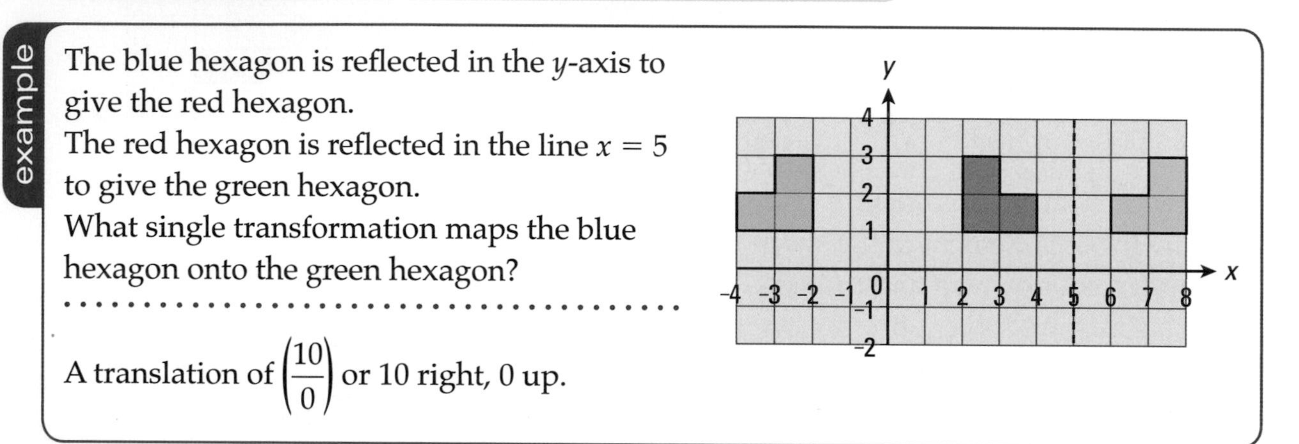

The blue hexagon is reflected in the y-axis to give the red hexagon.
The red hexagon is reflected in the line $x = 5$ to give the green hexagon.
What single transformation maps the blue hexagon onto the green hexagon?

A translation of $\begin{pmatrix}10\\0\end{pmatrix}$ or 10 right, 0 up.

example

a Reflect triangle A in the y axis.
Call the image B.
b Reflect triangle B in the line $y = x$.
Call the image C.
c Describe the single transformation that maps triangle A to triangle C.

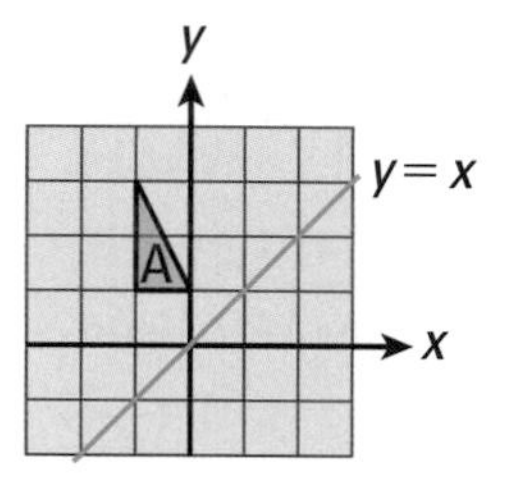

a

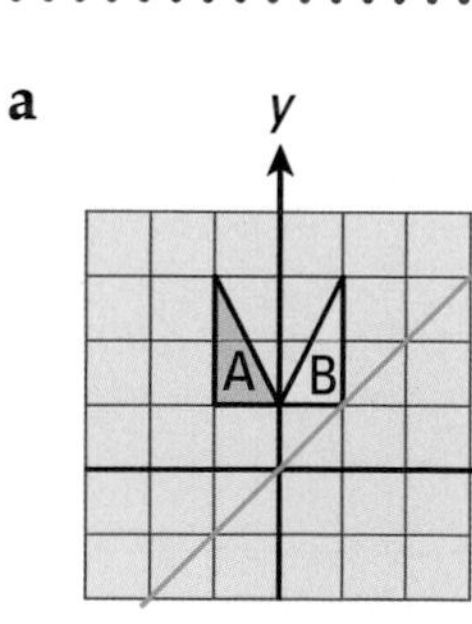

Reflection in the y axis.

b

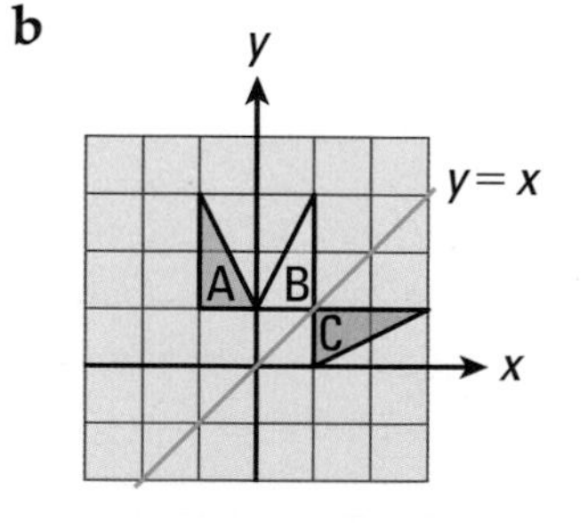

Reflection in the line $y = x$.

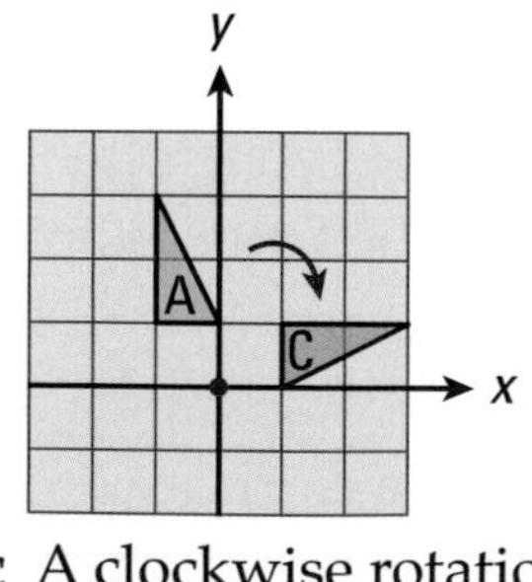

c A clockwise rotation of 90° about (0, 0).

Use tracing paper to find the centre of rotation.

Exercise 10c

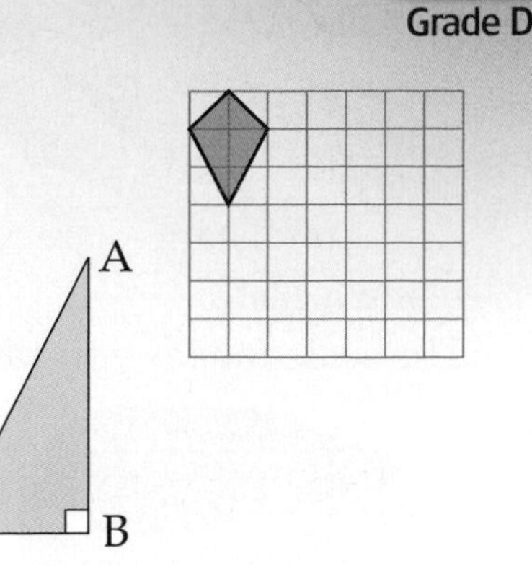

1 Use repeated rotations of 180° about the midpoints of the sides of the kite to form a tessellation.

2 The right-angled triangle ABC is reflected in the line AB. The triangle and the image are then reflected in the line CB extended to the right.

  a What is the mathematical name of the shape formed by the object and the image?

  b Give reasons to explain your decisions.

3 A shape is translated by $\begin{pmatrix}\text{5 right}\\ \text{1 up}\end{pmatrix}$

  The image is translated by $\begin{pmatrix}\text{4 left}\\ \text{3 down}\end{pmatrix}$

  Write a single transformation that is equivalent to the two translations.

4 The pink triangle is reflected in the line $y = x$.

  a Draw the image and label it I_1.

  b The triangle I_1 is reflected in the x axis. Draw the new image and label it I_2.

  c Describe the single transformation that maps the pink triangle to triangle I_2.

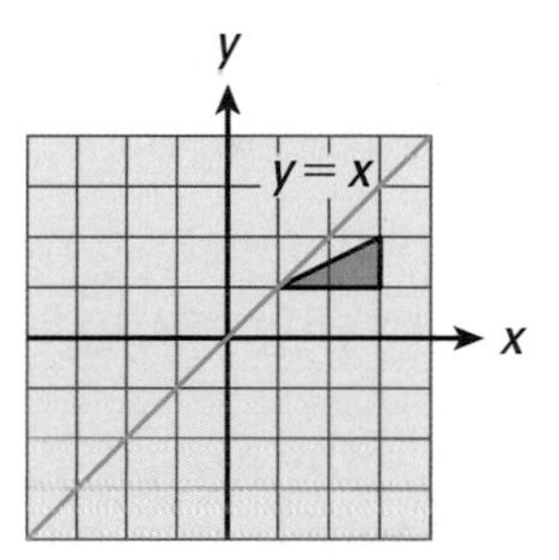

5 a Describe the single transformation that maps hexagon A to hexagon C.

  b Find a combination of rotations that maps hexagon A to hexagon C through hexagon B.

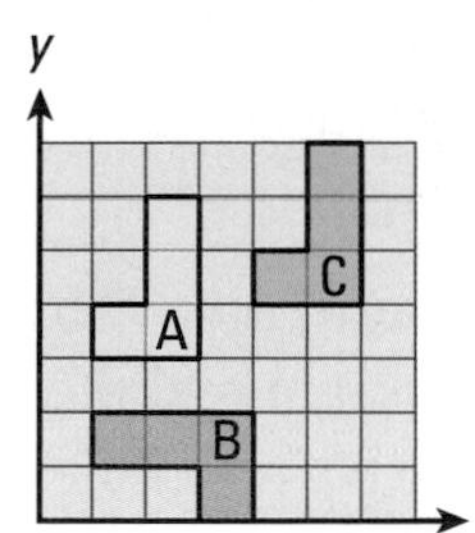

activity

Draw a 2 by 2 square.

Translate and rotate the triangles as shown.

Show that this shape tessellates using a combination of rotations and translations.

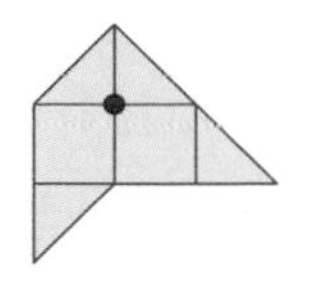

Maps and scale drawings

LEVEL 6/7

- Use and interpret maps and scale drawings

Keywords
Map *Scale*
Ratio *Scale drawing*

Real-life distances are reduced or enlarged in proportion using a **scale**.
The scale means you can interpret a **map** or **scale drawing**.

The angles stay the same.

p. 28

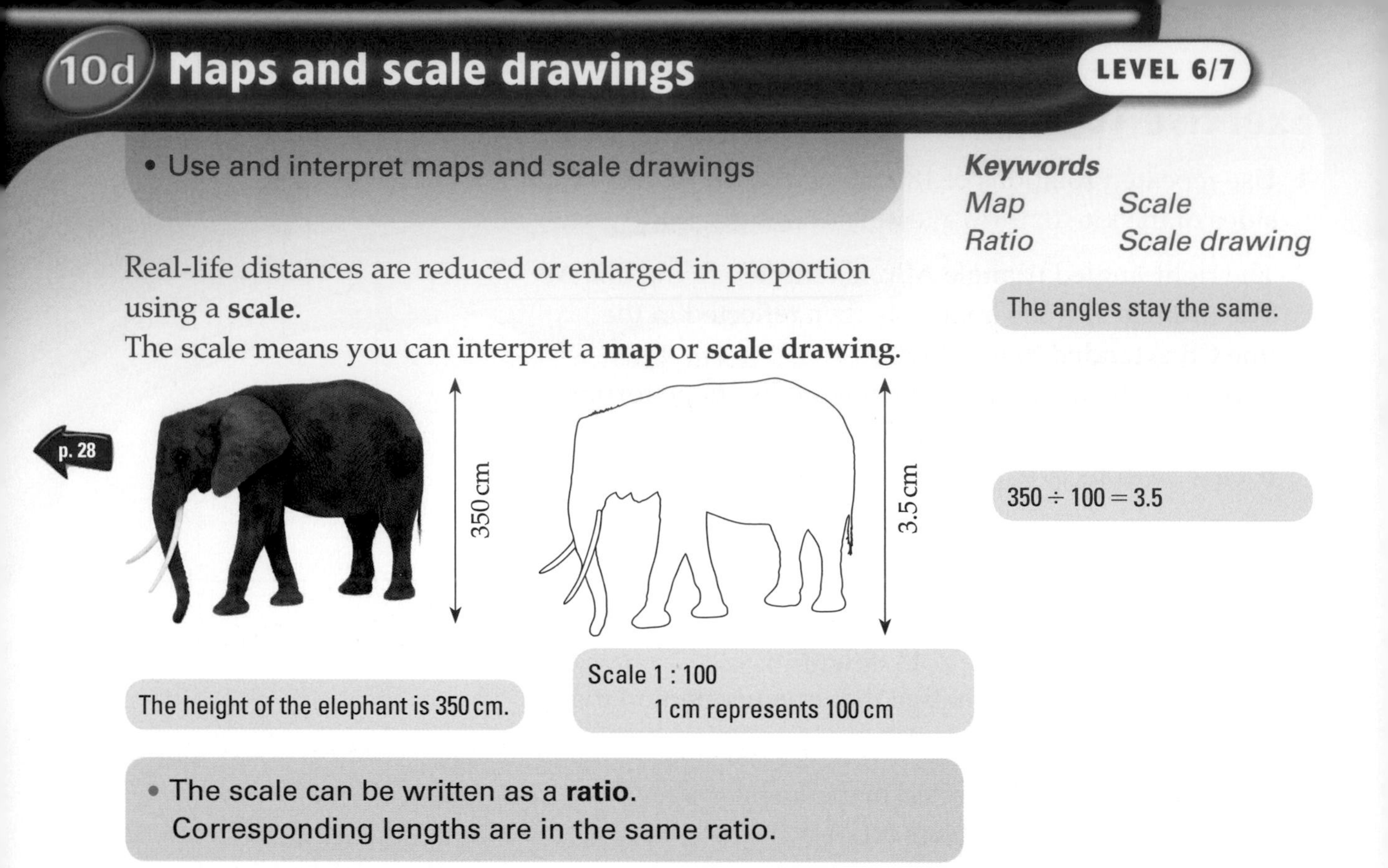

$350 \div 100 = 3.5$

The height of the elephant is 350 cm.

Scale 1 : 100
1 cm represents 100 cm

- The scale can be written as a **ratio**.
  Corresponding lengths are in the same ratio.

The lengths in the scale drawing are 100 times smaller then in real life.
The real-life lengths are an enlargement, scale factor 100, of the scale drawing.

example

The scale on the map is 1 : 50 000.

a The distance between Calver and Stoney Middleton on the map is 2 cm. Calculate the distance between the villages in real life.

b The distance between Baslow and Stoney Middleton in real life is 4.25 km. Find the distance between the villages on the map.

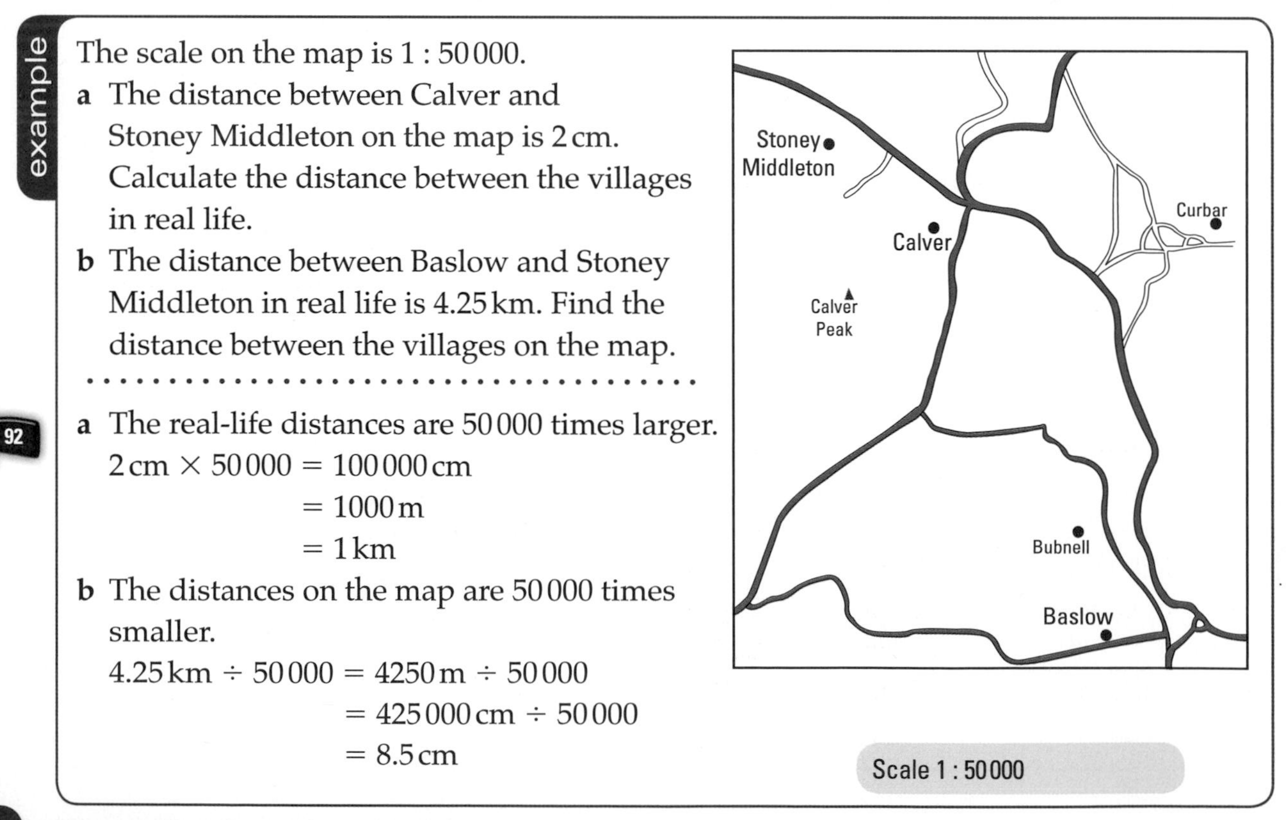

Scale 1 : 50 000

p. 92

a The real-life distances are 50 000 times larger.

$2\text{ cm} \times 50\,000 = 100\,000\text{ cm}$
$= 1000\text{ m}$
$= 1\text{ km}$

b The distances on the map are 50 000 times smaller.

$4.25\text{ km} \div 50\,000 = 4250\text{ m} \div 50\,000$
$= 425\,000\text{ cm} \div 50\,000$
$= 8.5\text{ cm}$

Exercise 10d

1 A scale drawing uses a scale of 1 cm represents 5 metres.
The height of the lighthouse in the scale drawing is 4.5 cm.
What is the height of the lighthouse in real life?

The angles remain the same.

2 Cath walks in a straight line for 75 metres.
She turns through 90° and walks for a further 45 metres.

a Draw a scale drawing of her journey using a scale of 1 cm represents 10 metres.

b How far is she from her starting point?

Finish
45 m
Start
75 m

Scale: 1 cm represents 5 m

3 A lorry has these dimensions.
Length: 16.5 m
Height: 4.4 m
Width: 2.5 m
A scale model is made using a scale of 1 : 20.
Calculate the length, height and width of the model in centimetres.

4 A map has a scale of 1 cm represents 5 km.

a Calculate the real-life distance represented by these lengths.

i 8 cm **ii** 15 cm **iii** 6.5 cm
iv 3.4 cm **v** 30 mm

b Calculate the distance on the map for these real-life distances.

i 15 km **ii** 60 km **iii** 125 km
iv 12.5 km **v** 2.5 km

Did you know?

A 1 : 16 scale model of the Angel of the North was valued at £1 000 000.

activity

Use a scale of 1 : 100 to draw a scale drawing to represent the heights and lengths of these animals.

	Height	**Length** (shoulder to tail)
Brachiosaurus	1500 cm	1400 cm
Tyrannosaurus	600 cm	300 cm
Giraffe	500 cm	200 cm
Hippopotamus	160 cm	350 cm

Now add your height to the scale drawing.

Bearings

- Use bearings to specify direction

Keywords
Bearing
Direction
Three-figure bearing

This photograph is taken looking east from Kala Patthar (5545 m) in Nepal. Mount Everest (8848 m) is in the background.

The **direction** of Everest from Kala Patthar is 090°.
This angle is called the **bearing**.

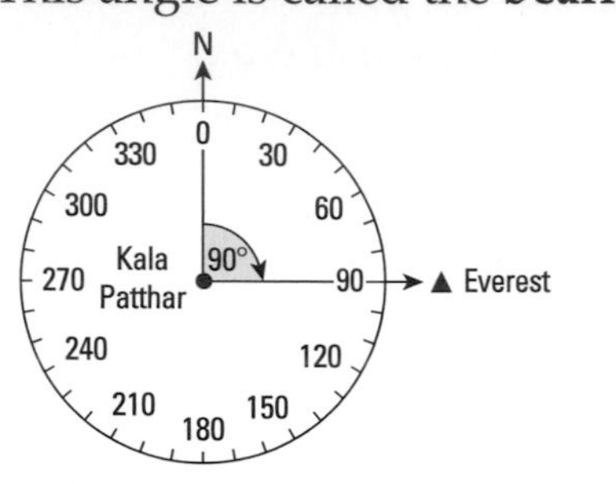

- When you give a **three-figure bearing**
  - measure from north
  - measure in a clockwise direction
  - use three digits.

example

Work out the bearing of
a the oil rig from the lighthouse
b the lighthouse from the oil rig.

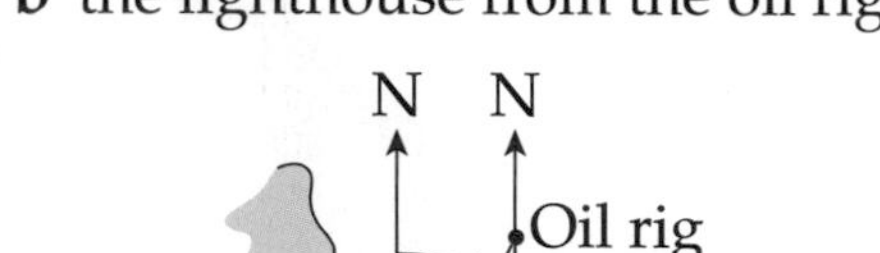

Not drawn accurately.

a To find the bearing of the oil rig from the lighthouse imagine you are at the lighthouse.
Measure clockwise from north.
The bearing is 025°.

b To find the bearing of the lighthouse from the oil rig imagine you are at the oil rig.
Measure clockwise from north.
The bearing is 180° + 25° = 205°.

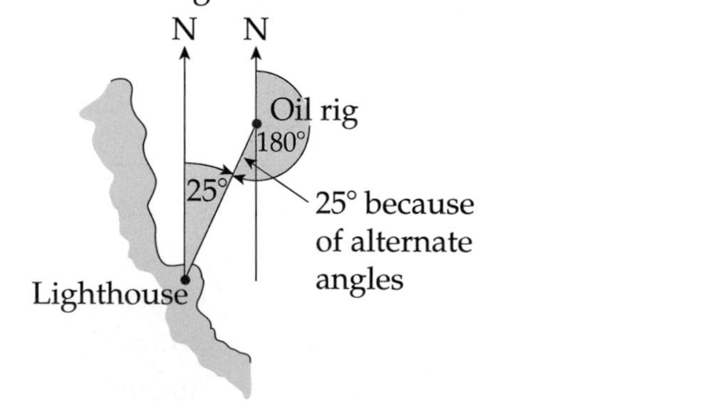

Notice that 25° + 180° = 205° and 205° − 180° = 25°.

- You either add or subtract 180° to find the reverse bearing.

This is also called the back bearing.

Exercise 10e

1 Measure the bearings of these points from the point O.

a Abbey **b** Barn
c Church **d** Dentist
e Estate **f** Field
g Gate **h** House
i Ice rink **j** Jetty

2 Draw accurate diagrams to show these bearings from a point O.
Remember to mark the direction of north.

a 045° **b** 190° **c** 300°
d 120° **e** 240°

3 Put a cross in the middle of your page.
Plot these sets of points and join them in order to form a shape.
Give the mathematical name of the shape and draw any lines of symmetry.

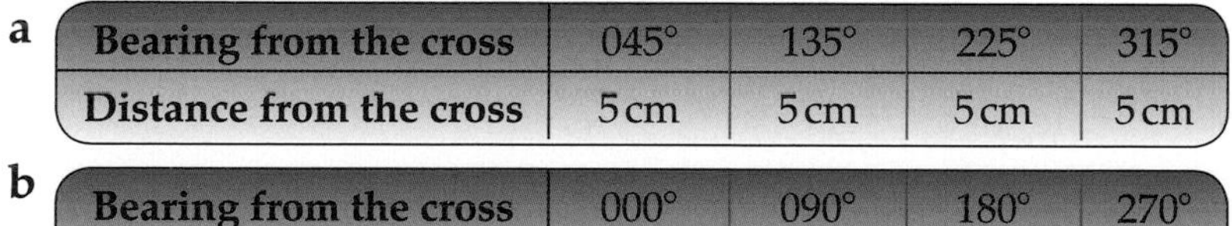

a

Bearing from the cross	045°	135°	225°	315°
Distance from the cross	5 cm	5 cm	5 cm	5 cm

b

Bearing from the cross	000°	090°	180°	270°
Distance from the cross	3 cm	5 cm	3 cm	5 cm

Did you know?

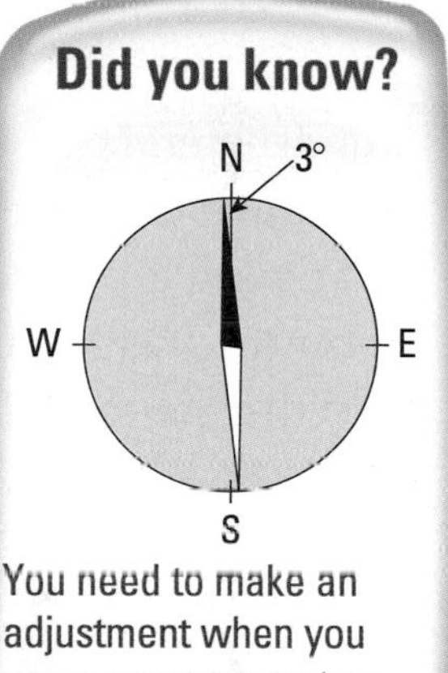

You need to make an adjustment when you use a compass as true north and magnetic north are different. Magnetic north varies with place and time. This difference is printed on every OS map.

4 **a** Give the bearing of B from A.
b Calculate the bearing of A from B.
c Give the bearing of D from C.
d Calculate the bearing of C from D.

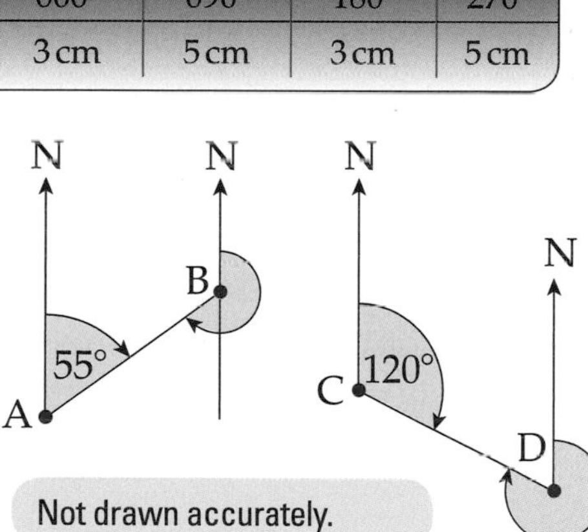

Not drawn accurately.

activity

A yacht sails on a bearing of 040° for 10 sea miles, then on a bearing of 160° for a further 7.5 sea miles.

a Draw a scale drawing to show the voyage.
b What is the yacht's distance and bearing from the starting point?
c What bearing should the yacht take to return to the starting point?

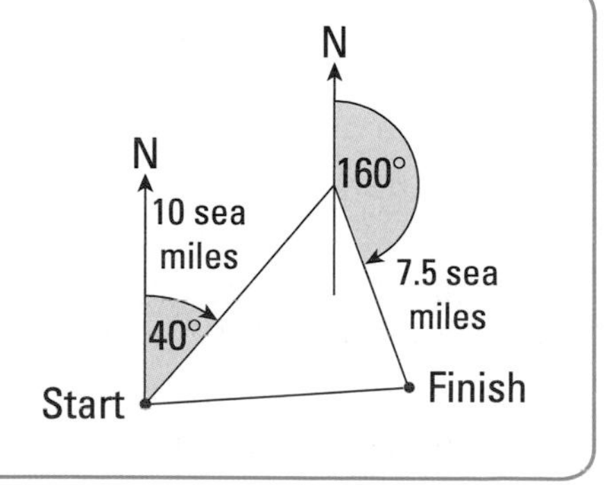

Not drawn accurately.

10 Consolidation

10a

1 A shape is rotated three times through a right angle about the point O. Write the mathematical name of the shape formed by the object and its images when the rotated shape is

a a right-angled isosceles triangle **b** a square.

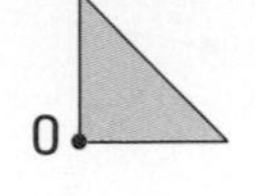

10b

2 **a** Draw an enlargement of the blue trapezium by scale factor 2.

b Show how four congruent blue trapeziums tessellate to make the image.

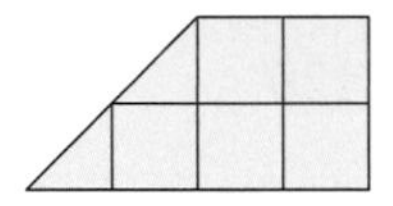

3 Draw coordinate axes from 0 to 10 on square grid paper. Plot and join the points (2, 1), (3, 2), (3, 3) and (2, 4) to form a quadrilateral.

a What is the mathematical name of the quadrilateral?

b Enlarge the quadrilateral by scale factor 3 using (0, 1) as the centre of enlargement.

c Write the coordinates of the vertices of the enlargement.

10c

4 Two mirrors M_1 and M_2 are 4 units apart.

a Reflect the green flag in the mirror M_1. Label the image I_1.

b Draw the reflection of I_1 using the mirror M_2. Label the image I_2.

c Describe the single transformation that maps the green flag to I_2.

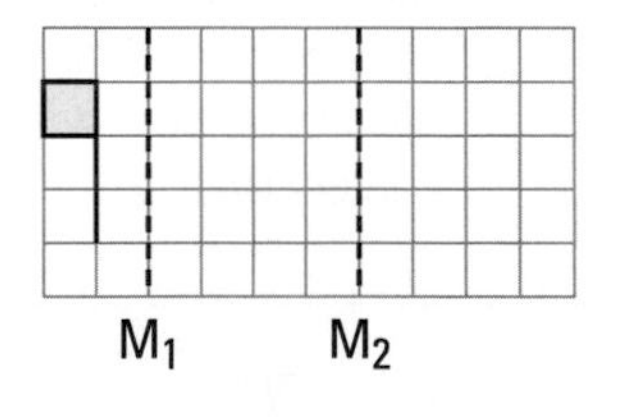

10d

5 The scale on a map is 1 : 25 000.

a Calculate the real-life distance represented by

i 7 cm **ii** 8.5 cm **iii** 4.5 cm **iv** 24 cm.

b Calculate the distance on the map for these real-life distances.

i 1200 m **ii** 850 m **iii** 8 km **iv** 4.5 km.

6 Calculate the real-life distance between these trees.

a Ash to Beech
b Ash to Cherry
c Ash to Date
d Beech to Cherry
e Beech to Date
f Cherry to Date

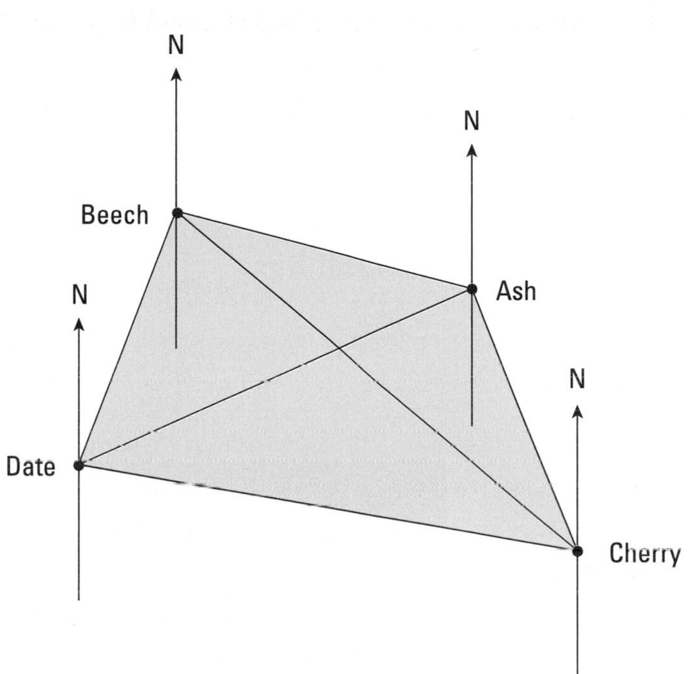

Scale: 1 cm represents 0.5 km

7 Use the diagram in question **6**. Measure the bearing of

a Ash from Date
b Beech from Date
c Beech from Ash
d Cherry from Ash
e Date from Ash
f Cherry from Beech
g Date from Beech
h Ash from Beech
i Ash from Cherry
j Beech from Cherry.

10 Summary

Assessment criteria

- Use and interpret maps and scale drawings in context **Level 6**
- Enlarge 2-D shapes given a centre of enlargement and a positive whole number scale factor **Level 6**

Level 6

1 James walks from Bridge to Hill Top.
Calculate

a the distance he walks in metres

b the bearing of Hill Top from Bridge

c the bearing of Bridge from Hill Top.

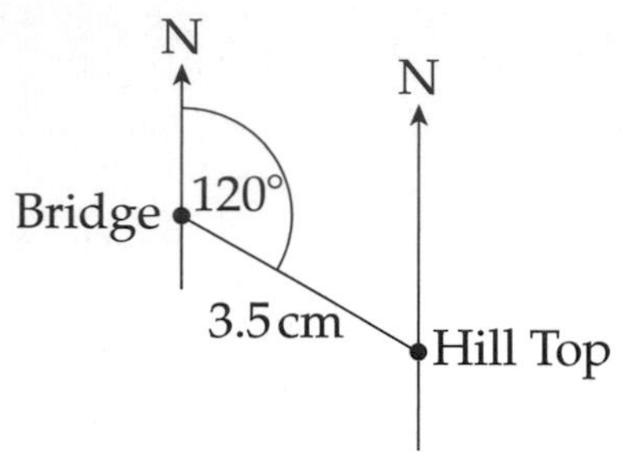

Scale 1:5000

Bethan's answer ✔

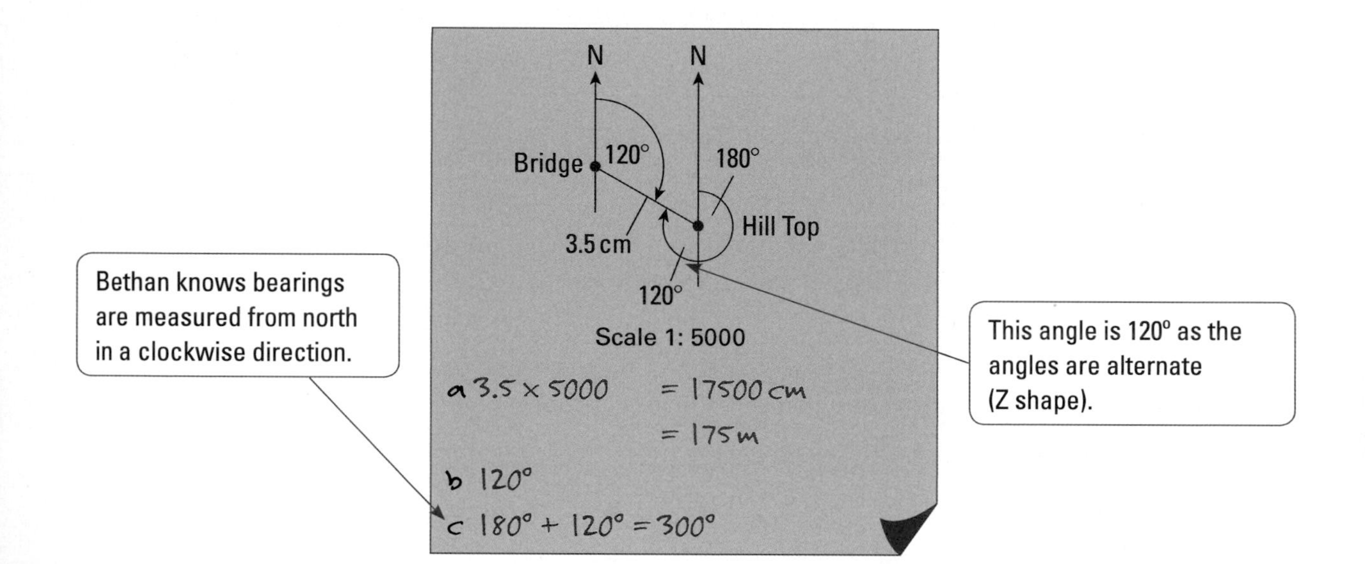

Level 6

2 Look at the rectangle drawn on a square grid.
Draw an enlargement of this rectangle with scale factor 2.
Use point A as the centre of enlargement.

A

Key Stage 3 2005 5–7 Paper 2

11 Algebra

Expressions and formulae

Sir Isaac Newton was a British scientist and lived from 1643 to 1727. He was a great mathematician, and described how gravity works, devised the laws of motion that are the foundations of classical mechanics and helped develop calculus.

What's the point? Although Newton lived over 300 years ago, many of his ideas form the basis of our understanding of the world around us.

Check in

Level 4

1 **a** Find the smallest whole number greater than 1 that can be divided exactly only by itself and 1.

b Find the four smallest prime numbers.

Level 5

2 **a** You think of a number n, treble it, and then add 4.

i Write an expression in terms of n for your final answer.

ii What is your final answer if n is 6?

b You think of a number, add 4, and then treble the result.

i Write an expression in terms of n for your final answer.

ii What is your final answer if n is 6?

Treble means multiply by three.

3 **a** Find the value of $5(6 - 2) + 3(5 - 1)$.

b Expand the brackets in this expression and collect like terms.

$5(2x + 2) + 3(x - 1)$

11a Factors, multiples and primes

LEVEL 6

- Revise and use factors, multiples and primes

Keywords
Factor
Factor pair
Factor tree
Highest common factor (HCF)
Indices
Lowest common multiple (LCM)
Multiple
Prime
Prime factor

- Any whole number can be written as the **product** of two **factors**.

The **factor pairs** of 12 are 1×12, 2×6 and 3×4. So the factors of 12 are 1, 2, 3, 4, 6 and 12.

- The highest common factor (**HCF**) of two numbers is the largest number that will divide into both of them.

Find the HCF of 12 and 20 by listing all their factors.

Number	Its factors						
12	1,	2,	3,	4,	6,	12	HCF = 4
20	1,	2,	4,	5,	10,	20	

- The lowest common multiple (**LCM**) of two numbers is the smallest **multiple** from their 'times tables'.

Find the LCM of 12 and 20 by listing their multiples.

Number	Its multiples						
12	12,	24,	36,	48,	60,	...	LCM = 60
20	20,	40,	60,	80,	...		

- A **prime** number only has two factors, 1 and itself. The first prime numbers are 2, 3, 5, 7, 11, 13, ...

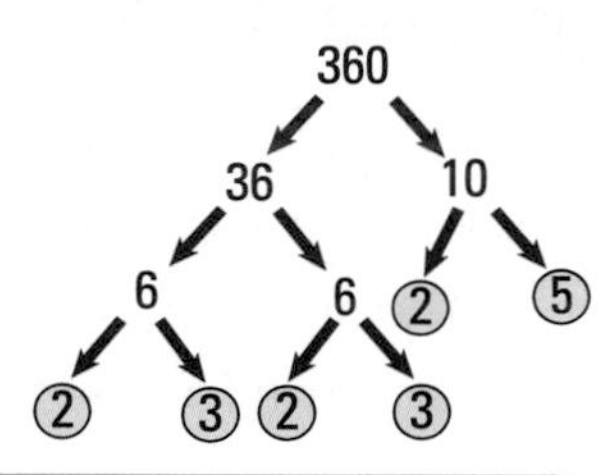

You can use a **factor tree** to find the **prime factors** of a number.

$360 = 2 \times 2 \times 2 \times 3 \times 3 \times 5 = 2^3 \times 3^2 \times 5$

example

Find the highest common factor and lowest common multiple of 126 and 105 using their factor trees.

$126 = 2 \times 3 \times 3 \times 7$

$105 = 3 \times 5 \times 7$

126 and 105 have the prime factors 3 and 7 in common. So the HCF of 126 and 105 is $3 \times 7 = 21$.

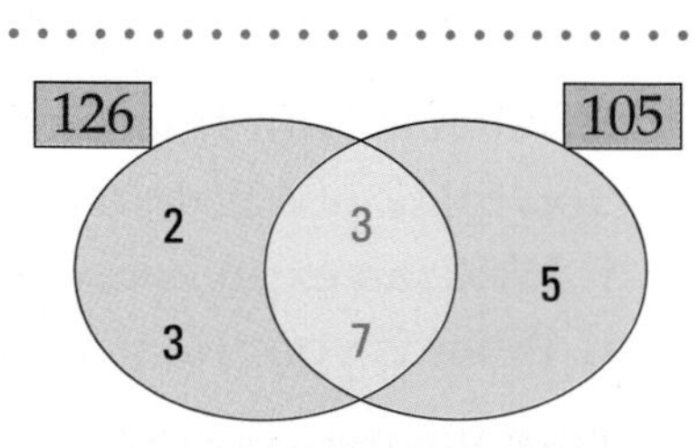

The shortest list you can have that includes all the prime factors of 126 and 105 is $2 \times 3 \times 3 \times 5 \times 7$.
So the LCM of 126 and 105 is
$2 \times 3 \times 3 \times 5 \times 7 = 630$.

Exercise 11a

Grade D–C

1 Find all the factor pairs for these numbers.
Then list all the factors for each number.

a 15 b 20 c 24 d 25
e 30 f 36 g 60 h 100

2 a Use this table to find the highest common factor of 16 and 24.

Number	Its factors
16	
24	

b Use the same method to find the highest common factor of these pairs of numbers.

i 12 and 28 ii 16 and 36 iii 32 and 40

3 a Use this table to find the lowest common multiple of 12 and 15.

Number	Its multiples
12	
15	

b Use the same method to find the lowest common multiple of these pairs of numbers.

i 8 and 10 ii 9 and 15 iii 6 and 14

4 a Write the next **three** prime numbers after these.
2, 3, 5, 7, …

b Use factor trees to write these numbers as the product of their prime factors.
Give your answers using indices.

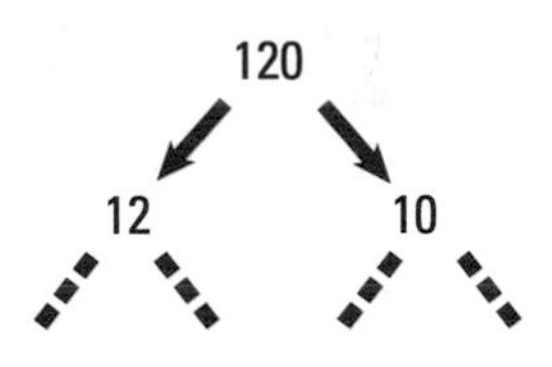

i 120 ii 48 iii 72 iv 200
v 300 vi 144 vii 1000 viii 720
ix 216 x 1080

5 a Copy this Venn diagram and write in all the prime factors of the numbers A and B.

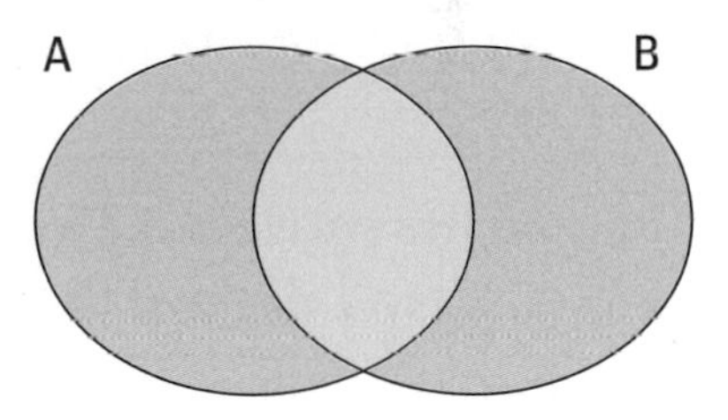

i A = 40, B = 110 ii A = 70, B = 42
iii A = 30, B = 54 iv A = 60, B = 210
v A = 150, B = 350 vi A = 90, B = 84

b Use your Venn diagrams to find the highest common factor and lowest common multiple of each pair of numbers.

rich task

a Find all the positive integers less than 50 which have only three factors.
What do these numbers have in common?

b Find all the factors of 60. There are twelve of them.
Find another integer less than 100 which also has exactly twelve factors.

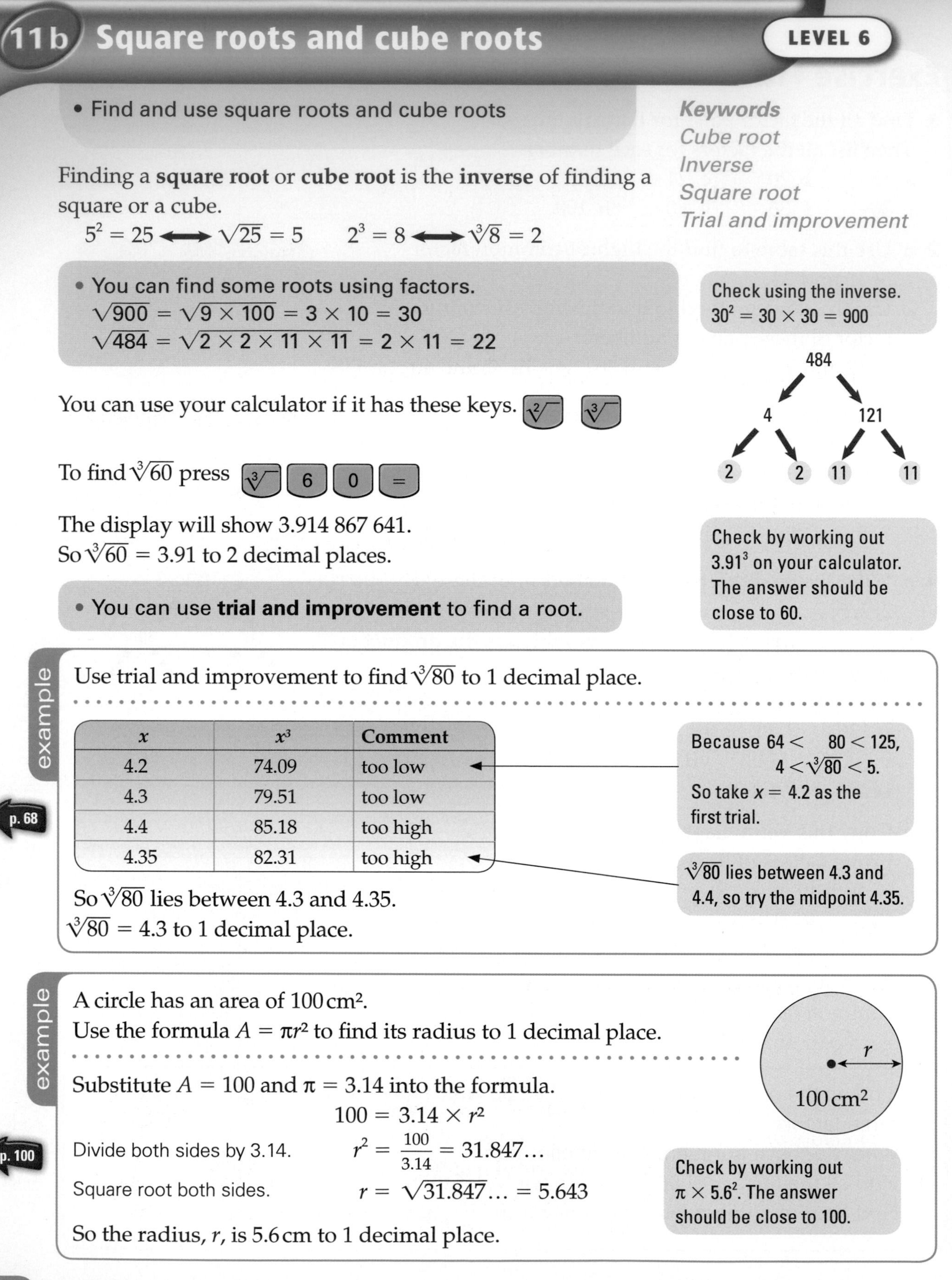

11b Square roots and cube roots

LEVEL 6

- Find and use square roots and cube roots

Keywords
Cube root
Inverse
Square root
Trial and improvement

Finding a **square root** or **cube root** is the **inverse** of finding a square or a cube.

$5^2 = 25 \longleftrightarrow \sqrt{25} = 5 \qquad 2^3 = 8 \longleftrightarrow \sqrt[3]{8} = 2$

- You can find some roots using factors.
  $\sqrt{900} = \sqrt{9 \times 100} = 3 \times 10 = 30$
  $\sqrt{484} = \sqrt{2 \times 2 \times 11 \times 11} = 2 \times 11 = 22$

Check using the inverse.
$30^2 = 30 \times 30 = 900$

You can use your calculator if it has these keys. [$\sqrt[2]{\ }$] [$\sqrt[3]{\ }$]

To find $\sqrt[3]{60}$ press [$\sqrt[3]{\ }$] [6] [0] [=]

The display will show 3.914 867 641.
So $\sqrt[3]{60} = 3.91$ to 2 decimal places.

Check by working out 3.91^3 on your calculator. The answer should be close to 60.

- You can use **trial and improvement** to find a root.

example

Use trial and improvement to find $\sqrt[3]{80}$ to 1 decimal place.

x	x^3	Comment
4.2	74.09	too low
4.3	79.51	too low
4.4	85.18	too high
4.35	82.31	too high

Because $64 < 80 < 125$, $4 < \sqrt[3]{80} < 5$. So take $x = 4.2$ as the first trial.

$\sqrt[3]{80}$ lies between 4.3 and 4.4, so try the midpoint 4.35.

So $\sqrt[3]{80}$ lies between 4.3 and 4.35.
$\sqrt[3]{80} = 4.3$ to 1 decimal place.

p. 68

example

A circle has an area of $100\,\text{cm}^2$.
Use the formula $A = \pi r^2$ to find its radius to 1 decimal place.

Substitute $A = 100$ and $\pi = 3.14$ into the formula.

$$100 = 3.14 \times r^2$$

Divide both sides by 3.14. $\quad r^2 = \frac{100}{3.14} = 31.847\ldots$

Square root both sides. $\quad r = \sqrt{31.847\ldots} = 5.643$

So the radius, r, is 5.6 cm to 1 decimal place.

Check by working out $\pi \times 5.6^2$. The answer should be close to 100.

p. 100

Exercise 11b

1 Work out these square roots.

a $\sqrt{400}$ **b** $\sqrt{1600}$ **c** $\sqrt{2500}$ **d** $\sqrt{10000}$ **e** $\sqrt{\frac{9}{100}}$ **f** $\sqrt{\frac{4}{100}}$

2 Find the prime factors of these numbers from their factor trees and then find their square roots.

a $\sqrt{196}$ **b** $\sqrt{225}$ **c** $\sqrt{1089}$ **d** $\sqrt{3025}$ **e** $\sqrt{1764}$

3 Use trial and improvement to find these roots to 1 decimal place.
Use this table of squares and cubes to help you choose your starting values.
You could use tables like these.

x	1	2	3	4	5	6	7	8
x^2	1	4	9	16	25	36	49	64
x^3	1	8	27	64	125			

a $\sqrt{30}$ **b** $\sqrt{46}$ **c** $\sqrt{62}$ **d** $\sqrt{85}$ **e** $\sqrt{105}$

f $\sqrt[3]{30}$ **g** $\sqrt[3]{10}$ **h** $\sqrt[3]{55}$ **i** $\sqrt[3]{100}$ **j** $\sqrt[3]{120}$

Check your answers.

x	x^2	Comment

x	x^3	Comment

4 The area A of a circle of radius r is given by the formula $A = \pi r^2$.
Find the radius, to 2 decimal places, of circles with these areas.

a 24 cm² **b** 50 cm² **c** 75 cm² **d** 120 cm² **e** 240 cm²

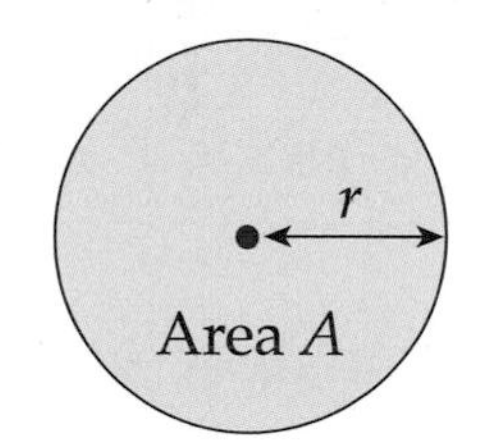

5 A circular garden pond has an area of 20 m².
Find its radius, to 1 decimal place.

6 The area of one side of a £2 coin is 6.33 cm².
What is its radius, to 1 decimal place?

7 A circular helipad has an area of 725 m².
Find its radius and its diameter, to the nearest whole metre.

8 A light bulb with a wattage W and resistance R needs an electrical current I given by $I = \sqrt{\frac{W}{R}}$.
Calculate I for

a an old-style light bulb with $W = 60$ and $R = 960$

b a modern low-energy light bulb with $W = 12$ and $R = 4800$.

ICT research

A sphere of radius r has a surface area A given by $A = 4\pi r^2$.

a If the surface area of a standard football is 1550 cm², calculate its radius.

b Use the Internet to find the dimensions of a standard (size 5) football and an indoor (size 4) football.

c Who would use the even smaller size 3 football?

11c Indices

- Learn the rules of indices and use them to simplify expressions

Keywords
Index
Rule
Power

- An **index** or **power** is used when a number or letter is multiplied by itself.
  $3^4 = 3 \times 3 \times 3 \times 3$ $\quad x^5 = x \times x \times x \times x \times x$

You say '3 to the power 4' and 'x to the power 5'.

There are three **rules** that you should know about indices.

example

Simplify these expressions giving your answers as a power.

a $2^4 \times 2^3$ **b** $\frac{5^7}{5^4}$ **c** $(4^2)^3$

a $2^4 \times 2^3 = (2 \times 2 \times 2 \times 2) \times (2 \times 2 \times 2) = 2^7$

b $\frac{5^7}{5^4} = \frac{\cancel{5} \times \cancel{5} \times \cancel{5} \times \cancel{5} \times 5 \times 5 \times 5}{\cancel{5} \times \cancel{5} \times \cancel{5} \times \cancel{5}} = 5 \times 5 \times 5 = 5^3$

c $(4^2)^3 = 4^2 \times 4^2 \times 4^2 = (4 \times 4) \times (4 \times 4) \times (4 \times 4) = 4^6$

- Rule 1: $x^a \times x^b = x^{a+b}$ In part **a**, the powers $4 + 3 = 7$.

- Rule 2: $\frac{x^a}{x^b} = x^{a-b}$ In part **b**, the powers $7 - 4 = 3$.

- Rule 3: $(x^a)^b = x^{a \times b}$ In part **c**, the powers $2 \times 3 = 6$.

example

Simplify **a** $\frac{z^4 \times z^6}{z^8}$ **b** $\frac{8(y^4)^3}{2y^2 \times y^7}$

a $\frac{z^4 \times z^6}{z^8} = \frac{z^{10}}{z^8} = z^2$ using rule 1 and then rule 2.

b $\frac{8(y^4)^3}{2y^2 \times y^7} = \frac{8y^{12}}{2y^2 \times y^7} = \frac{8y^{12}}{2y^9} = 4y^3$

using rules 3, 1 and then 2.

LEVEL 6

Grade C

Exercise 11c

You can only use the rules to simplify indices of the same letter.

1 Simplify these expressions, using indices in your answers.

a $x \times x \times x \times x$ **b** $y \times y \times y \times y \times y$

c $x \times x \times x \times x \times z \times z \times z$ **d** $r \times s \times s \times r \times r \times r \times s$

e $2 \times 2 \times p \times p \times 2 \times p$ **f** $3 \times x \times 3 \times y \times x \times x \times y$

2 Use the rule $x^a \times x^b = x^{a+b}$ to simplify these expressions.

a $x^4 \times x^5$ **b** $y^6 \times y^4$ **c** $z^7 \times z$

d $p \times p^5$ **e** $k^3 \times k^2 \times k$ **f** $q^2 \times q^4 \times r^6 \times r^3$

g $m^2 \times t^3 \times m^5 \times t^2$ **h** $a^2 \times b^3 \times a \times b^4$ **i** $x^2y^3 \times x^4y$

3 Use the rule $\frac{x^a}{x^b} = x^{a-b}$ to simplify these expressions.

a $\frac{x^7}{x^3}$ **b** $\frac{y^8}{y^2}$ **c** $\frac{z^4}{z^3}$ **d** $\frac{a^8b^5}{a^2b^2}$

e $\frac{p^7q^6}{p^5q}$ **f** $\frac{x^3y^4}{xy^3}$ **g** $\frac{s^4t^3}{s^3t^2}$ **h** $\frac{y^4z^2}{y^4z}$

4 Use the rule $(x^a)^b = x^{a \times b}$ to simplify these expressions.

a $(x^2)^3$ **b** $(y^4)^2$ **c** $(z^5)^3$ **d** $(m^3)^5$

e $(n^4)^2$ **f** $(x^3y^4)^2$ **g** $(a^4b^2)^3$ **h** $(m^2n)^5$

5 Simplify these expressions.

a $2x^3 \times 4x^5$ **b** $6y^7 \times 3y^2$ **c** $\frac{8z^6}{4z^2}$ **d** $\frac{p^4 \times p^6}{p^7}$

e $\frac{q^6 \times q^4}{q^2 \times q^3}$ **f** $\frac{r^2 \times r^5}{r^4 \times r^2}$ **g** $\frac{8a^5 \times a^6}{2a^7}$ **h** $\frac{3c^5 \times 4c^6}{6c^8}$

i $\frac{5x^6 \times 4x^3}{10x^8}$ **j** $\frac{6(x^4)^3}{3x^2}$ **k** $\frac{12(y^5)^3}{4y^7 \times y^3}$ **l** $3(y^3)^2 \times 5y^4$

6 A billion in the USA is a thousand million $= 10^3 \times 10^6$.

A billion in the UK can also mean a million million $= 10^6 \times 10^6$.

A US trillion is (a million)^2

A UK trillion is (a million)^3

Write these four numbers in the form 10^a.

Did you know?

April 09

In April 2009, the International Monetary Fund warned that 'credit crunch' losses could reach $4 trillion.

challenge

a Work out the value of $\frac{2^3}{2^3}$ **i** using $\frac{2 \times 2 \times 2}{2 \times 2 \times 2}$ **ii** using rule 2.

What can you say about the value of 2^0 and x^0?

b Work out the value of **i** $9^{\frac{1}{2}} \times 9^{\frac{1}{2}}$ **ii** $\sqrt{9} \times \sqrt{9}$

What can you say about the value of $9^{\frac{1}{2}}$ and $x^{\frac{1}{2}}$?

Factors in algebra

LEVEL 6

- Know that factorising an algebraic expression is the inverse of expanding brackets.

Keywords
Common Factor
Expression Inverse

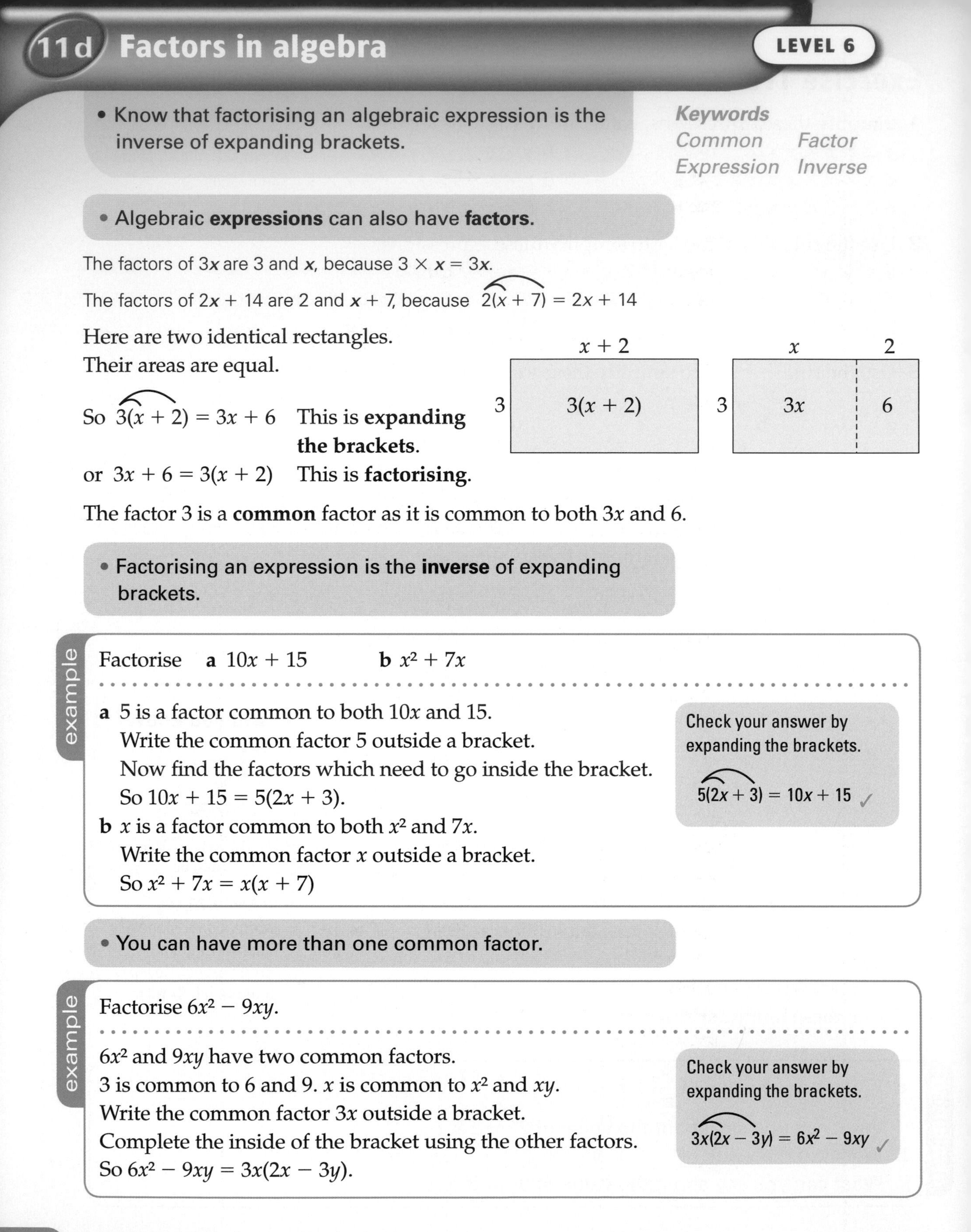

- Algebraic **expressions** can also have **factors.**

The factors of $3x$ are 3 and x, because $3 \times x = 3x$.

The factors of $2x + 14$ are 2 and $x + 7$, because $2(x + 7) = 2x + 14$

Here are two identical rectangles.
Their areas are equal.

So $3(x + 2) = 3x + 6$ This is **expanding the brackets.**

or $3x + 6 = 3(x + 2)$ This is **factorising.**

The factor 3 is a **common** factor as it is common to both $3x$ and 6.

- Factorising an expression is the **inverse** of expanding brackets.

example

Factorise **a** $10x + 15$ **b** $x^2 + 7x$

a 5 is a factor common to both $10x$ and 15.
Write the common factor 5 outside a bracket.
Now find the factors which need to go inside the bracket.
So $10x + 15 = 5(2x + 3)$.

b x is a factor common to both x^2 and $7x$.
Write the common factor x outside a bracket.
So $x^2 + 7x = x(x + 7)$

Check your answer by expanding the brackets.

$5(2x + 3) = 10x + 15$ ✓

- You can have more than one common factor.

example

Factorise $6x^2 - 9xy$.

$6x^2$ and $9xy$ have two common factors.
3 is common to 6 and 9. x is common to x^2 and xy.
Write the common factor $3x$ outside a bracket.
Complete the inside of the bracket using the other factors.
So $6x^2 - 9xy = 3x(2x - 3y)$.

Check your answer by expanding the brackets.

$3x(2x - 3y) = 6x^2 - 9xy$ ✓

LEVEL 6

Grade D-C

Exercise 11d

1 Write the factor which is common to the two terms in each of these expressions.

a $2x + 6$ **b** $3x + 6$ **c** $5z - 20$ **d** $4p + 16$

e $6q + 8$ **f** $9r - 6$ **g** $8x + 6$ **h** $15x - 20$

2 Factorise these expressions.

a $2x - 8$ **b** $3y + 9$ **c** $4x - 12$ **d** $5m + 30$

e $9n + 6$ **f** $6x - 10$ **g** $15y + 25$ **h** $8z - 10$

i $6 - 9x$ **j** $18 + 4x$ **k** $25 - 10x$ **l** $12 - 4x$

m $12x - 8$ **n** $10x + 5$ **o** $6x + 3$ **p** $7x - 14$

3 Factorise these expressions.

a $x^2 + 5x$ **b** $y^2 + 7y$ **c** $z^2 - 3z$ **d** $4p + p^2$

e $x^2 + 5xy$ **f** $a^2 - 2ab$ **g** $t^2 + 3st$ **h** $6yz - z^2$

i $8y + y^2$ **j** $8xy + y^2$ **k** $3z^2 + z$ **l** $5x^2 - x$

m $x^3 + 5x$ **n** $x^3 - 2x^2$ **o** $z^3 - z^2 + 3z$ **p** $2y + y^2 - y^3$

4 Factorise these expressions.
Look for two common factors.

a $2x^2 + 6xy$ **b** $9x^2 + 3xy$ **c** $2y^2 - 8yz$ **d** $6p^2 + 3pq$

e $4q^2 - 8pq$ **f** $6z^2 + 8yz$ **g** $9xy + 6yz$ **h** $4ab - 6bc$

i $6mn + 8np$ **j** $4x^2 - 6x$ **k** $6x^2 - 4x$ **l** $6x^2 - 2x$

m $9x^2 + 3xy$ **n** $12z + 8z^2$ **o** $9z^2 - 3z$ **p** $2y^3 + 4y$

5 Factorise these expressions.

a $8z^3 - 6z$ **b** $8z^3 - 6z^2$ **c** $8z^3 + 4z$ **d** $8z^3 + 4z^2$

6 The area of a rectangle is $3x^2 + 6x$.

a Factorise this expression in several different ways.

b Find at least three possible pairs of values for its length and width.

length

width

Area $= 3x^2 + 6x$

7 **a** The number x is an integer.
Write the next two integers greater than x.

b Write an expression for the total, T, when you add together x and the next two integers.

c Prove that T is always a multiple of 3.

puzzle

A whole number x is added to its square to give a total, T.

a Prove that T is always equal to the product of two consecutive numbers.

b Find expressions for these consecutive numbers.

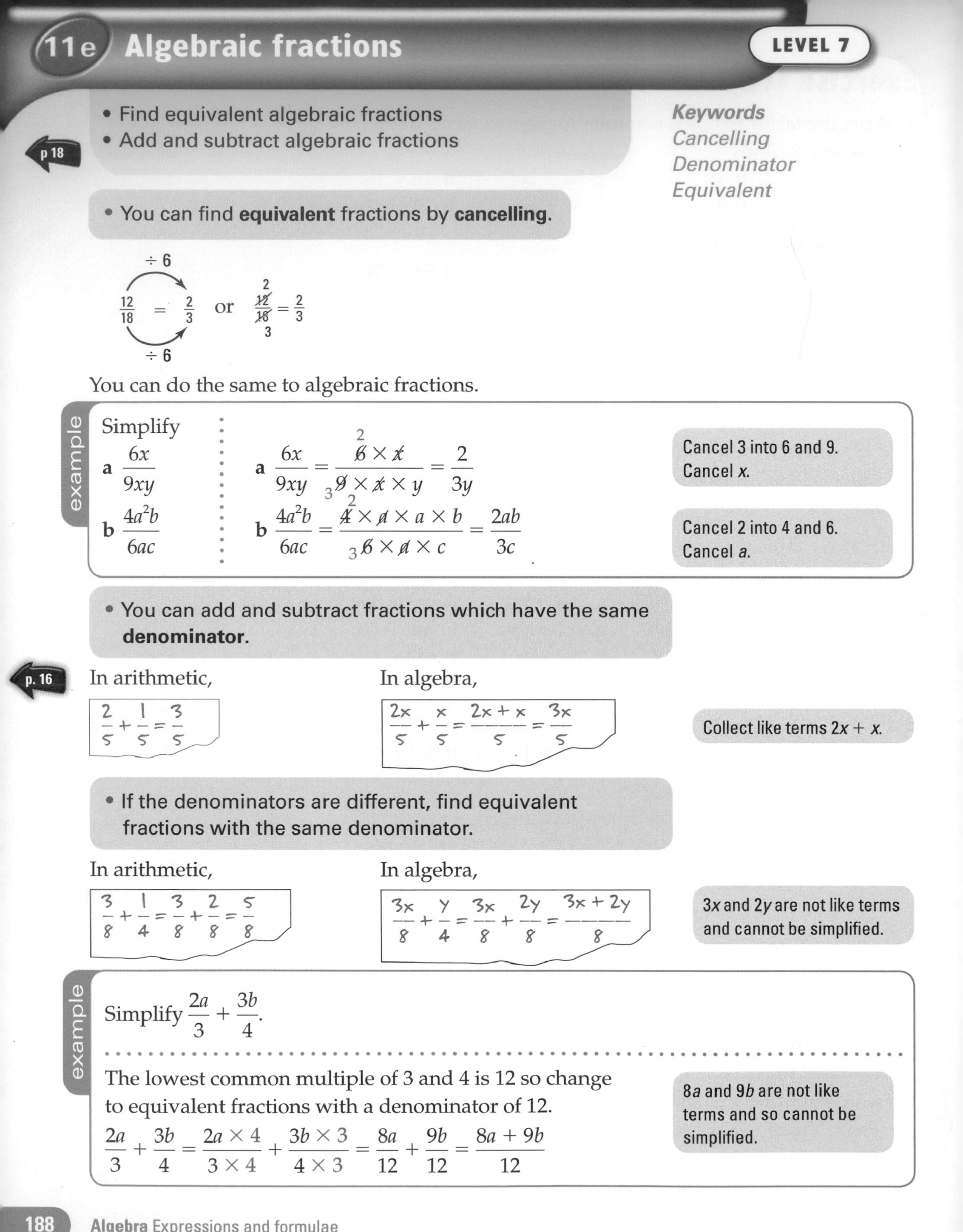

11e Algebraic fractions

LEVEL 7

- Find equivalent algebraic fractions
- Add and subtract algebraic fractions

p 18

Keywords
Cancelling
Denominator
Equivalent

- You can find **equivalent** fractions by **cancelling**.

$$\frac{12}{18} = \frac{2}{3} \quad (\div 6) \quad \text{or} \quad \frac{\cancel{12}^{2}}{\cancel{18}_{3}} = \frac{2}{3}$$

You can do the same to algebraic fractions.

example

Simplify

a $\frac{6x}{9xy}$

b $\frac{4a^2b}{6ac}$

a $\frac{6x}{9xy} = \frac{{}^{2}\cancel{6} \times \cancel{x}}{{}_{3}\cancel{9} \times \cancel{x} \times y} = \frac{2}{3y}$

Cancel 3 into 6 and 9. Cancel x.

b $\frac{4a^2b}{6ac} = \frac{{}^{2}\cancel{4} \times \cancel{a} \times a \times b}{{}_{3}\cancel{6} \times \cancel{a} \times c} = \frac{2ab}{3c}$

Cancel 2 into 4 and 6. Cancel a.

- You can add and subtract fractions which have the same **denominator**.

p. 16

In arithmetic,

$$\frac{2}{5} + \frac{1}{5} = \frac{3}{5}$$

In algebra,

$$\frac{2x}{5} + \frac{x}{5} = \frac{2x + x}{5} = \frac{3x}{5}$$

Collect like terms $2x + x$.

- If the denominators are different, find equivalent fractions with the same denominator.

In arithmetic,

$$\frac{3}{8} + \frac{1}{4} = \frac{3}{8} + \frac{2}{8} = \frac{5}{8}$$

In algebra,

$$\frac{3x}{8} + \frac{y}{4} = \frac{3x}{8} + \frac{2y}{8} = \frac{3x + 2y}{8}$$

$3x$ and $2y$ are not like terms and cannot be simplified.

example

Simplify $\frac{2a}{3} + \frac{3b}{4}$.

The lowest common multiple of 3 and 4 is 12 so change to equivalent fractions with a denominator of 12.

$$\frac{2a}{3} + \frac{3b}{4} = \frac{2a \times 4}{3 \times 4} + \frac{3b \times 3}{4 \times 3} = \frac{8a}{12} + \frac{9b}{12} = \frac{8a + 9b}{12}$$

$8a$ and $9b$ are not like terms and so cannot be simplified.

LEVEL 7

Grade D-C

Exercise 11e

1 Find equivalent fractions by cancelling.

a $\frac{2x}{6}$ b $\frac{3y}{9}$ c $\frac{6z}{8}$ d $\frac{ab}{5a}$

e $\frac{uv}{4u}$ f $\frac{3pq}{p^2}$ g $\frac{2mn}{n^2}$ h $\frac{4x}{5xy}$

2 Simplify each fraction by cancelling as much as possible.

a $\frac{2xy}{8x}$ b $\frac{3mm}{9m}$ c $\frac{8ab}{100}$ d $\frac{6yz}{9xz}$ e $\frac{5pq}{10qr}$ f $\frac{8st}{4s}$

g $\frac{x^2}{xy}$ h $\frac{a^2}{abc}$ i $\frac{m^2n}{2mn}$ j $\frac{6yz}{9y^2}$ k $\frac{4h^2k}{6h}$ l $\frac{9xyz}{6xz^2}$

3 Add or subtract these fractions.

a $\frac{3x}{7}+\frac{2x}{7}$ b $\frac{3x}{7}+\frac{2y}{7}$ c $\frac{4a}{9}+\frac{a}{9}$ d $\frac{4a}{9}+\frac{b}{9}$

e $\frac{4s}{5}-\frac{3s}{5}$ f $\frac{4s}{5}-\frac{3t}{5}$ g $\frac{9y}{11}-\frac{3y}{11}$ h $\frac{9y}{11}-\frac{3z}{11}$

4 Add or subtract these fractions.
Your first step will be to find a common denominator.

a $\frac{x}{2}+\frac{x}{3}$ b $\frac{y}{5}+\frac{y}{3}$ c $\frac{3z}{2}-\frac{z}{5}$ d $\frac{x}{3}+\frac{2x}{5}$ e $\frac{3a}{7}+\frac{2a}{3}$ f $\frac{3c}{5}-\frac{c}{2}$

g $\frac{4m}{3}+\frac{3m}{8}$ h $\frac{3x}{8}+\frac{x}{4}$ i $\frac{11y}{12}-\frac{y}{3}$ j $\frac{5p}{6}-\frac{3p}{4}$ k $\frac{7q}{10}+\frac{3q}{4}$ l $\frac{3s}{8}-\frac{s}{6}$

5 Add or subtract these fractions.

a $\frac{2x}{3}+\frac{y}{4}$ b $\frac{5c}{2}-\frac{3d}{5}$ c $\frac{2e}{7}+\frac{f}{2}$ d $\frac{2x}{5}+\frac{x}{2}$

e $\frac{3p}{5}-\frac{3q}{4}$ f $\frac{5y}{4}+\frac{3z}{5}$ g $\frac{3z}{4}-\frac{z}{2}$ h $\frac{x}{8}-\frac{3y}{4}$

i $\frac{5y}{6}+\frac{z}{4}$ j $\frac{8a}{9}-\frac{5}{6}$ k $\frac{3p}{10}+\frac{1}{2}$ l $\frac{2x}{3}-\frac{1}{4}$

challenge

A student wrote these two calculations.
They are both wrong.
Explain the mistakes and find the correct answers.

a. $\frac{1}{2}+\frac{1}{3}=\frac{1+1}{2+3}=\frac{2}{5}$

b. $\frac{x}{2}+\frac{y}{3}=\frac{x+y}{2+3}=\frac{x+y}{5}$

11f Formulae in context

LEVEL 7

- Substitute into formulae in different contexts

Keywords
Equation
Formula
Subject
Value
Variable

You can find **formulae** in science, engineering, business and medicine.

- A **variable** is a quantity which can change its **value**.

You use a formula to calculate a value of one variable when you know the values of other variables.

example

In science, the energy E needed to send a current I through a light bulb with resistance R is given by the formula $E = RI^2$.

Find the value of E when $R = 16$ and $I = 5$.

Substitute the values of R and I into the formula.

$E = RI^2$
$= 16 \times 5^2$
$= 16 \times 25$
$= 400$

- Often the variable you are finding is not the **subject** of the formula.
  Then you can think of the formula as an **equation**.

The subject is the variable by itself on the left-hand side of the formula.

example

When a car accelerates from an initial speed u for a time t with an acceleration a, its final speed v is given by this formula.

$v = u + at$

a Find the value of u when $v = 20$, $a = 4$ and $t = 3$.

b Find the value of t when $v = 40$, $u = 10$ and $a = 5$.

a Substitute the values you know into the formula.

$v = u + at$

$20 = u + 4 \times 3$

This is an equation. $20 = u + 12$

Subtract 12 from both sides. $8 = u$

The car's initial speed u is 8.

b Substitute the values you know into the formula.

$v = u + at$

$40 = 10 + 5 \times t$

This is an equation. $40 = 10 + 5t$

Subtract 10 from both sides. $30 = 5t$

Divide both sides by 5. $6 = t$

The car accelerates over a time $t = 6$.

Exercise 11f

Grade D-C

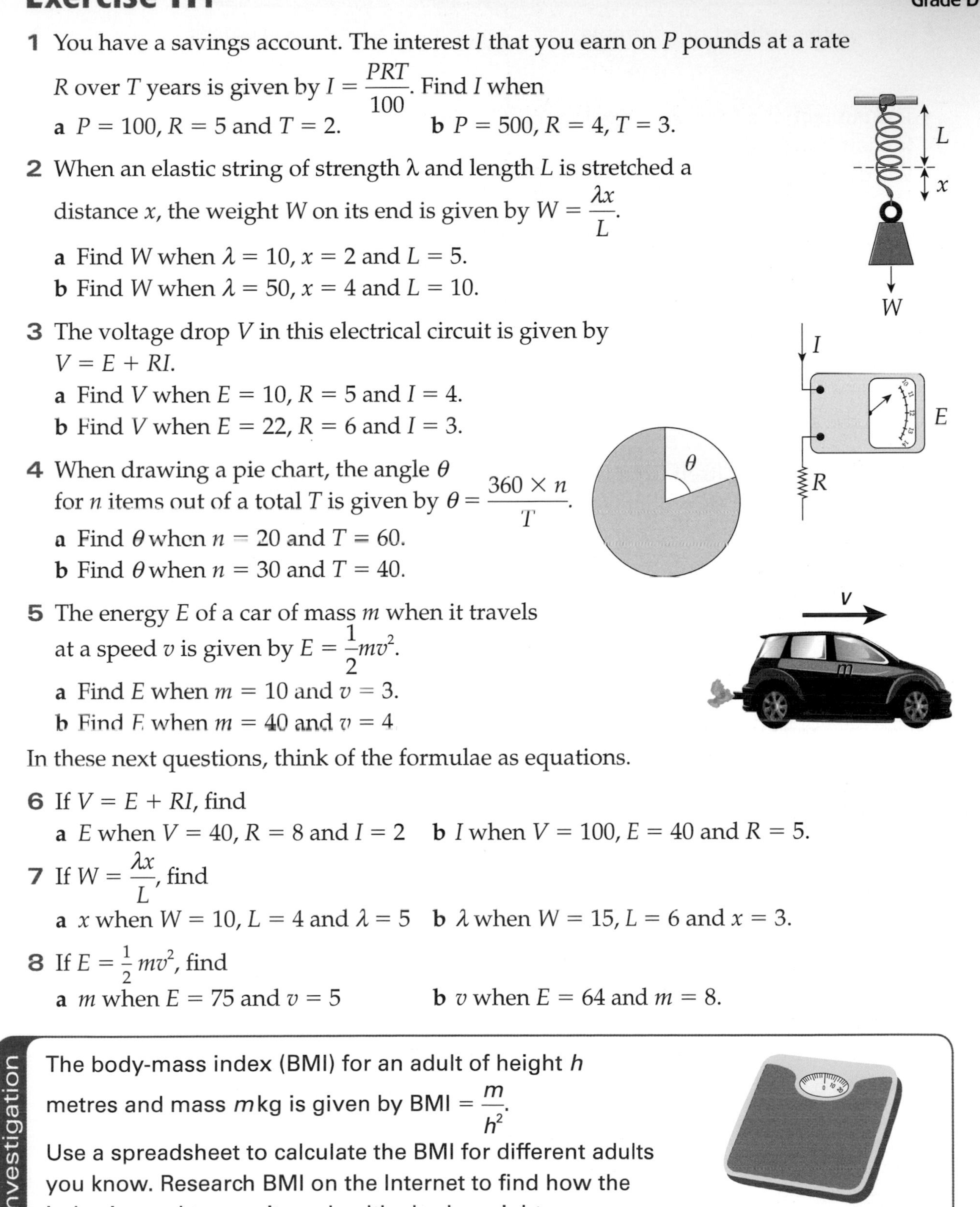

1 You have a savings account. The interest I that you earn on P pounds at a rate R over T years is given by $I = \frac{PRT}{100}$. Find I when

a $P = 100$, $R = 5$ and $T = 2$. **b** $P = 500$, $R = 4$, $T = 3$.

2 When an elastic string of strength λ and length L is stretched a distance x, the weight W on its end is given by $W = \frac{\lambda x}{L}$.

a Find W when $\lambda = 10$, $x = 2$ and $L = 5$.

b Find W when $\lambda = 50$, $x = 4$ and $L = 10$.

3 The voltage drop V in this electrical circuit is given by $V = E + RI$.

a Find V when $E = 10$, $R = 5$ and $I = 4$.

b Find V when $E = 22$, $R = 6$ and $I = 3$.

4 When drawing a pie chart, the angle θ for n items out of a total T is given by $\theta = \frac{360 \times n}{T}$.

a Find θ when $n = 20$ and $T = 60$.

b Find θ when $n = 30$ and $T = 40$.

5 The energy E of a car of mass m when it travels at a speed v is given by $E = \frac{1}{2}mv^2$.

a Find E when $m = 10$ and $v = 3$.

b Find E when $m = 40$ and $v = 4$.

In these next questions, think of the formulae as equations.

6 If $V = E + RI$, find

a E when $V = 40$, $R = 8$ and $I = 2$ **b** I when $V = 100$, $E = 40$ and $R = 5$.

7 If $W = \frac{\lambda x}{L}$, find

a x when $W = 10$, $L = 4$ and $\lambda = 5$ **b** λ when $W = 15$, $L = 6$ and $x = 3$.

8 If $E = \frac{1}{2}mv^2$, find

a m when $E = 75$ and $v = 5$ **b** v when $E = 64$ and $m = 8$.

investigation

The body-mass index (BMI) for an adult of height h metres and mass m kg is given by $\text{BMI} = \frac{m}{h^2}$.

Use a spreadsheet to calculate the BMI for different adults you know. Research BMI on the Internet to find how the index is used to monitor a healthy body weight.

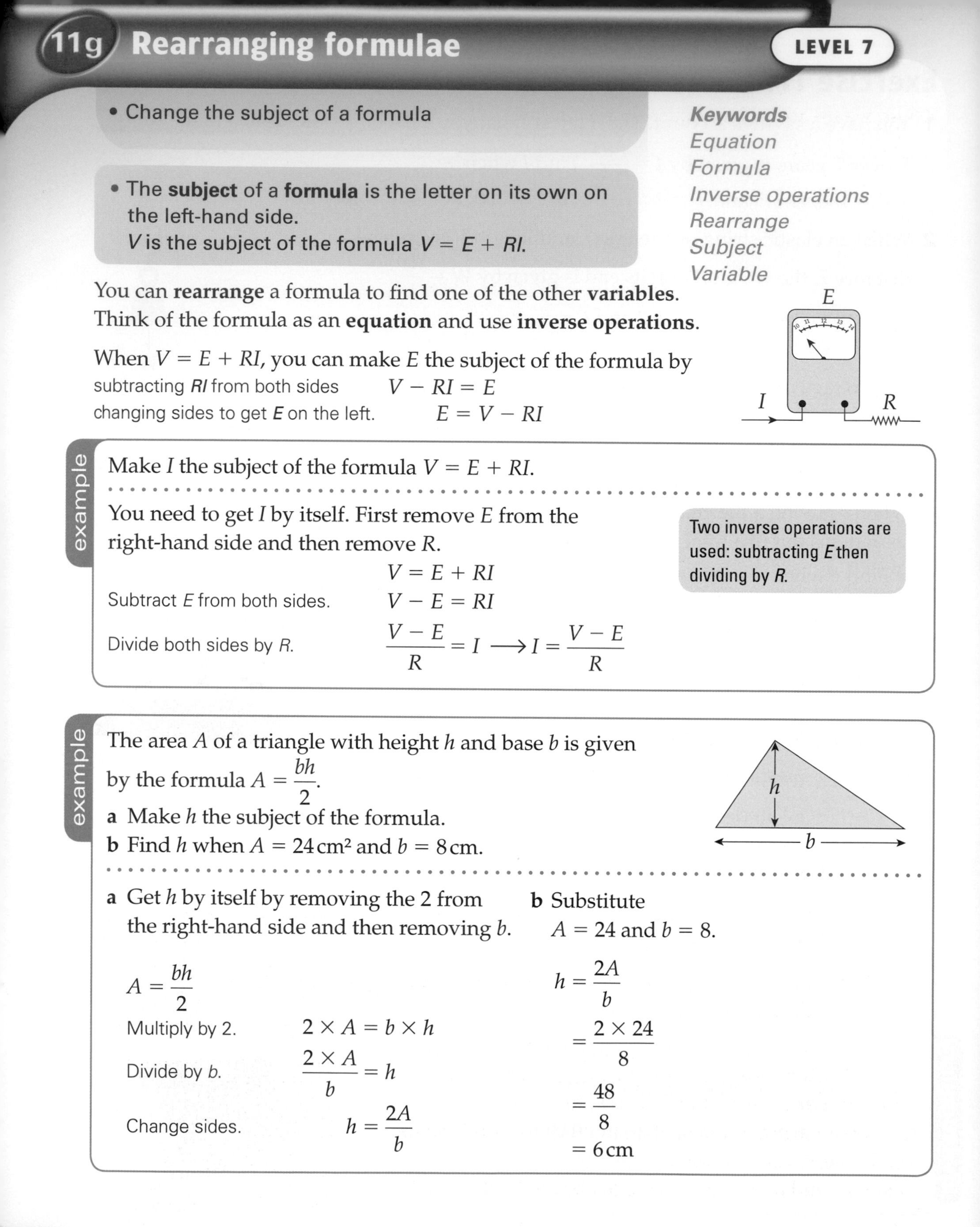

11g Rearranging formulae

LEVEL 7

- Change the subject of a formula

Keywords
Equation
Formula
Inverse operations
Rearrange
Subject
Variable

- The **subject** of a **formula** is the letter on its own on the left-hand side.
  V is the subject of the formula $V = E + RI$.

You can **rearrange** a formula to find one of the other **variables**. Think of the formula as an **equation** and use **inverse operations**.

When $V = E + RI$, you can make E the subject of the formula by

subtracting RI from both sides $\quad V - RI = E$

changing sides to get E on the left. $\quad E = V - RI$

example

Make I the subject of the formula $V = E + RI$.

You need to get I by itself. First remove E from the right-hand side and then remove R.

Two inverse operations are used: subtracting E then dividing by R.

$$V = E + RI$$

Subtract E from both sides. $\quad V - E = RI$

Divide both sides by R. $\quad \frac{V - E}{R} = I \longrightarrow I = \frac{V - E}{R}$

example

The area A of a triangle with height h and base b is given by the formula $A = \frac{bh}{2}$.

a Make h the subject of the formula.

b Find h when $A = 24\,\text{cm}^2$ and $b = 8\,\text{cm}$.

a Get h by itself by removing the 2 from the right-hand side and then removing b.

$$A = \frac{bh}{2}$$

Multiply by 2. $\quad 2 \times A = b \times h$

Divide by b. $\quad \frac{2 \times A}{b} = h$

Change sides. $\quad h = \frac{2A}{b}$

b Substitute $A = 24$ and $b = 8$.

$$h = \frac{2A}{b} = \frac{2 \times 24}{8} = \frac{48}{8} = 6\,\text{cm}$$

Exercise 11g

These are the formulae used in this exercise.

For moving vehicles	From science	For shapes	From medicine
$s = vt$	$V = RI$	$V = \frac{lbh}{3}$	$D = kW$
$v = u + at$	$E = V + RI$	$C = \pi d$	$\text{BMI} = \frac{m}{h^2}$
$E = \frac{mv^2}{2}$	$P = RI^2t$	$A = \pi r^2$	
		$V = \pi r^2 h$	

1 a Make t the subject of $s = vt$. b Find t when $s = 30$ and $v = 6$.

2 a Make R the subject of $V = RI$. b Find R when $V = 42$ and $I = 7$.

3 a Make W the subject of $D = kW$. b Find W when $D = 18$ and $k = 3$.

4 a Make u the subject of $v = u + at$. b Find u when $v = 42$, $a = 2$ and $t = 9$.

5 a Make V the subject of $E = V + RI$. b Find V when $E = 32$, $R = 12$ and $I = 2$.

6 a Make I the subject of $E = V + RI$. b Find I when $E = 52$, $V = 28$ and $R = 4$.

7 a Make m the subject of $\text{BMI} = \frac{m}{h^2}$ b Find m when BMI $= 24$ and $h = 10$.

8 a Make m the subject of $E = \frac{mv^2}{2}$. b Find m when $E = 48$ and $v = 4$.

9 a Make h the subject of $V = \frac{lbh}{3}$. b Find h when $V = 24$, $l = 6$ and $b = 2$.

10 a Make R the subject of $P = RI^2t$. b Find R when $P = 150$, $I = 5$ and $t = 2$.

11 The energy absorbed by a resistor in an electrical circuit is given by the formula $E = RI^2$.
Make I the subject of the formula.

12 A rectangle has a perimeter given by the formula $P = 2l + 2w$.
Make l the subject of the formula.

13 The volume V of a cylinder is given by the formula $V = \pi r^2 h$.
Make r the subject of this formula.

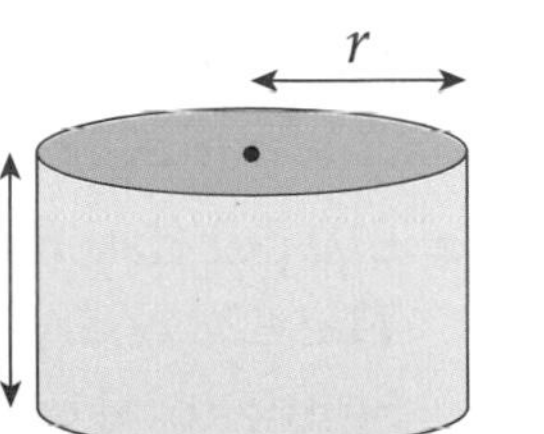

investigation

Isaac Newton, born in 1643 in Lincolnshire, is one of the most influential men in human history.
Use the internet to find out about his contributions to mathematics and science.
Can you find any formulae associated with Newton?

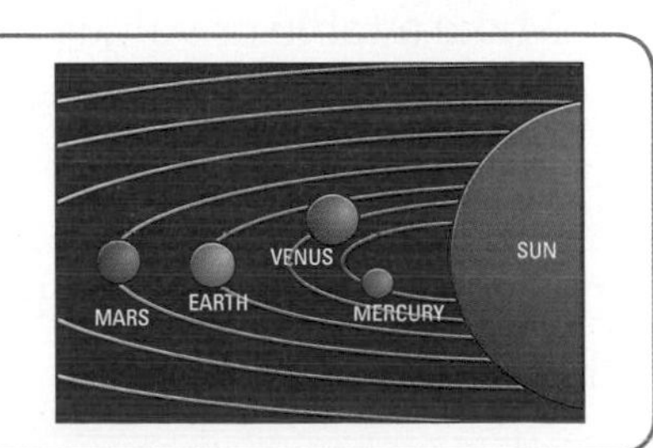

11h Deriving and graphing formulae

LEVEL 7

- Derive formulae in practical situations
- Draw graphs based on formulae

Keywords
Derive
Formula

- You can often write your own formula for a situation.

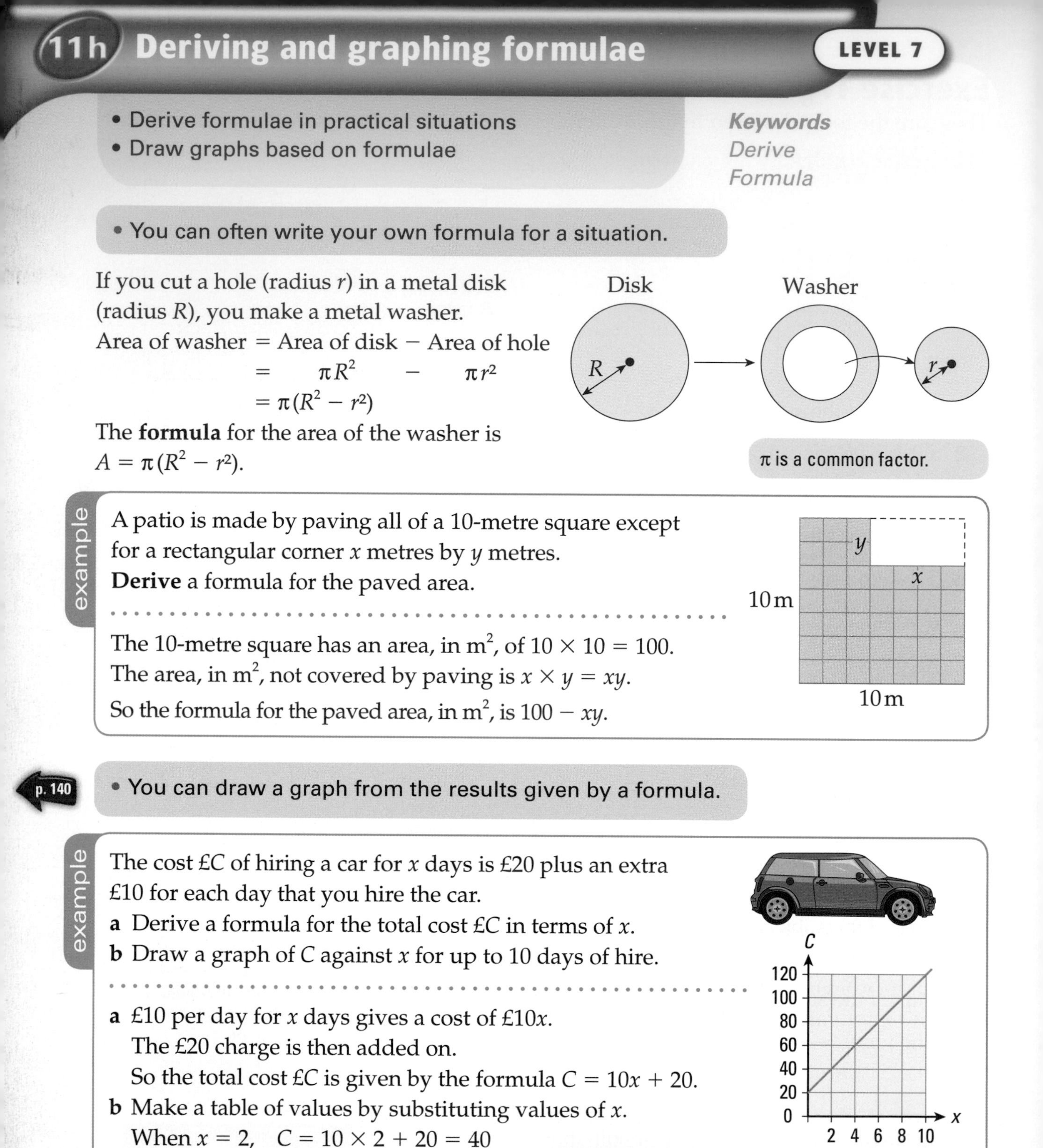

If you cut a hole (radius r) in a metal disk (radius R), you make a metal washer.

Area of washer = Area of disk − Area of hole

$= \pi R^2 - \pi r^2$

$= \pi(R^2 - r^2)$

The **formula** for the area of the washer is $A = \pi(R^2 - r^2)$.

π is a common factor.

example

A patio is made by paving all of a 10-metre square except for a rectangular corner x metres by y metres.
Derive a formula for the paved area.

The 10-metre square has an area, in m², of $10 \times 10 = 100$.
The area, in m², not covered by paving is $x \times y = xy$.
So the formula for the paved area, in m², is $100 - xy$.

p. 140

- You can draw a graph from the results given by a formula.

example

The cost £C of hiring a car for x days is £20 plus an extra £10 for each day that you hire the car.

a Derive a formula for the total cost £C in terms of x.
b Draw a graph of C against x for up to 10 days of hire.

a £10 per day for x days gives a cost of £$10x$.
The £20 charge is then added on.
So the total cost £C is given by the formula $C = 10x + 20$.

b Make a table of values by substituting values of x.
When $x = 2$, $C = 10 \times 2 + 20 = 40$
When $x = 4$, $C = 60$
When $x = 6$, $C = 80$ …

x (days)	2	4	6	8	10
C (£)	40	60	80	100	120

This table gives the coordinates of the points you plot to give the graph of C against x.

Exercise 11h

1 Derive formulae for the shaded area A in each of these diagrams.
All lengths are in centimetres.

a **d**

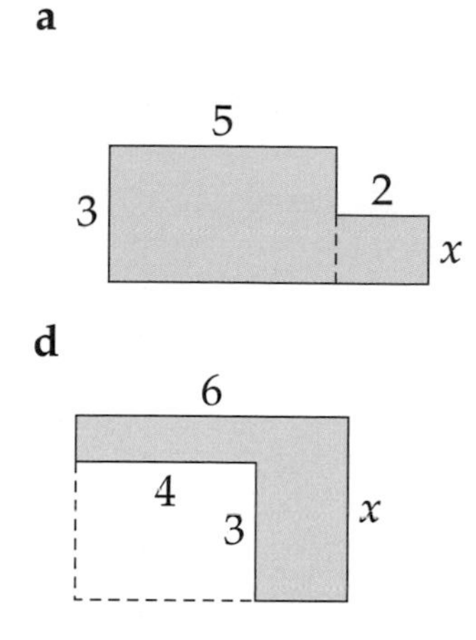

b **e**

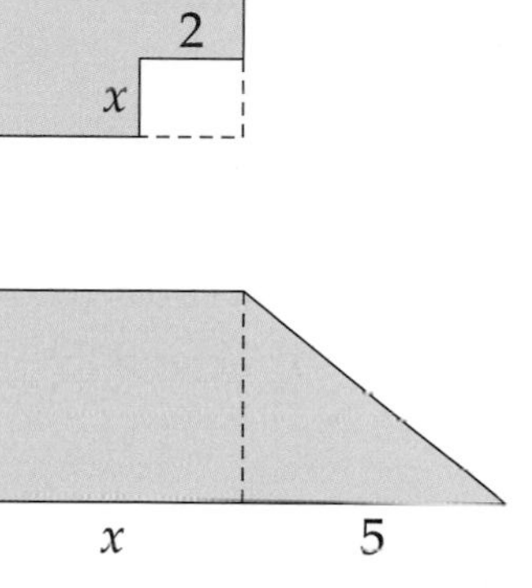

c **f**

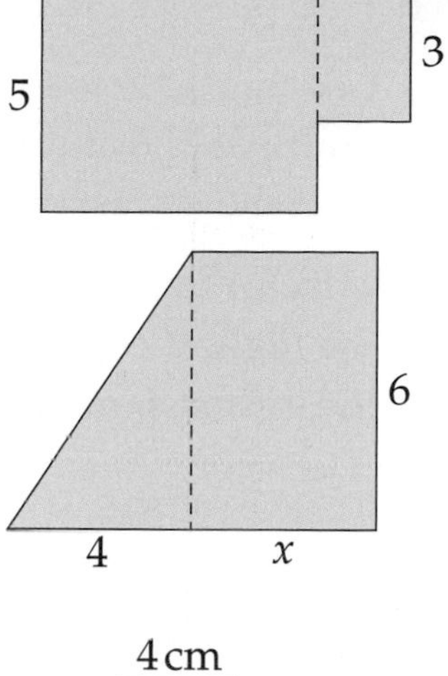

2 **a** Find a formula in terms of x for the area A of this shape.

b Copy and complete this table of values.

x (cm)	2	4	6	8	10
A (cm^2)					

c Draw a graph of A against x.

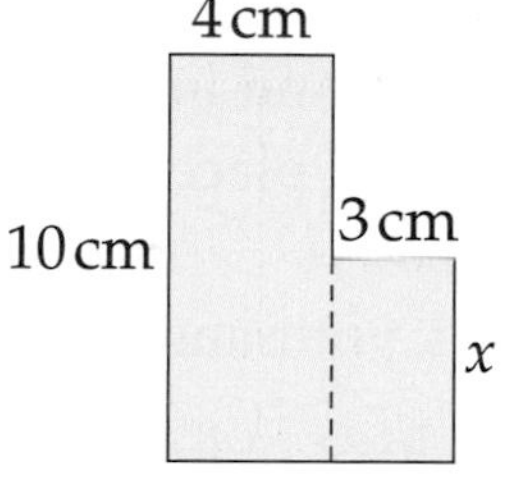

3 To cook a chicken, you allow 50 minutes per kilogram (kg) and then an extra 20 minutes.

a Write a formula for the number of minutes, n, to cook a chicken with a mass of x kg. This flow diagram might help you.

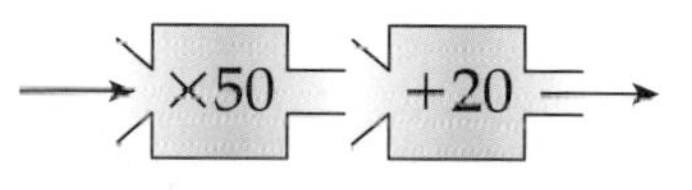

b Find the cooking time n for $x = 6, 8, 10, 12$.
Construct a table of values and draw a graph of n against x.

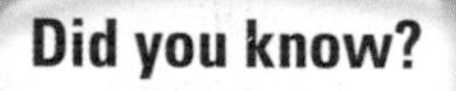

Did you know?

Life expectancies estimated in 2008 range from 84.33 years in Macau to 31.99 years in Swaziland.

4 **a** The average life expectancy in the UK is 80 years.
If a person is x years old now, write a formula for the number of years, n, they might still be expected to live.

b Find n for values of x from 10 to 70 and draw a graph of n against x.

challenge

The formula $F = \frac{9 \times C}{5} + 32$ changes temperatures in degrees Fahrenheit to temperatures in degrees Celsius.
Construct a table of values for F with $C = 60, 30, 0, -30$ and -60.
Draw a graph of your results.
How cold has it to be for the temperature to have the same value in degrees Fahrenheit and in degrees Celsius?

11 Consolidation

11a

1 a Use this table to find the highest common factor of 18 and 30.

b Find the highest common factor of 20 and 45.

Number	Its factors
18	
30	

2 a Use this table to find the lowest common multiple of 8 and 10.

b Find the lowest common multiple of 6 and 9.

Number	Its multiples
8	
10	

3 Use factor trees and prime factors to find

a the highest common factor of i 60 and 260 ii 210 and 270

b the lowest common multiple of i 12 and 20 ii 60 and 126

11b

4 Work out these square roots.

a $\sqrt{1600}$ b $\sqrt{4900}$ c $\sqrt{14400}$ d $\sqrt{\frac{81}{100}}$

5 Use trial and improvement to find these roots to 1 decimal place.

a $\sqrt{38}$ b $\sqrt{62}$ c $\sqrt[3]{38}$ d $\sqrt[3]{250}$

Check your answers by finding squares or cubes.

x	x^2	Comment

x	x^3	Comment

6 A circle of radius r has an area $A = \pi r^2$.
Find r to 1 decimal place when $A = 240\,\text{cm}^2$.

7 An ice cube has a volume of $10\,\text{cm}^3$.
Find the length x of its edges, to 1 decimal place.

11c

8 Simplify these expressions using indices in your answers.

a $y \times y \times y \times y \times y$ b $x \times x \times z \times z \times x$ c $n \times 4 \times n \times n \times 4$

9 Use the rules of indices to simplify these expressions.

a $x^6 \times x^7$ b $2x^6 \times 4x^7$ c $a^2 \times b^4 \times a^3 \times b^2$ d $s^3t^2 \times s^4t$

e $\frac{x^8}{x^2}$ f $\frac{x^8y^5}{x^2y^3}$ g $(x^4)^2$ h $(2y^5)^3$

11d

10 Factorise these expressions.

a $4x - 20$ b $5y + 15$ c $4 - 6z$ d $8p - 6$ e $x^2 + 6x$ f $3y + y^2$

11 Factorise these expressions. Look for two common factors.

a $3xy + 6xz$ b $9pq + 3pr$ c $6x^2 - 4x$ d $8y^2 + 2yz$ e $6ab - 3a^2$ f $5xy + x^2y$

11e

12 Find equivalent fractions by cancelling.

a $\frac{3x}{6}$ b $\frac{2y}{8}$ c $\frac{6z}{10}$ d $\frac{mn}{3n}$ e $\frac{3xy}{6y}$ f $\frac{2yz}{8z}$

g $\frac{4a^2}{8a}$ h $\frac{4b^3}{6b}$ i $\frac{s^2t^3}{s^3t}$ j $\frac{x^3y}{x^2y}$ k $\frac{9ab^2}{6b}$ l $\frac{3y^2z}{6y^2z^2}$

13 Add or subtract these fractions.

a $\frac{x}{5}+\frac{2x}{5}$ b $\frac{2y}{7}+\frac{3y}{7}$ c $\frac{2x}{3}+\frac{y}{3}$ d $\frac{7v}{9}-\frac{5v}{9}$ e $\frac{z}{2}+\frac{z}{4}$ f $\frac{3a}{8}+\frac{a}{4}$

g $\frac{5c}{9}-\frac{c}{3}$ h $\frac{9x}{10}-\frac{3x}{5}$ i $\frac{z}{2}+\frac{z}{3}$ j $\frac{2a}{3}+\frac{a}{5}$ k $\frac{4x}{5}-\frac{3x}{4}$

11f

14 I cycle for x hours and walk for y hours. The total distance travelled, D miles, is given by the formula $D = 12x + 2y$.

a Find D when $x = 4$ and $y = 3$.

b Find x when $D = 46$ and $y = 2$.

15 The speed, S, of water pouring from a tank is given by $S = \frac{rt}{2h}$.

a Find S when $r = 10$, $t = 6$ and $h = 15$.

b Find t when $S = 24$, $r = 36$ and $h = 3$.

11g

16 a Make t the subject of the formula $v = u + at$.

b Find t when $v = 30$, $u = 18$ and $a = 2$.

17 a Make w the subject of the formula $P = 2l + 2w$.

b Find w when $P = 50$ and $l = 6$.

18 a Make n the subject of the formula $C = \frac{2n}{3}$.

b Find n when $C = 30$.

11h

19 I buy one packet of nails for 30 pence and x boxes of screws at 50 pence per box.

a Write a formula for the total cost, C, of the nails and screws.

b Find the value of C when $x = 2, 4, 6, 8$ and 10 and draw a graph of C against x.

c Find the value of x when $C = 680$.

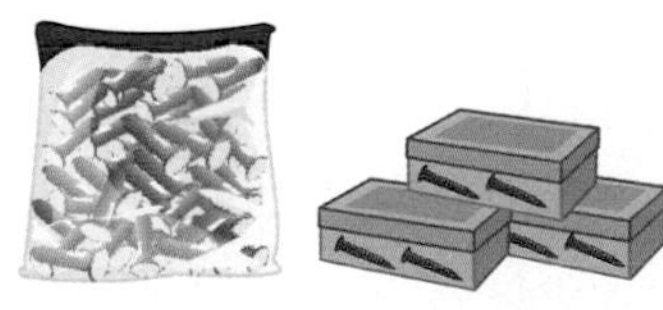
1 Packet x Boxes

Maths life

Why do bikes have gears?

Bikes are ingeniously simple structures which are very efficient at getting us around quickly and cheaply. This case study shows how bikes have developed over the years into the sophisticated machines they are today.

The pedals of a penny-farthing bicycle were fixed directly to the front wheel so the wheel turned once for every turn of the pedals. The larger the wheel, the further the bike travelled for each turn of the pedals.

The largest wheel in common use on a penny-farthing had a diameter of about 1.5 m

- How far would it travel for one turn of the pedals?

  THAT WOULD BE THE SAME DISTANCE AS THE CIRCUMFERENCE OF THE WHEEL $c = \pi d$
- how many turns of the pedals would be needed to travel 1km?

If you remember riding a tricycle like this, you will know that you had to pedal quite quickly even at low speeds!

With a 30 cm diameter front wheel, how many turns of the pedals would be needed to travel 500 m?

Why does a child have to pedal quickly on this type of tricycle?

As bikes developed, their wheels became smaller and a crank and chain drive was used. The larger front sprocket means that the wheel turns several times for each turn of the pedals.

- *How far would a bike with a 60 cm diameter wheel travel for each turn of the wheel?*
- *For one turn of the pedals on the bike to match the distance travelled by one turn of the pedals on the penny-farthing, how many times would the rear wheel have to turn for each turn of the pedals?*
- *If the rear sprocket has 18 teeth, how many teeth will the front sprocket have?*

If the cyclist turns the pedals once a second, how fast in kph will this bike be travelling?

t just 280g, they're across, yet they still me abuse.
: pedal designs – the in and Mag Lite.
veigh in at 385g and lue, red, black, gold, . They contain two gs and a bush, and o service with a 5m ket.
e similar but with a and bolts that are of the pedal instead from the front. RRP n gunmetal, gold or
the Mag Lites are eeping the weight hey have a slightly other two models black.
le for bringing the Even without this the lightest flat s. We've got a pair how how they fare.

75

Complete this table to compare the gears of a typical 7 speed touring bike, giving the values to 2 decimal places:

Wheel diameter: 700 mm

Distance travelled for each turn of the wheel: ______ metres

number of teeth front sprocket	number of teeth rear sprocket	number of turns of the wheel per turn of the pedals	distance travelled per turn of the pedals (m)
48	12	4	
48	14		
48	16		6.60
48	18		
48	20		
48	24		
48	28		

Which gear would you use to cycle up a sleep hill?

What is the fewest number of turns of the pedal that would be needed to travel 1 km?

When riding comfortably, a cyclist makes between 40 and 90 turns of the pedals per minute.
What range of speeds will they travel at in each gear?

- Draw a graph showing the speed ranges for each gear.
- How much overlap is there between the gears?

- What would the speed ranges be in miles per hour? 1 km ≈ ⅝ mile
- What would the speed ranges be if they were using their 52 teeth front sprocket?

If you have a bike, find out how quickly you turn the pedals and work out the speed ranges for your gears.

11 Summary

Assessment criteria

- Use index notation for integer powers **Level 6**
- Use formulae from mathematics and other subjects **Level 7**
- Substitute numbers into expressions and formulae **Level 7**

Level 6

1 Find the values of a and b.

$10^6 \times 10^2 = 10^a$ $\qquad \dfrac{10^6}{10^2} = 10^b$

Alistair's answer ✔

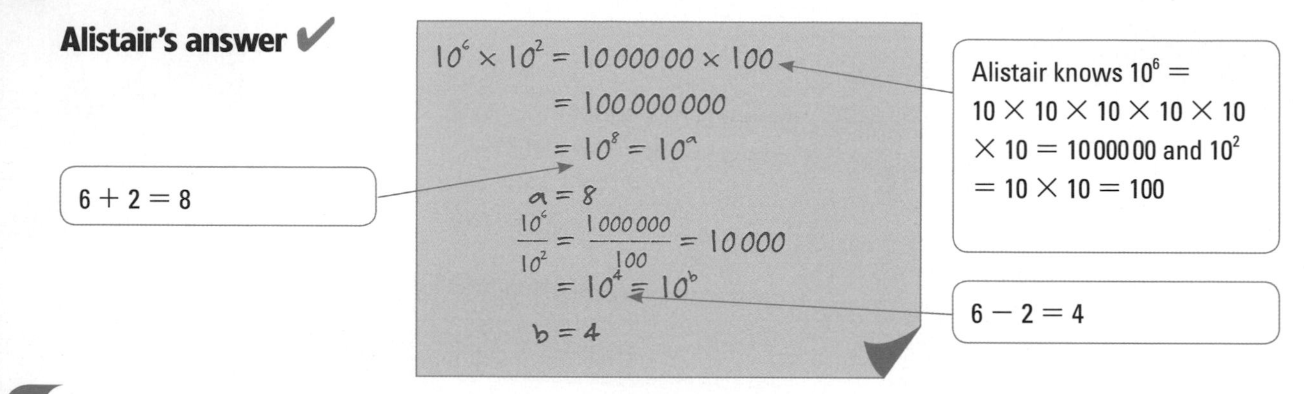

Level 7

2 I am going to use a wooden beam to support a load.
The cross-section of the beam is a rectangle.

Cross-section

The formula below gives the greatest load, M kg, that a beam of this length can support.

$M = 5d^2w$ where d is the depth of the beam in cm, w is the width of the beam in cm.

I can place the cross-section of the beam in two different ways.

1st way: $d = 11$, $w = 8$

2nd way: $d = 8$, $w = 11$

In which way will the beam be able to support the greater load?
Calculate the difference.

Key Stage 3 2007 5–7 Paper 2

12 Statistics

Interpreting statistics

We usually don't go out without a hat on a cold winter day. This thinking comes from a US military study where volunteers were put in very cold conditions wearing Arctic survival suits. The researchers found that the volunteers lost most heat from their heads.

What's the point? Although the volunteers in the study wore survival suits, none of them wore hats. So they lost most heat from their head as this was the only bit left uncovered! We are faced with many facts and statistics every day so it is important to be able to judge which are helpful and which are misinterpreted or misleading.

Check in

Level 5

1 Find the mean of each of these sets of data.

a 5, 8, 4, 9, 9

b 16, 13, 24, 24

c 3.9, 7.2, 4.5, 6.8, 7.2, 5.3

86

2 Here are the test scores of 10 students.
Draw a stem-and-leaf diagram to show the data.
58 54 78 93 42 75 70 69 63 72

Level 4

3 A researcher asked 10 shoppers at two different supermarkets how much they had spent (to the nearest pound) on their weekly shopping.

Weekly shopping bills (£)

Supermarket A	74, 108, 36, 54, 98, 67, 102, 77, 111, 83
Supermarket B	45, 103, 62, 42, 65, 85, 92, 66, 71, 49

Use the mean and range to compare these two distributions.

12a Interpreting graphs

LEVEL 6

- Interpret graphs and charts
- Use information from statistical diagrams to answer statistical questions

Keywords
Data
Interpret
Scale

- Statistical diagrams can help you **interpret data** and answer statistical questions.

example

The Arscott family are going on holiday. They look at this chart that summarises the climate where they are going.
What mistakes have they made in reading this chart?

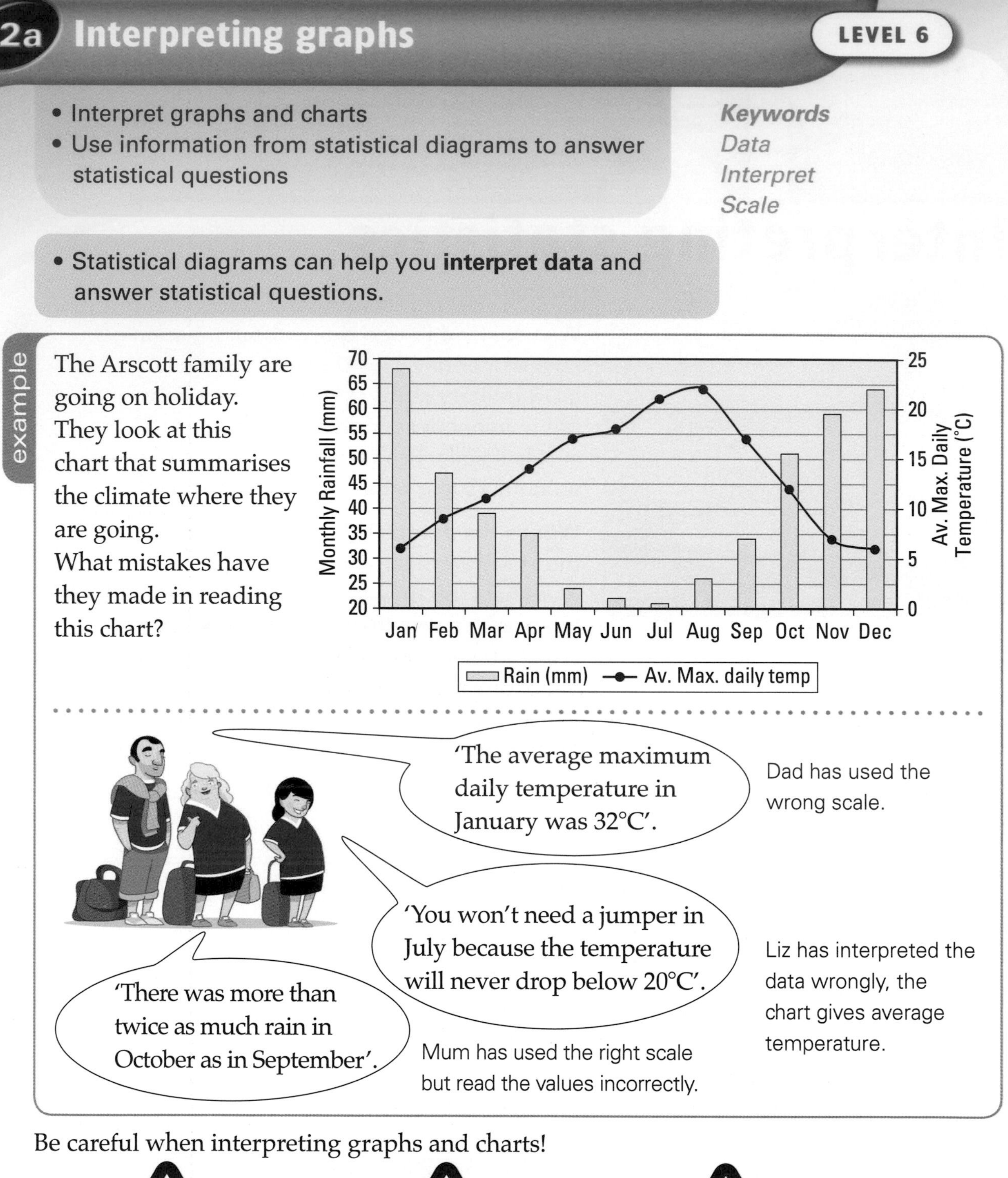

Dad has used the wrong scale.

Liz has interpreted the data wrongly, the chart gives average temperature.

Mum has used the right scale but read the values incorrectly.

Be careful when interpreting graphs and charts!

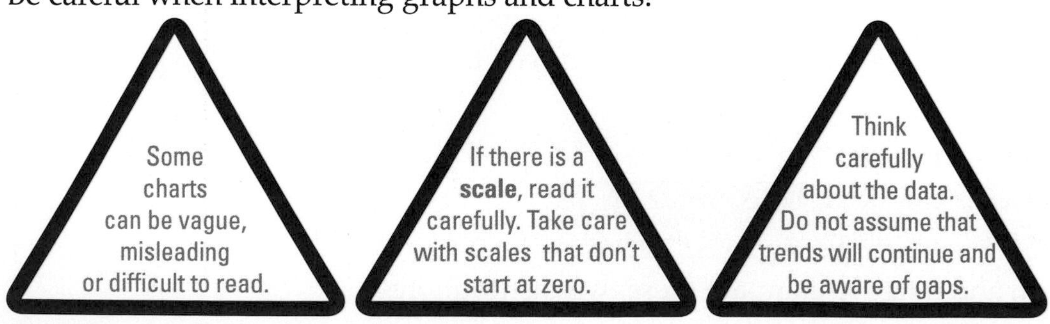

Exercise 12a

1 This chart and table of data shows the telephone votes for four finalists A, B, C and D in a TV talent competition by country.

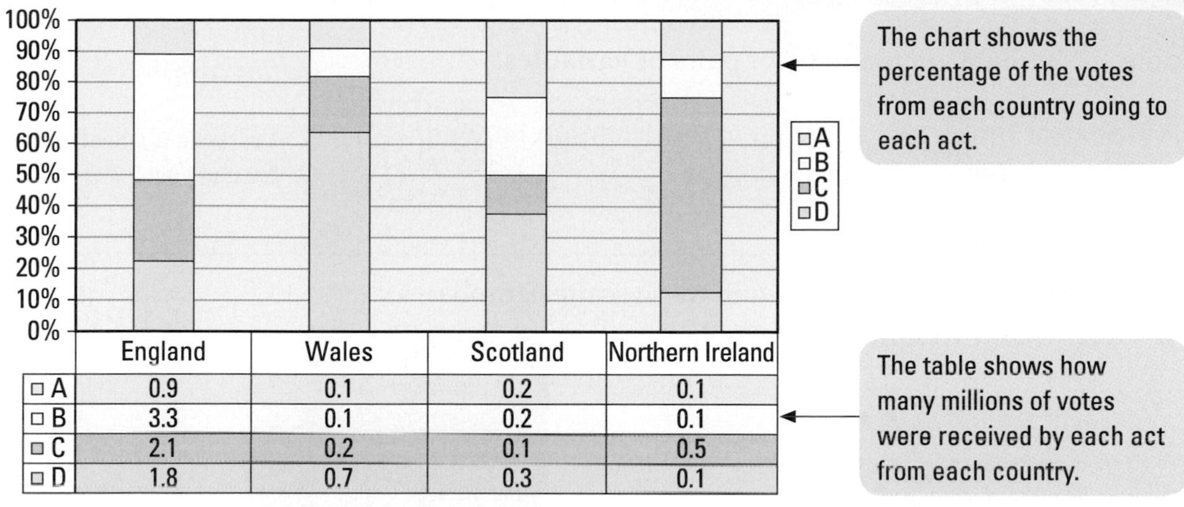

	England	Wales	Scotland	Northern Ireland
A	0.9	0.1	0.2	0.1
B	3.3	0.1	0.2	0.1
C	2.1	0.2	0.1	0.5
D	1.8	0.7	0.3	0.1

The chart shows the percentage of the votes from each country going to each act.

The table shows how many millions of votes were received by each act from each country.

a Which act (A, B, C or D) won the competition?

b Can you suggest which countries some of the acts came from?

Can you be sure?

c Re-draw the chart as a series of stacked bars showing the **actual** numbers of votes received (rather than the percentages).

d Draw a pie chart for each act to show the total number of votes cast for them by each country.

e Which of the three charts gives the fairest impression of the votes cast? Explain your answer.

2 The table shows the speed of a river, measured every hour.

T	1	2	3	4	5	6	7	8	9
v	5.9	1.6	4.8	0.8	3.2	0.4	2.6	0.3	1.5

T = Time (hours), v = speed (metres per second)

84, 144

a Plot a time-series graph for this set of data.

b 'When $T = 12$ hours, the graph shows that the speed will be about 6 metres per second.'

i Explain how somebody could make this prediction.

ii Do you think this is a sensible prediction? Can you make another suggestion? Explain your answer.

Draw lines on your graph to illustrate your answer

challenge

The table shows the average number of copies sold for two daily newspapers.

Daily News	Gazette
485 000	446 000

Produce a bar chart for the Daily News that makes it look as if they sold twice as many copies as the Gazette.

12b Correlation

LEVEL 6

- Draw and interpret scatter graphs
- Understand correlation

Keywords
Correlation *Positive*
Data *Variable*
Negative
Scatter graph

Some sets of **data** are made up of pairs of **variables**.

- A **scatter graph** will show up any **correlation** between the variables.

A variable is something you can count or measure.

example

Describe the correlation shown in these scatter graphs.

a Heights and weights of 20 people

p. 84

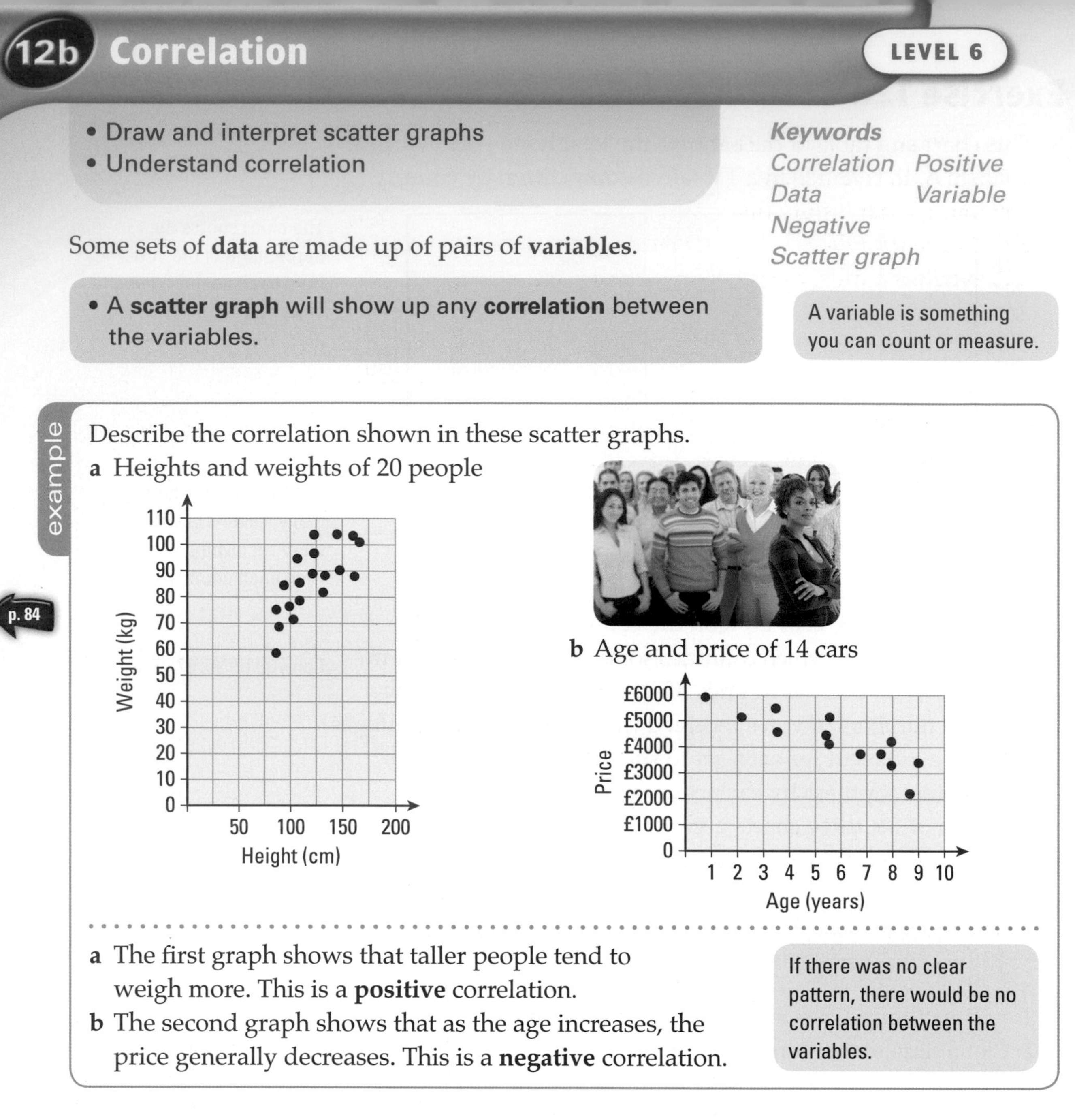

b Age and price of 14 cars

a The first graph shows that taller people tend to weigh more. This is a **positive** correlation.

b The second graph shows that as the age increases, the price generally decreases. This is a **negative** correlation.

If there was no clear pattern, there would be no correlation between the variables.

Correlation describes the connection between two variables.

Positive correlation

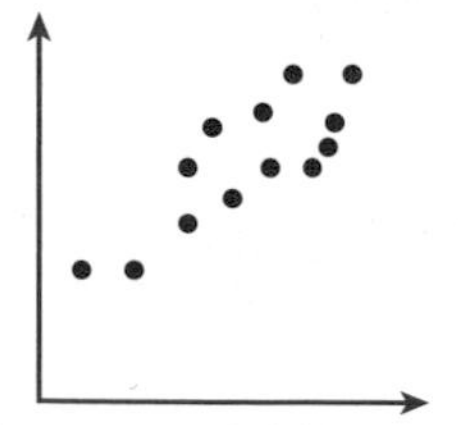

As one variable increases so does the other.

Negative correlation

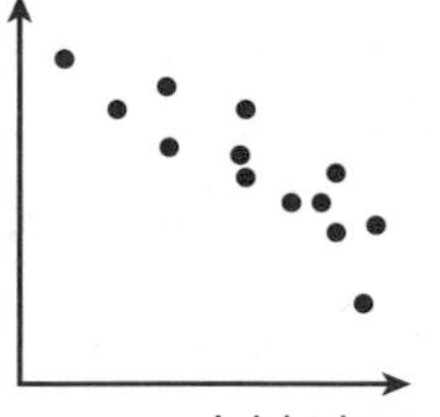

As one variable increases, the other decreases.

Zero correlation

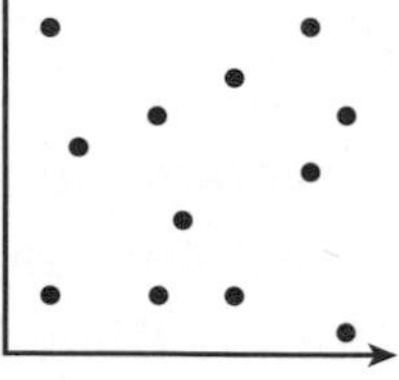

No clear connection between the variables.

Exercise 12b

1 Choose the correlation for each situation.

a There is no connection between height and eye colour of year 9 students.

b Children get taller as they get older.

c As you eat a cake, there are fewer slices left.

Positive
Negative
Zero

2 a Use the data in the table to plot a scatter graph.

b Describe the correlation shown in the graph.

Region	Number of burglaries per 10 000 households	Number of car thefts per 10 000 people
North East	99	28
North West	137	34
Yorks & Humber	167	38
East Midlands	135	30
West Midlands	129	32
East of England	95	26
London	193	45
South East	89	24
South West	87	23

Source: British Crime Survey 2007–2008

3 a This table shows the GDP and the average fertility rate (number of children born per woman) for selected countries. Plot a scatter graph for this set of data.

b Describe the correlation between the variables.

Country	Fertility rate	GDP US$ per head
Italy	1.26	26 700
Hong Kong	1.32	28 800
Switzerland	1.48	32 700
Cuba	1.61	2900
Finland	1.70	27 400
Croatia	1.93	10 600
Indonesia	2.50	3200
Malaysia	3.13	9000
Turkmenistan	3.50	5800
Zimbabwe	3.66	1900
Gabon	4.83	5500
Laos	4.94	1700
Nigeria	5.40	900
Somalia	6.98	500

investigation

GDP (Gross domestic product – a measure of a country's income per head) is a useful measure of how wealthy the inhabitants of a country are.
What would you expect the relationship between GDP and life expectancy to be? Investigate the GDP and life expectancy for various countries.

You can find useful information at https://www.cia.gov/library/publications/the-world-factbook/

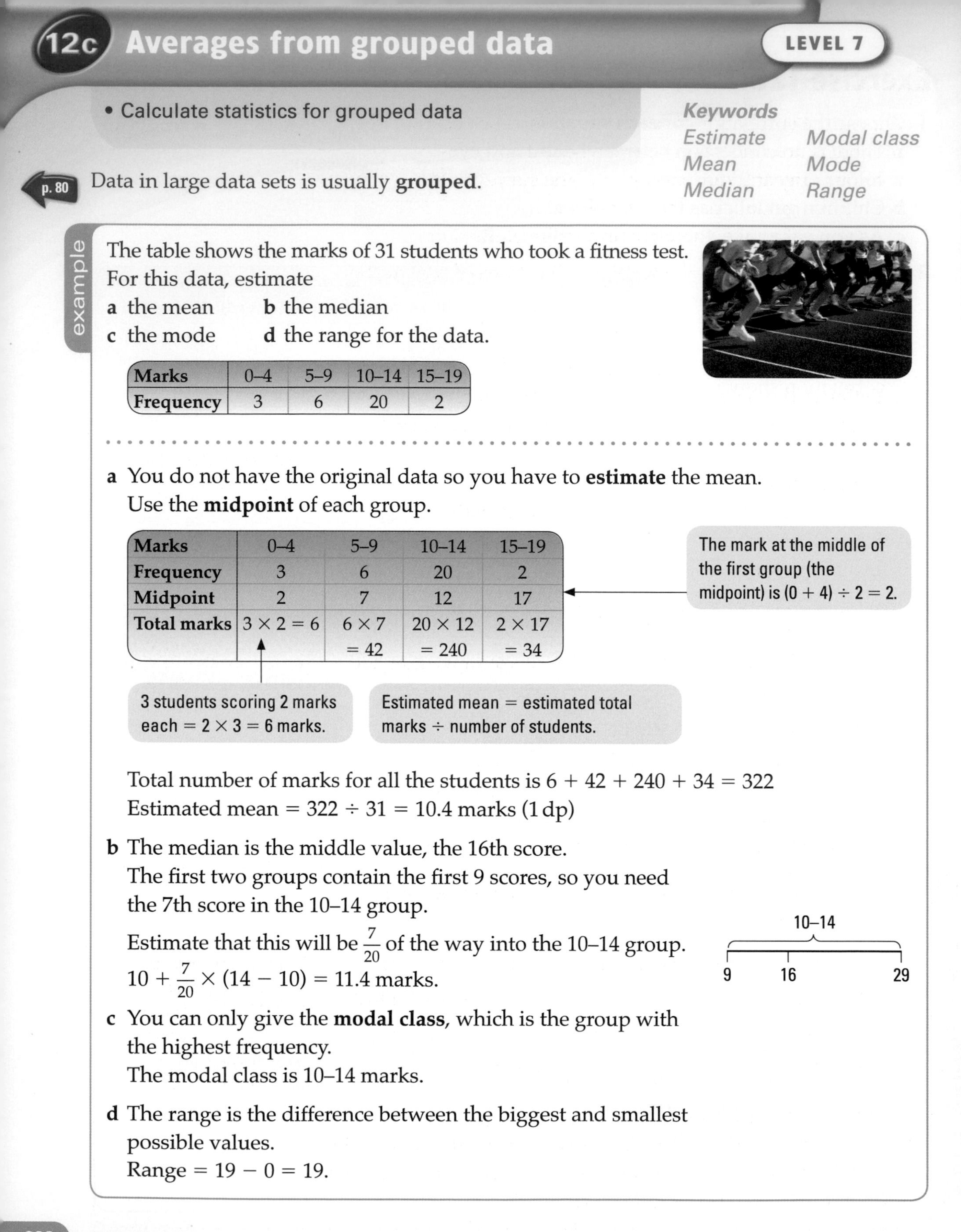

12c Averages from grouped data

LEVEL 7

- Calculate statistics for grouped data

Keywords
Estimate, Mean, Median, Modal class, Mode, Range

p. 80

Data in large data sets is usually **grouped**.

example

The table shows the marks of 31 students who took a fitness test.
For this data, estimate

a the mean **b** the median
c the mode **d** the range for the data.

Marks	0–4	5–9	10–14	15–19
Frequency	3	6	20	2

a You do not have the original data so you have to **estimate** the mean.
Use the **midpoint** of each group.

Marks	0–4	5–9	10–14	15–19
Frequency	3	6	20	2
Midpoint	2	7	12	17
Total marks	$3 \times 2 = 6$	$6 \times 7 = 42$	$20 \times 12 = 240$	$2 \times 17 = 34$

The mark at the middle of the first group (the midpoint) is $(0 + 4) \div 2 = 2$.

3 students scoring 2 marks each $= 2 \times 3 = 6$ marks.

Estimated mean = estimated total marks ÷ number of students.

Total number of marks for all the students is $6 + 42 + 240 + 34 = 322$
Estimated mean $= 322 \div 31 = 10.4$ marks (1 dp)

b The median is the middle value, the 16th score.
The first two groups contain the first 9 scores, so you need the 7th score in the 10–14 group.
Estimate that this will be $\frac{7}{20}$ of the way into the 10–14 group.
$10 + \frac{7}{20} \times (14 - 10) = 11.4$ marks.

c You can only give the **modal class**, which is the group with the highest frequency.
The modal class is 10–14 marks.

d The range is the difference between the biggest and smallest possible values.
Range $= 19 - 0 = 19$.

Exercise 12c

1 A group of students took part in a survey and recorded the number of text messages they sent one day.

Messages sent	0–4	5–9	10–14
Frequency	6	5	4

a How many students took part in the survey?
b Find the modal class for this set of data.
c Estimate the mean, median and range of the data.

2 20 teenagers recorded the number of portions of fruit and vegetables they ate in a week.

Portions	0–9	10–19	20–29	30–39	40–49	50–59
Frequency	2	4	6	4	3	1

a Estimate the range of the number of portions.
b Explain why the range is an estimate and not an exact answer.
c Find the modal class of the data.
d Explain why the modal class is not an estimate.
e Estimate the mean of the data.
f Estimate the median of the data.

Hint: The midpoint of the first group is 4.5.

Hint: The median is the 10.5th value.

3 In a science experiment, Gemma planted batches of 100 seeds into trays.
After a week, she counted the number of seedlings that had germinated in each tray.

Number of Seedlings	0–24	25–49	50–74	75–99
Frequency	7	9	14	3

a How many trays of seeds were there altogether?
b What was the modal class for these results?
c Estimate the median, mean and range of the data.

challenge

A researcher measured the lengths, in centimetres, of a sample of fish.

119.9	137.1	129.8	116.9	104.3	136.0	126.7	112.7
110.6	108.2	125.3	128.4	119.7	117.3	137.6	120.8
112.8	114.2	130.4	138.4	127.6	115.4	105.0	130.5
123.5	118.9	118.0	128.8	124.5	129.3	123.7	

This is **continuous** data. You can use groups like 100–109, 110–119 and so on, but make sure you know where 109.4 or 109.6 would go.

a Use a tally chart to organise the data into groups.
b Use the grouped data to estimate the mean and median length.
c Use the original data to calculate the exact mean and median.
d Compare the estimated and exact results.

12d Comparing distributions 1

- Compare two or more distributions using appropriate statistics and make comments

Keywords
Average *Mode*
Mean *Range*
Median *Spread*
Modal class

- To compare **distributions** you can use
  – an **average** (**mean, median, mode** or **modal class**) to compare typical values
  – the **range** to show how widely spread the values are.

example

Jez says, *'United had the best season by far'*.
Pete says, *'Rovers had some fantastic matches – they did much better.'*
The table shows the mean and the range of the numbers of goals scored.
Compare the performance of the two teams.
Can you say which team had the better season?

Team	Mean	Range
Rovers	2.8	7
United	1.6	4

Mean: on average, Rovers scored more goals per match than United.
Range: Rovers had more variation in the number of goals scored.
Rovers could have scored seven goals in one (or more) matches and no goals in some of their matches.
There is not enough information to say which team won most games. You also know nothing about the number of goals scored **against** each team.

You can sometimes make comments from statistics but sometimes you need to explain why you cannot.

- Think about both an average and the spread of values because consistency and reliability can be important.

The captain of a hockey team has to choose one forward player from two players. The table shows their goals so far this season. What does this tell the captain?

	Anne	Cara
Mean	0.9	2.3
Range	1	5

Cara's high mean score may make her the obvious choice but the large range shows that her performance is inconsistent – the high mean may be just one or two high scores.
Anne is much more consistent. She scores a goal (but no more!) in most games.

LEVEL 7

Grade D-C

Exercise 12d

1 A group of students did two tests on the same day.
Both tests were marked out of 100.
Which test was easiest? Explain your answer.

	Median	Range
Test 1	34	65
Test 2	27	47

2 Two groups of students took a French test marked out of 100.
The table shows their marks.

Group	Marks
A	45 50 41 60 56 90 68 63 82 74 83 47 66 52
	35 73 81 71 52 75 46 63 74 84 42 62 60 90
	58 82 50 87 94 47 92 66 60 58 54 68 64 74
B	36 31 29 52 58 54 13 62 19 41 14 45 56 61
	59 43 36 15 25 22 16 15 15 53 46 28 13 50
	17 13 24 51 34 54 14 32 33 33 20 13 36 15

a Draw a back-to-back stem-and-leaf diagram for this data.

b Find the median and the range of each set of data.

c Use the statistics you calculated to compare the performance of the two groups.

d The teacher said 'The students in Group A did more preparation for the test than those in Group B'.
Do you agree? Explain your answer.

3 This frequency table shows the number of people living in the houses in two streets.

Number of people	1	2	3	4	5	6
Frequency (King Street)	8	14	16	5	2	0
Frequency (Queen Street)	0	0	5	14	13	4

a Calculate the mean, median, mode and range of the number of people living in the houses in each street.

b Using suitable statistics, compare the two distributions.

c What sort of houses would you expect to find on each street? Justify your answer.

challenge

The table shows some results from a homework survey in Year 9.

Time spent on homework (minutes)		
Class	Mean	Range
9X	48.6	98
9Y	57.9	28

a Which class spent longer on their homework, on average?

b Class 9Y's teacher looked at the table and said, 'Nobody in my class spent less than 20 minutes on their homework'.
Explain how she knew this.

c Jodie spent 90 minutes on her homework.
Which class is she in? Explain your answer.

d 'Students in 9Y spend longer on homework than those in 9X.'
Is this statement justified? Explain your answer.

12e Comparing distributions 2

LEVEL 7

- Draw frequency polygons for sets of data
- Compare the distribution of sets of data using statistical diagrams

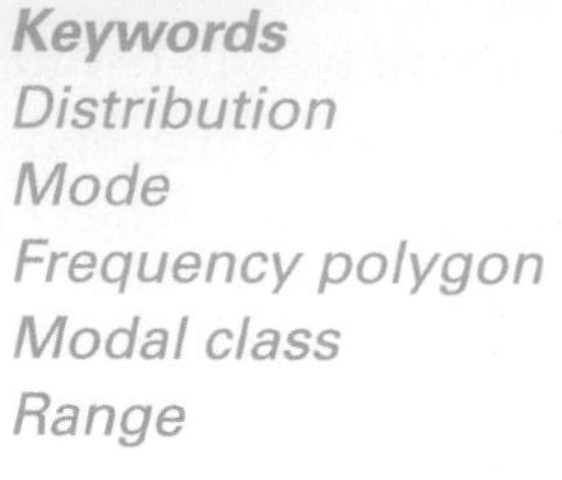

Keywords
Distribution
Mode
Frequency polygon
Modal class
Range

- You can compare the **distributions** of two sets of data using statistical diagrams such as **frequency polygons**.

p. 82

You can draw a frequency polygon instead of bars on a bar chart.

example

A scientist placed 20 insect traps at location A and the same at location B.
She left the traps overnight and in the morning counted the number of insects in each trap.

Number of insects	3	4	5	6	7
Frequency at location A	2	5	6	4	3
Frequency at location B	8	4	4	3	1

Use a pair of frequency polygons to compare these sets of data.

The frequency polygons show that there were more traps containing three insects at B than at A. However, there were more traps containing higher numbers of insects at A than at B. Overall, there were more insects trapped at A than at B.

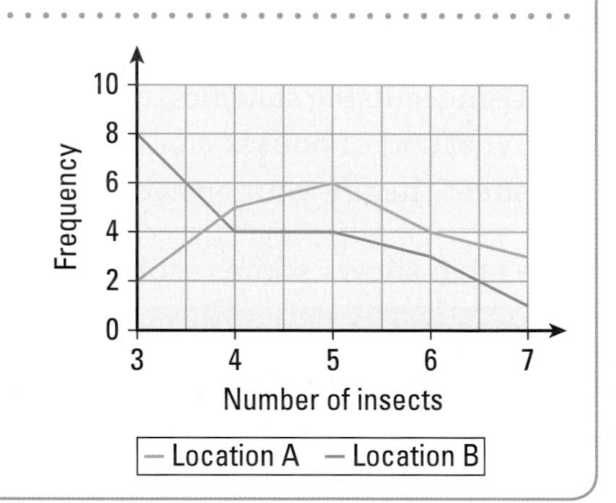

The modal number of insects per trap was five at location A and three at location B.
The range of both distributions was the same.

A frequency polygon allows you to see both data sets on the same diagram.
You can also draw frequency polygons for continuous data. Join the midpoints of the tops of the bars of the frequency diagram.

- Frequency polygons make it particularly easy to compare the **modes** (or **modal classes**) and **ranges** of two sets of data.

Grade D-C

Exercise 12e

1 This comparative bar chart shows the numbers of people in the cars using a road between 9 a.m. and 10 a.m. on two days.

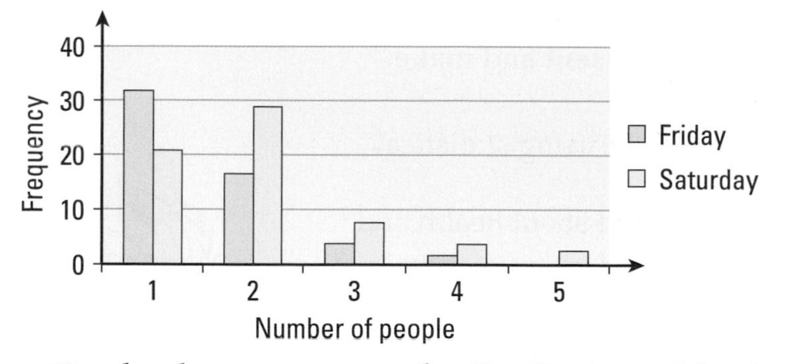

Ask questions like: On which day was there more traffic? What is the modal number of people in the cars each day? What is the range of each set of data?

a Use the chart to compare the distributions of the data sets.
b Re-draw the chart as a pair of frequency polygons.

2 The table shows the grades awarded to students in two classes who took part in a recycling project.

This is categorical data. A is the best possible grade and D is the lowest.

	A	B	C	D
9A	18	5	4	3
9B	10	16	4	0

p. 82

a Draw a pair of pie charts to represent this data.
b Now draw a diagram showing the data as a pair of frequency diagrams.
c Use the diagrams to describe the differences between the distributions of grades for the two classes.
d Explain which diagram makes it easier to compare the distributions and why.

Do you know how to produce both sorts of diagrams by hand and using a spreadsheet?

challenge

For a science project, Carla and Dan measured the height, in centimetres, of dandelions in two portions of a field. Compare the two distributions.

Carla's data				
20.7	19.0	20.3	20.1	23.0
24.4	15.4	17.6	21.6	17.1
18.8	21.2	19.8	18.7	18.4
19.2	18.8	16.2	18.8	28.8
20.4	18.9	14.9	16.3	25.2
19.7	20.5	25.4	20.7	16.1

Dan's data				
22.5	19.7	19.6	23.4	21.8
19.4	18.5	20.7	21.6	22.0
16.9	19.3	21.4	21.3	21.8
17.1	18.4	22.1	20.0	20.5
23.7	21.8	20.0	23.3	18.6
19.6	18.9	21.0	17.1	21.0

This is continuous data and you will need to organise it into suitable groups.

12f Communicating the results of an enquiry

LEVEL 6

- Communicate the interpretations and results of a statistical enquiry using selected tables, graphs and diagrams

Keywords
Conclusions
Present

The final stage of a statistical enquiry is to **present** and make sense of your findings.
Answer your initial questions where possible, using statistical

Jenny did some research for a geography project about health and poverty. She made comparisons between the G8 group of industrialised countries, South American countries (SAM) and countries in sub-Saharan Africa (SSM). She collected this data from the World Heath Organization.

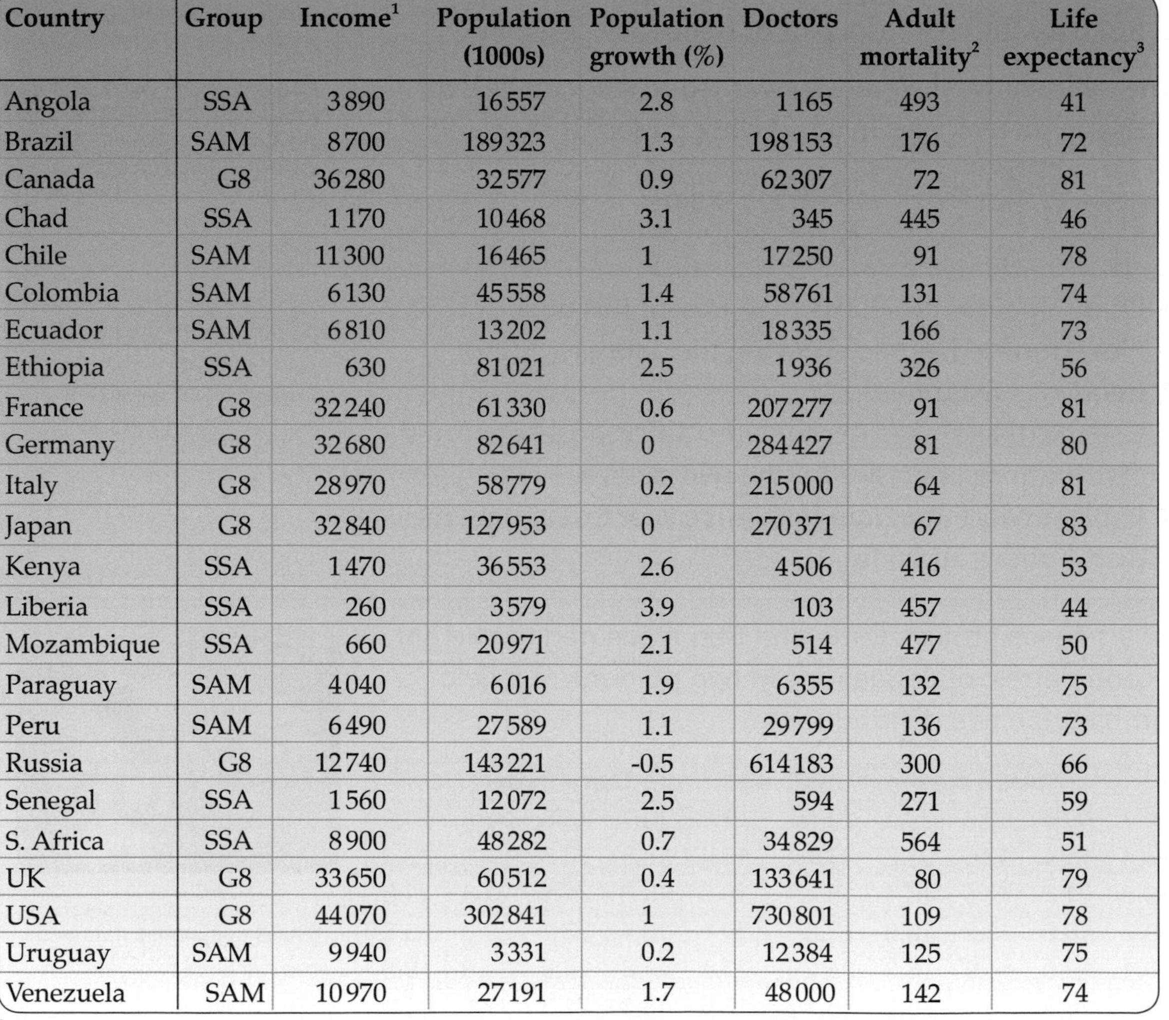

Country	Group	Income[1]	Population (1000s)	Population growth (%)	Doctors	Adult mortality[2]	Life expectancy[3]
Angola	SSA	3890	16557	2.8	1165	493	41
Brazil	SAM	8700	189323	1.3	198153	176	72
Canada	G8	36280	32577	0.9	62307	72	81
Chad	SSA	1170	10468	3.1	345	445	46
Chile	SAM	11300	16465	1	17250	91	78
Colombia	SAM	6130	45558	1.4	58761	131	74
Ecuador	SAM	6810	13202	1.1	18335	166	73
Ethiopia	SSA	630	81021	2.5	1936	326	56
France	G8	32240	61330	0.6	207277	91	81
Germany	G8	32680	82641	0	284427	81	80
Italy	G8	28970	58779	0.2	215000	64	81
Japan	G8	32840	127953	0	270371	67	83
Kenya	SSA	1470	36553	2.6	4506	416	53
Liberia	SSA	260	3579	3.9	103	457	44
Mozambique	SSA	660	20971	2.1	514	477	50
Paraguay	SAM	4040	6016	1.9	6355	132	75
Peru	SAM	6490	27589	1.1	29799	136	73
Russia	G8	12740	143221	-0.5	614183	300	66
Senegal	SSA	1560	12072	2.5	594	271	59
S. Africa	SSA	8900	48282	0.7	34829	564	51
UK	G8	33650	60512	0.4	133641	80	79
USA	G8	44070	302841	1	730801	109	78
Uruguay	SAM	9940	3331	0.2	12384	125	75
Venezuela	SAM	10970	27191	1.7	48000	142	74

[1]Mean income per person, US Dollars

http://www.who.int/whosis/en/

[2]Mean number of deaths per 1000 population, between ages of 15 and 60

[3]Life expectancy at birth, years

Exercise 12f

Jenny could use her data to answer many questions.
Here are some questions that you could answer and some techniques that you could use to produce statistics and diagrams to support your conclusions.
There could be different interpretations for some of the data so you should explain your evidence and reasoning carefully!

1 How do the average incomes of people in the three groups of countries (G8, SAM and SSA) compare?
Find the median of the incomes for each group of countries.
Write a short conclusion and present the statistics you calculated in a table.

The median is a more meaningful average than the mean here. Why?

2 How many doctors are there per 1000 people in each group of countries?
For each country, divide the 'Doctors' figure by the population size.
Find the median of the calculated values for each group of countries.

You can use different symbols for the countries in each group to provide additional information to readers.

3 What connection is there between average income and life expectancy?
Draw a scatter diagram using income and life expectancy as your variables.
Explain any patterns in the data.

4 You might expect the last two variables in the table (adult mortality and life expectancy) to be related.
What sort of correlation would you expect for these variables?
Draw a scatter diagram to check your suggestion.

5 How do the annual population growth rates for each group of countries compare?
Is there any connection between population growth rates and average incomes?

6 What are the overall conclusions that Jenny could reach about the connections between health and poverty in different countries of the world?

Did you know?

The WHO is part of the United Nations system. It provides leadership, research and support for health issues around the world.

research

Devise some other questions about health, international development and poverty. (Alternatively, you may prefer to investigate the questions raised here in more depth, for example, by looking at data for more countries.)

Visit the WHO website www.who.int/en/ to find any information you need to answer your questions. Present statistical evidence to support the conclusions that you reach.

12 Consolidation

12a

1 This chart shows the number of sofas sold one weekend in three different branches of a furniture store.

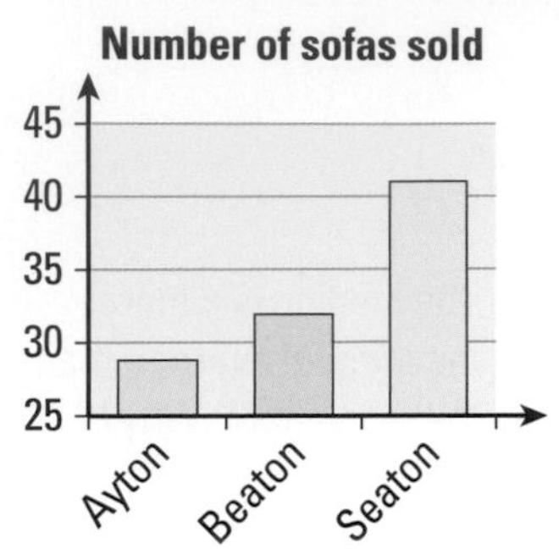

a Explain why this chart is misleading.

b Draw a new version of the chart to give a fairer impression of the data.

12b

2 Students on a PE course did a fitness test at the beginning of the course and repeated the same test at the end.

Student	A	B	C	D	E	F	G	H	I	J
Test 1	24	37	16	23	29	42	31	22	21	29
Test 2	39	42	34	35	30	44	40	33	35	39

a Plot a scatter graph for this set of data.

b What does the graph tell you about the course? Explain your answer.

12c

3 This frequency table shows the number of points awarded to competitors in a skating competition.

Points	1	2	3	4	5
Frequency	2	9	18	12	3

a Find the range of this set of data.

b Find the mean, median and mode of the number of points awarded.

4 Molly counted the number of people leaving a lift each time it arrived at the ground floor of a building.
The table shows her results.

Number of people	1–3	4–6	7–9	10–12
Frequency	12	8	4	1

a Find the modal class for this set of data.

b Estimate the mean, median and range of the data.

c Explain why your answers to part **b** are estimates.

12d

5 The table shows the number of parking tickets issued to vehicles parked on two streets each day during one week.

Day	Mon	Tue	Wed	Thu	Fri	Sat	Sun
King Street	8	7	6	6	3	8	0
Queen Street	4	3	5	2	4	11	0

a Find the mean, median, mode and range of the number of tickets issued each day in each street.

b Use the statistics you calculated in part **a** to compare the two distributions.

12e

6 The table shows the number of points awarded to boys and girls in Year 9 in a charity quiz.

Points	1	2	3	4	5	6
Boys	2	6	6	8	4	2
Girls	0	5	6	5	7	4

Draw a pair of frequency polygons to compare the two sets of scores.

7 Draw a frequency diagram for this set of data.

Height, h cm	$0 < h \leq 5$	$5 < h \leq 10$	$10 < h \leq 15$	$15 < h \leq 20$
Frequency	5	8	12	6

12f

8 Gather information similar to that shown in the table on page 212 for a selection of countries in Asia. Investigate any link between health and poverty in these countries, and report your findings.

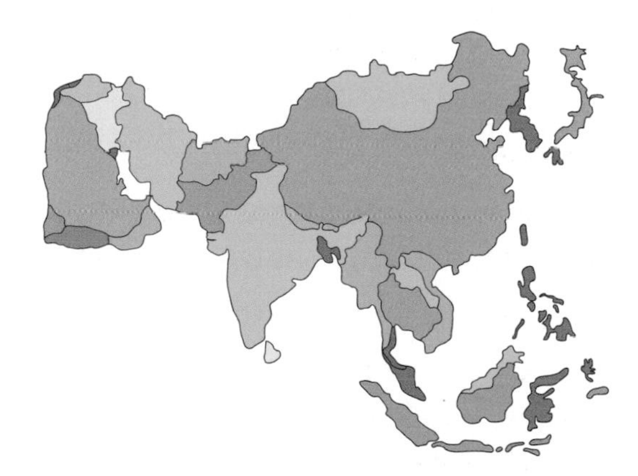

12 Summary

Assessment criteria

- Examine critically the results of a statistical enquiry and justify the choice of statistical representation in written presentation **Level 7**

Level 7

1 Here are four charts drawn by a computer.

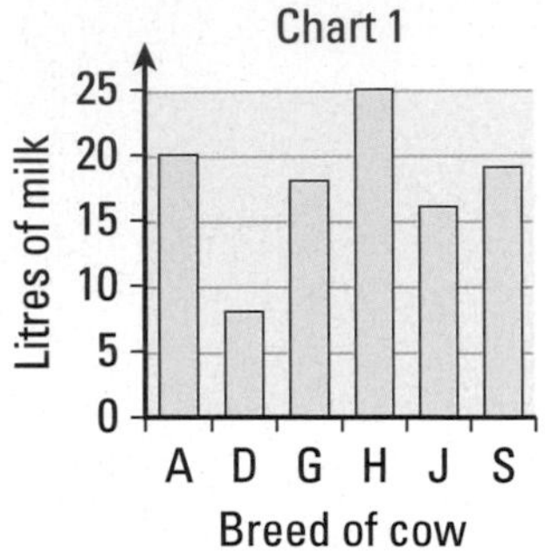

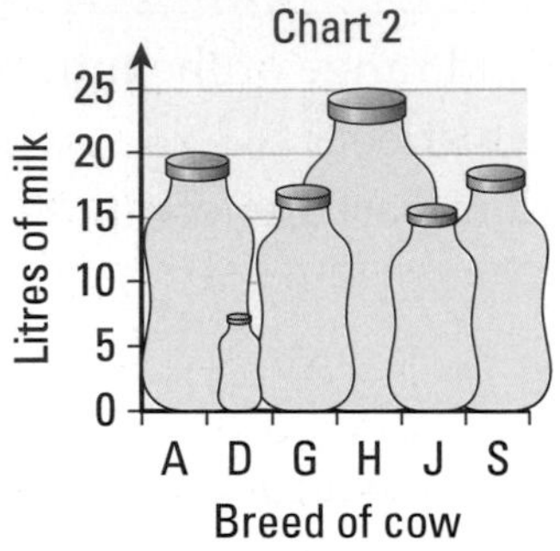

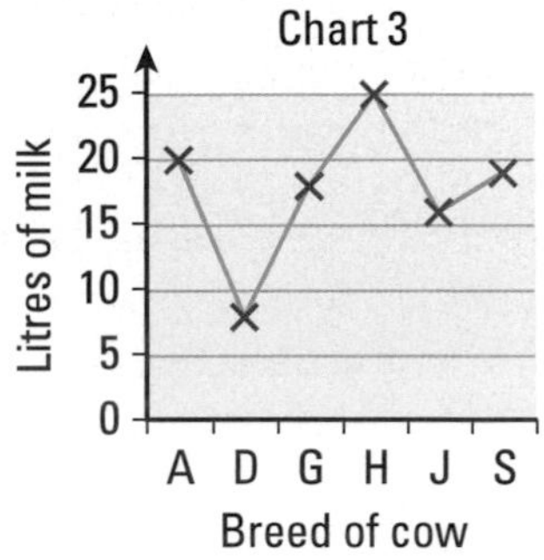

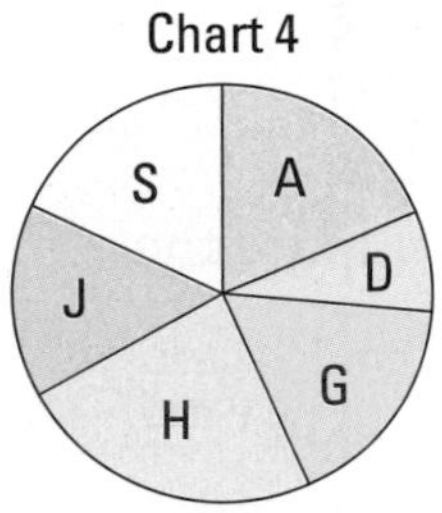

Chart 1

Litres of milk
25
20
15
10
5
0
A D G H J S
Breed of cow

Chart 2

Litres of milk
25
20
15
10
5
0
A D G H J S
Breed of cow

Chart 3

Litres of milk
25
20
15
10
5
0
A D G H J S
Breed of cow

Chart 4

S A D G H J

Key: A – Ayrshire D – Dexter G – Guernsey
H – Holstein J – Jersey S - Shorthorn

Which is the best way of showing the data?

For each of the other three charts, explain why the type of chart is not a good way of showing the data.

Key Stage 3 2005 5–7 Paper 2

13 Geometry

3-D shapes

Ancient Greek mathematicians studied 3-D shapes in great detail.
Plato tried to match solids to the four elements of the universe.

Tetrahedron – fire
Cube – earth
Octahedron – air
Icosahedron – water

Euclid wrote about the properties of 3-D shapes in one of his many mathematical books.

What's the point? There are only five solids made from regular polygons that have identical faces and vertices. These five 3-D shapes are called the Platonic solids.

Check in

Level 4

1 Write the mathematical name of these 2-D shapes.

a b c d e

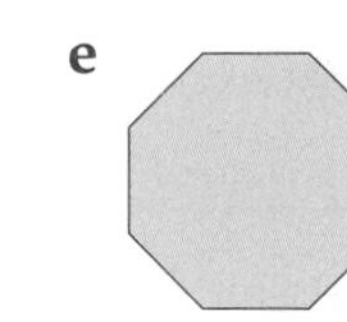

Level 5

2 Calculate the surface area and volume of these cuboids.
Give the units of your answer.

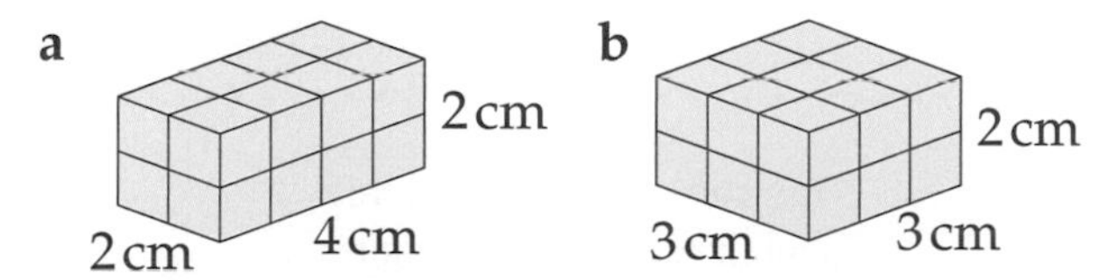

p. 98

3 Calculate the area of these shapes.

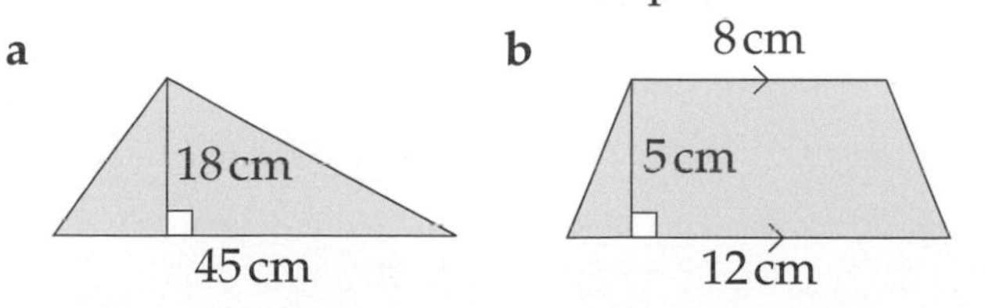

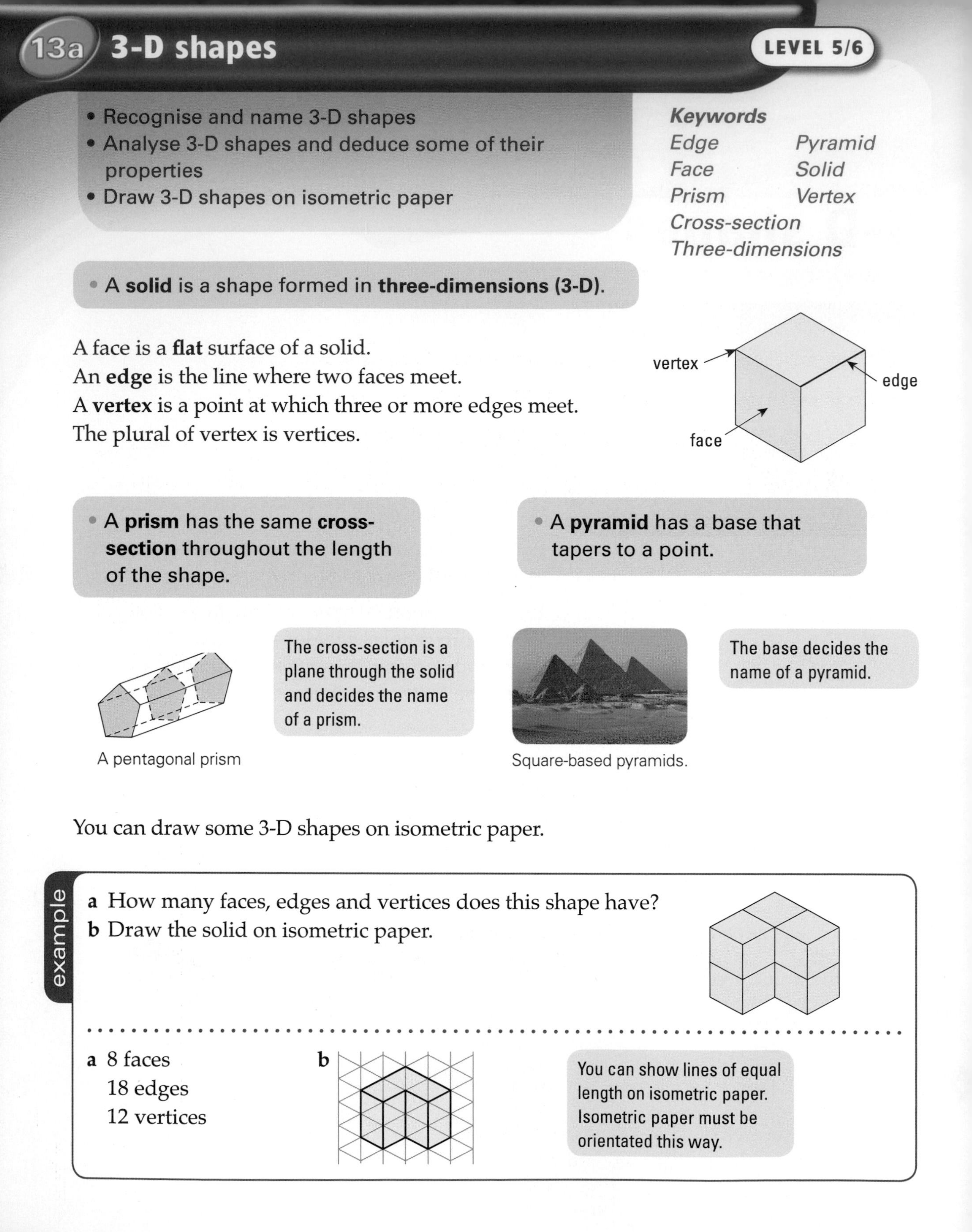

13a 3-D shapes

LEVEL 5/6

- Recognise and name 3-D shapes
- Analyse 3-D shapes and deduce some of their properties
- Draw 3-D shapes on isometric paper

Keywords
Edge
Face
Prism
Cross-section
Three-dimensions
Pyramid
Solid
Vertex

- A **solid** is a shape formed in **three-dimensions (3-D)**.

A face is a **flat** surface of a solid.
An **edge** is the line where two faces meet.
A **vertex** is a point at which three or more edges meet.
The plural of vertex is vertices.

- A **prism** has the same **cross-section** throughout the length of the shape.

- A **pyramid** has a base that tapers to a point.

A pentagonal prism

The cross-section is a plane through the solid and decides the name of a prism.

Square-based pyramids.

The base decides the name of a pyramid.

You can draw some 3-D shapes on isometric paper.

example

a How many faces, edges and vertices does this shape have?
b Draw the solid on isometric paper.

a 8 faces
18 edges
12 vertices

b

You can show lines of equal length on isometric paper. Isometric paper must be orientated this way.

Exercise 13a

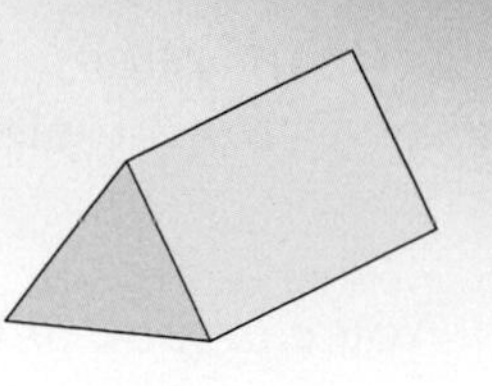

1 A triangular prism is made from three blue rectangles and two pink triangles.
Find the number of edges where
a a blue face meets a blue face **b** a blue face meets a pink face
c a pink face meets a pink face.

2 Three cubes are used to make a solid.
a On isometric paper, draw as many different solids as possible using the three cubes.
b Write the number of faces, edges and vertices of each solid.

3 **a** Copy and complete the table. **b** Find a rule connecting f, v and e.

Name of solid	Number of faces (f)	Number of vertices (v)	Number of edges (e)
Cube			
Cuboid			
Square-based pyramid			
Tetrahedron			
Triangular prism			
Hexagonal-based pyramid			
Hexagonal prism			
Octagonal-based pyramid			
Octahedron			

Did you know?

Salt crystals are always cubes.

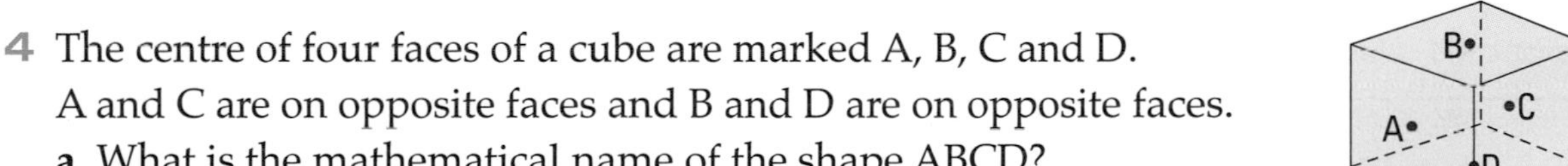

4 The centre of four faces of a cube are marked A, B, C and D.
A and C are on opposite faces and B and D are on opposite faces.
a What is the mathematical name of the shape ABCD?
b Explain how you know.

B

C

A

D

activity

a Draw these seven solids on isometric paper.

i ii iii iv v

b Calculate the total volume of all the solids.

c Make these shapes using Multilink cubes and fit them together to form a cube.

d What are the dimensions of the cube?

vi vii

13b Plans and elevations

LEVEL 6

- Analyse 3-D shapes through 2-D projections
- Draw the plan and elevations of a 3-D shape

Keywords
Front elevation
Plan
Side elevation

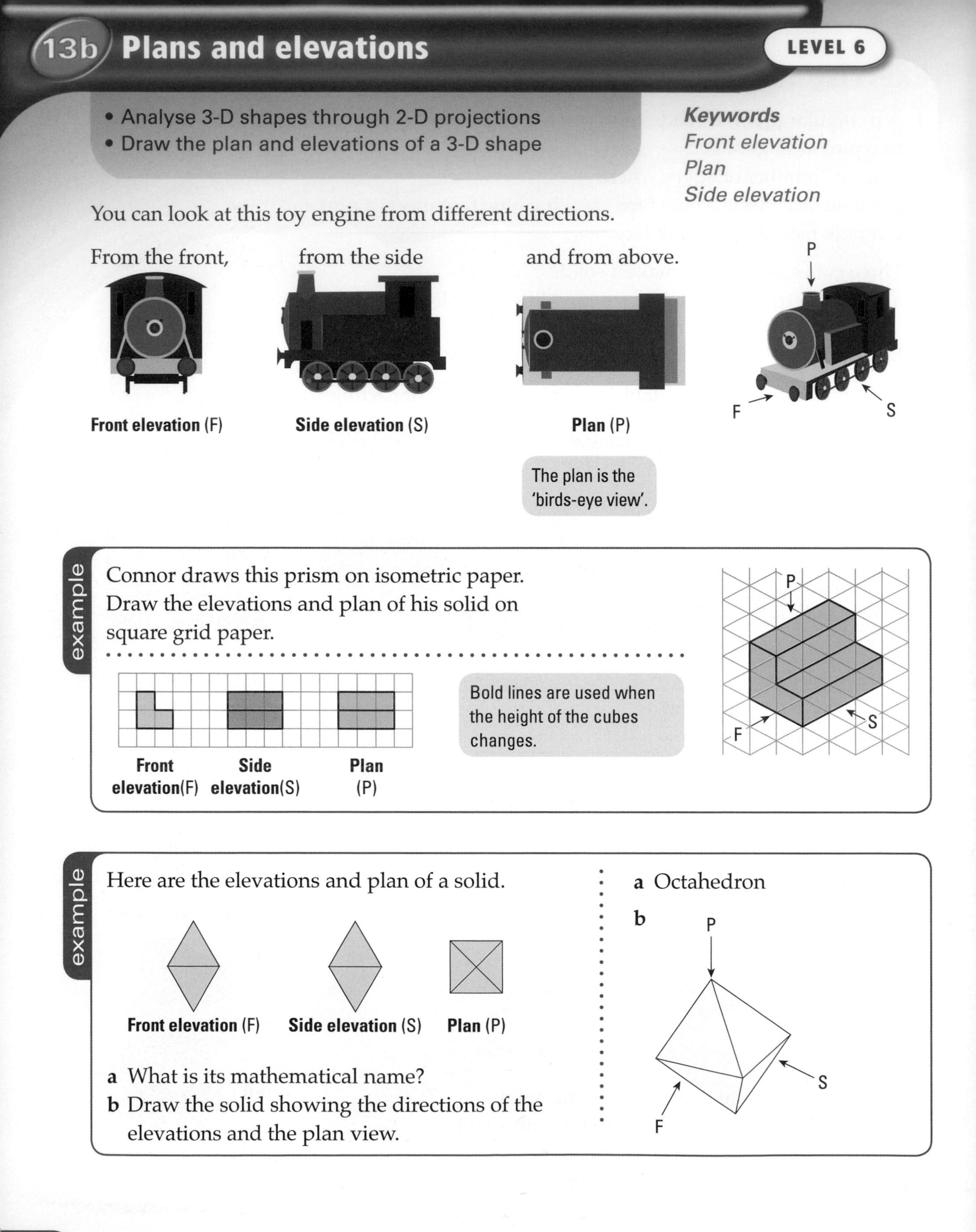

Grade D

Exercise 13b

1 This shape is made of 12 cubes.
Here are four drawings of the views.
Match each diagram to the correct view.

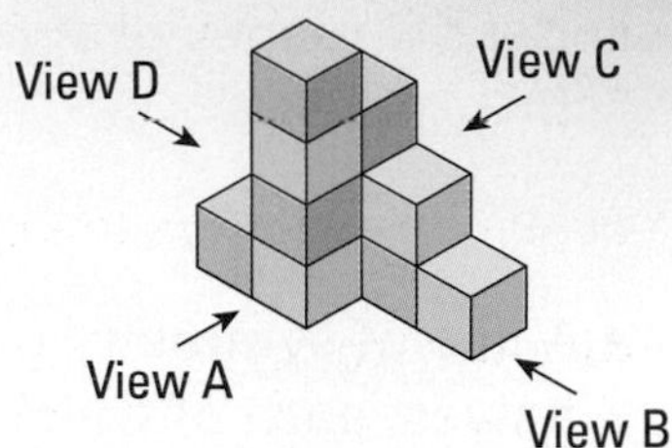

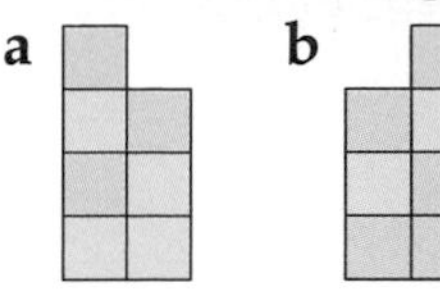

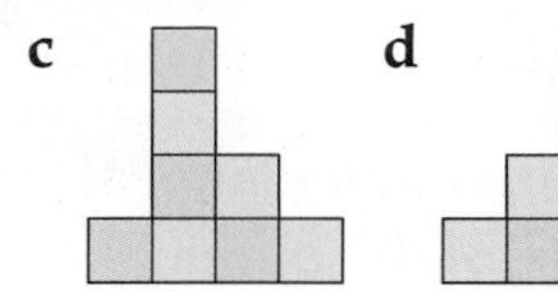

2 Sketch the front elevation (F), the side elevation (S) and the plan (P) of each of these prisms.

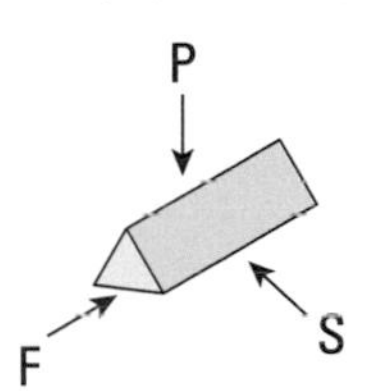

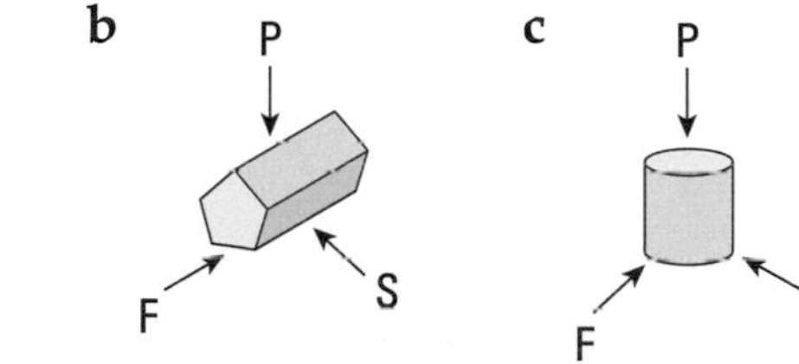

3 Bryony makes a 3-D shape from cubes.
Here are the elevations and the plan.

Front elevation (F) | **Side elevation** (S) | **Plan** (P)

a Draw her shape on isometric paper.
b How many cubes are needed to make the shape?

4 The front elevation of a square-based pyramid is a triangle.
Find a 3-D shape that has a front elevation of

a a square **b** a rectangle
c a circle **d** a hexagon.

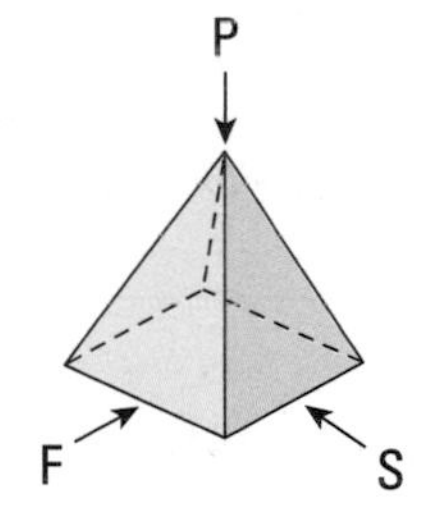

A square-based pyramid

Did you know?

Architects use very accurate scale drawings of the elevations and the plan when they design buildings.

activity

Draw an object of your choice.
Mark on your drawing the directions of the elevations and the plan view.
Draw the front elevation, the side elevation and the plan of your object.

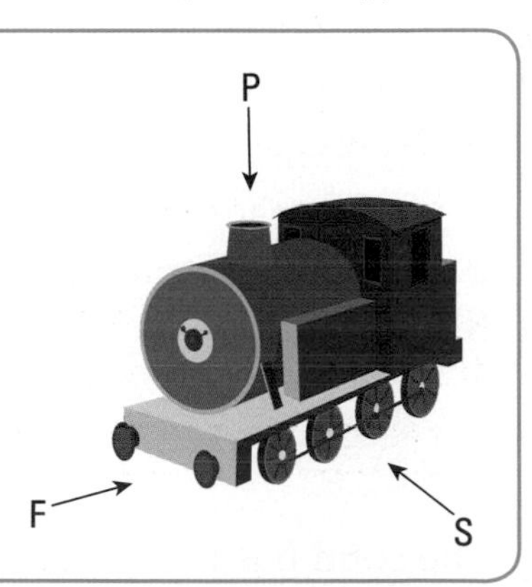

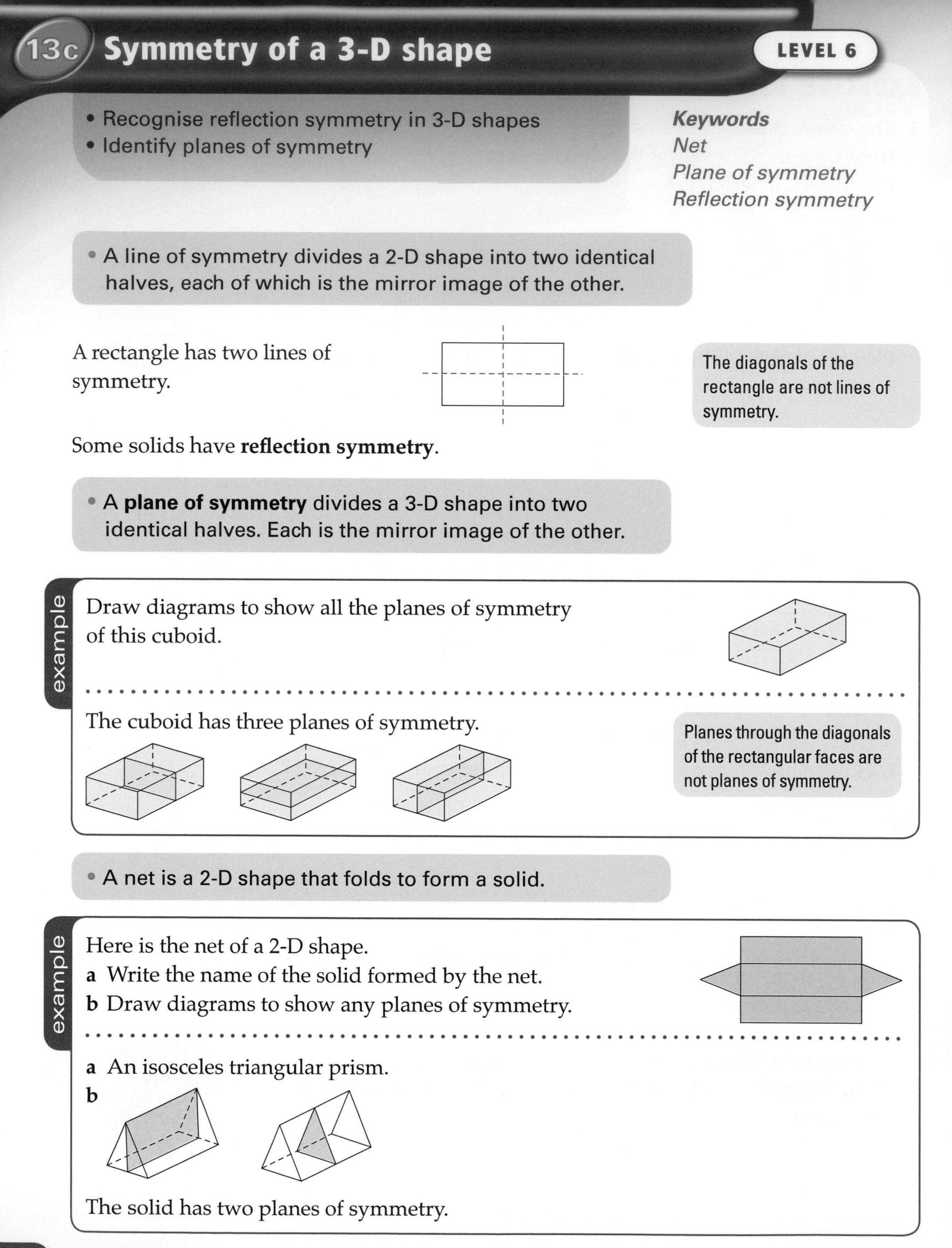

13c Symmetry of a 3-D shape

LEVEL 6

- Recognise reflection symmetry in 3-D shapes
- Identify planes of symmetry

Keywords
Net
Plane of symmetry
Reflection symmetry

- A line of symmetry divides a 2-D shape into two identical halves, each of which is the mirror image of the other.

A rectangle has two lines of symmetry.

The diagonals of the rectangle are not lines of symmetry.

Some solids have **reflection symmetry**.

- A **plane of symmetry** divides a 3-D shape into two identical halves. Each is the mirror image of the other.

example

Draw diagrams to show all the planes of symmetry of this cuboid.

The cuboid has three planes of symmetry.

Planes through the diagonals of the rectangular faces are not planes of symmetry.

- A net is a 2-D shape that folds to form a solid.

example

Here is the net of a 2-D shape.

a Write the name of the solid formed by the net.

b Draw diagrams to show any planes of symmetry.

a An isosceles triangular prism.

b

The solid has two planes of symmetry.

Exercise 13c

1 For each of these solids, decide if the shaded plane is a plane of symmetry. Explain your reasoning.

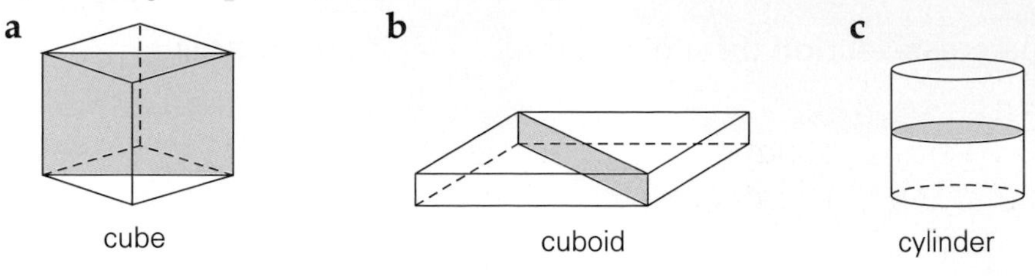

a cube **b** cuboid **c** cylinder

2 Draw diagrams to show all the planes of symmetry of these solids.

a

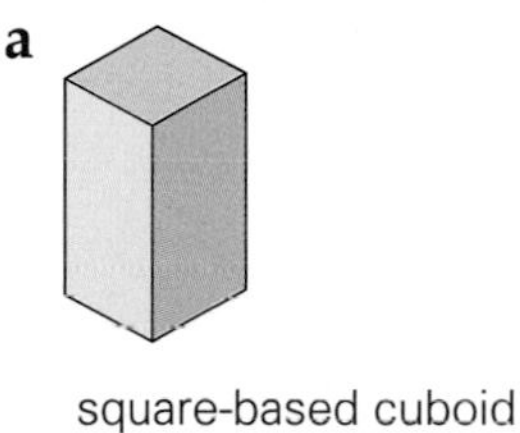

square-based cuboid

b

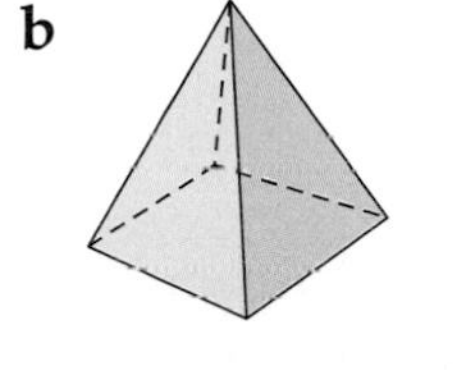

square-based pyramid

c

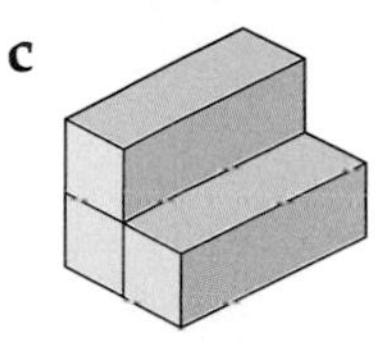

hexagonal prism

3 The net of a 3-D shape consists of three isosceles triangles and one equilateral triangle.

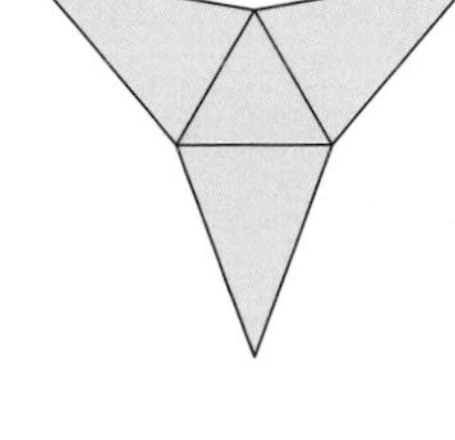

a Give the name of the solid formed by the net.
b How many planes of symmetry does the solid have?

4 You can slice a cube to give a square cross-section. Draw diagrams that show how a cube can be sliced so that the cross-section is
a a rectangle
b a triangle
c a pentagon.

5 **a** Construct a regular tetrahedron of length 5 cm.
b How many edges does the solid have?
c How many planes of symmetry does the regular tetrahedron have?

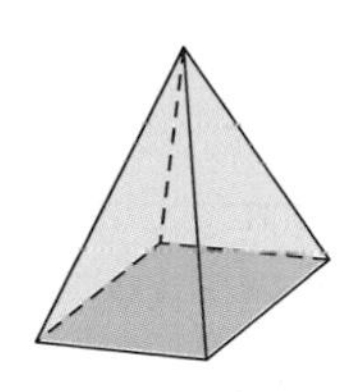

activity

a Construct a cube.
b Use your solid to decide the number of planes of symmetry of a cube.

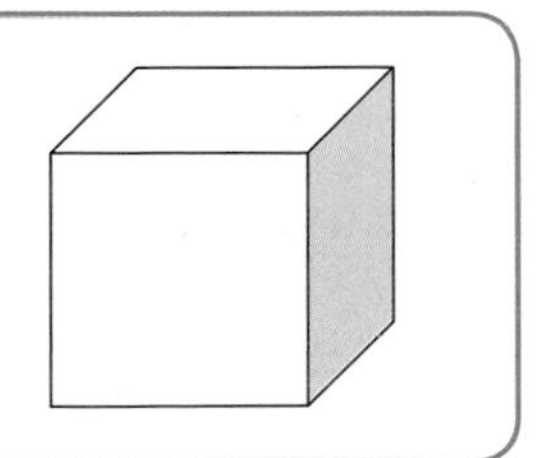

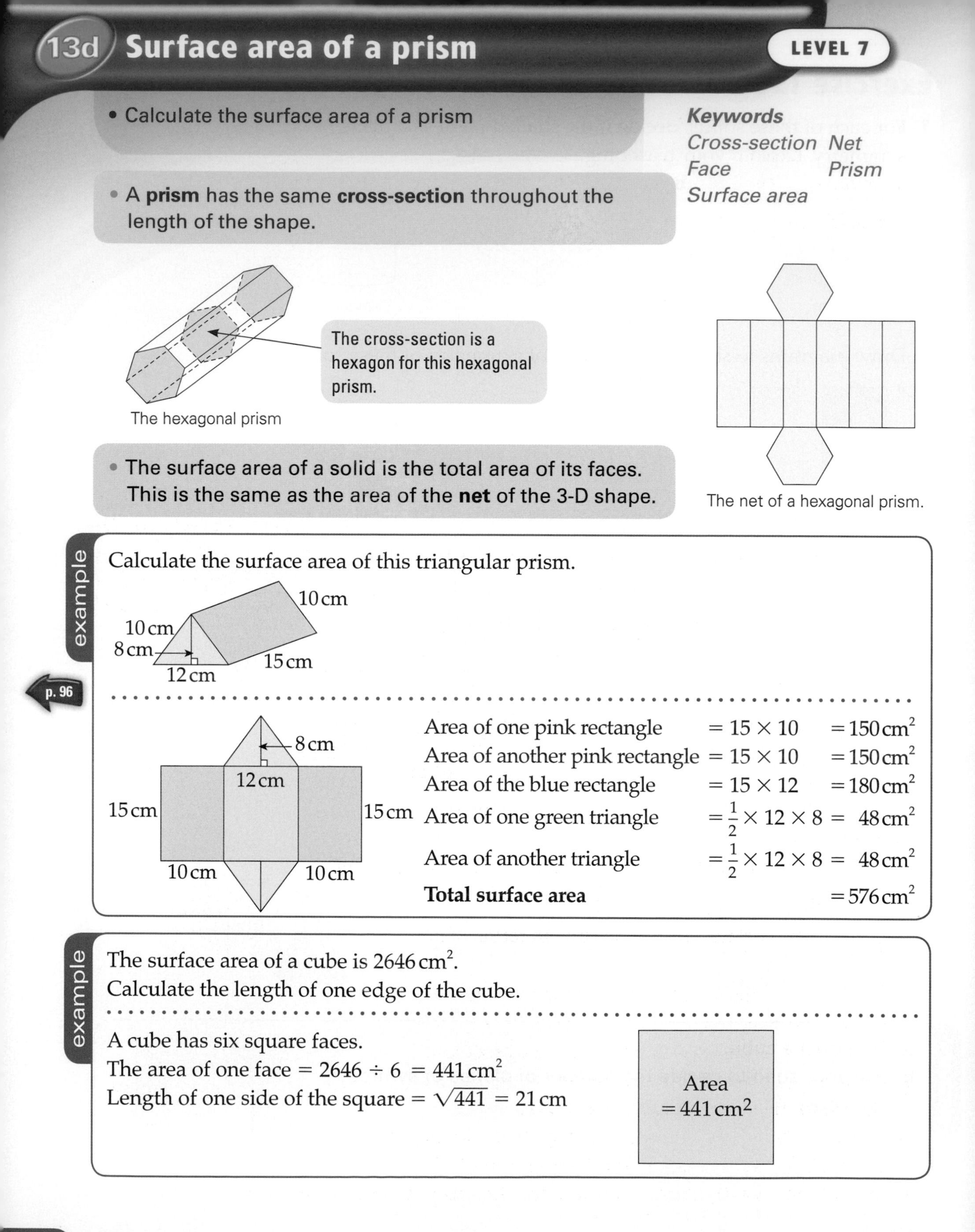

13d Surface area of a prism

LEVEL 7

- Calculate the surface area of a prism

Keywords
Cross-section *Net*
Face *Prism*
Surface area

- A **prism** has the same **cross-section** throughout the length of the shape.

The hexagonal prism

The net of a hexagonal prism.

- The surface area of a solid is the total area of its faces. This is the same as the area of the **net** of the 3-D shape.

example

Calculate the surface area of this triangular prism.

p. 96

Area of one pink rectangle	$= 15 \times 10$	$= 150\,\text{cm}^2$
Area of another pink rectangle	$= 15 \times 10$	$= 150\,\text{cm}^2$
Area of the blue rectangle	$= 15 \times 12$	$= 180\,\text{cm}^2$
Area of one green triangle	$= \frac{1}{2} \times 12 \times 8$	$= 48\,\text{cm}^2$
Area of another triangle	$= \frac{1}{2} \times 12 \times 8$	$= 48\,\text{cm}^2$
Total surface area		$= 576\,\text{cm}^2$

example

The surface area of a cube is $2646\,\text{cm}^2$.
Calculate the length of one edge of the cube.

A cube has six square faces.
The area of one face $= 2646 \div 6 = 441\,\text{cm}^2$
Length of one side of the square $= \sqrt{441} = 21\,\text{cm}$

Exercise 13d

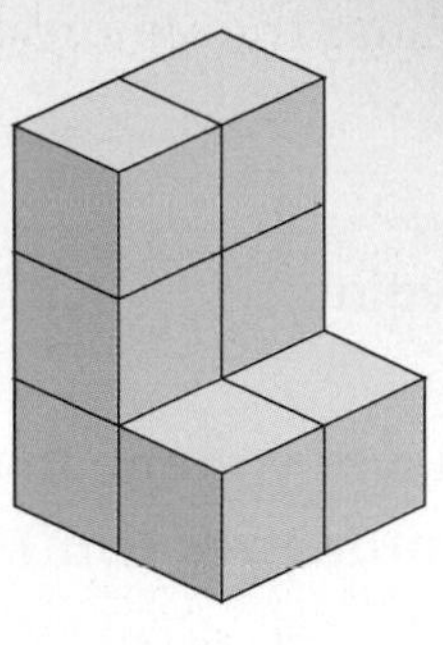

1 A prism is made from eight cubes.
Each cube measures 5 metres by 5 metres by 5 metres.
Calculate the surface area of the solid.

2 Calculate the surface area of this prism.

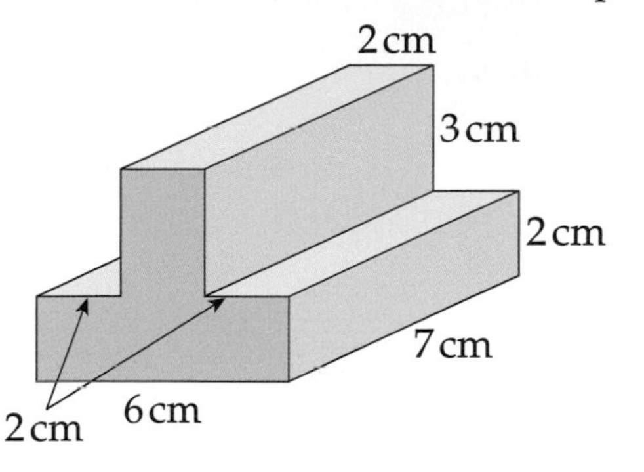

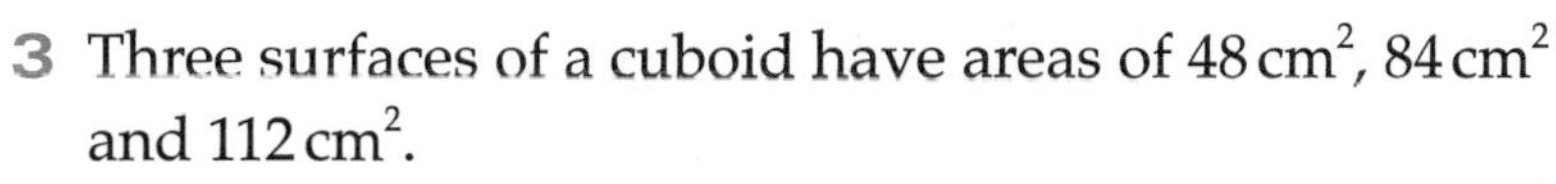

3 Three surfaces of a cuboid have areas of $48\,\text{cm}^2$, $84\,\text{cm}^2$ and $112\,\text{cm}^2$.
   a Calculate the total surface area
   b Find the length, width and height of the cuboid.

4 Calculate the surface area of these triangular prisms.

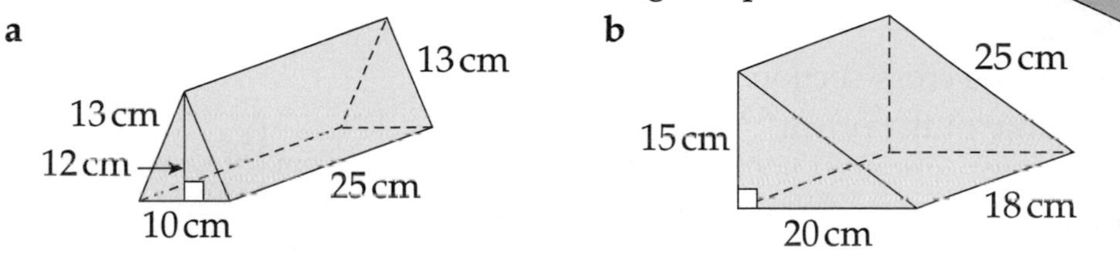

5 Calculate the length of one side of a cube if the cube has a surface area of
   a $600\,\text{cm}^2$ b $1350\,\text{cm}^2$ c $37.5\,\text{cm}^2$ d $121.5\,\text{cm}^2$

6 The length of one side of a cube is a.
Calculate the surface area of the cube in terms of a.

rich task

Candle Pack makes candles in the shape of cubes.
They want to pack eight candles in a box.

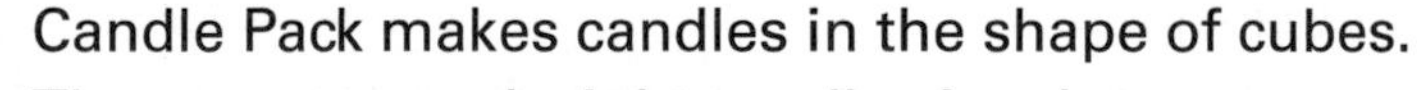

a Write the dimensions of three possible boxes.
b Draw each box on isometric paper.
c Calculate the surface area of each box.
d Describe the boxes that give the smallest and largest surface area. Which would be cheaper to make?
e Extend the investigation by designing a box to pack twelve candles.

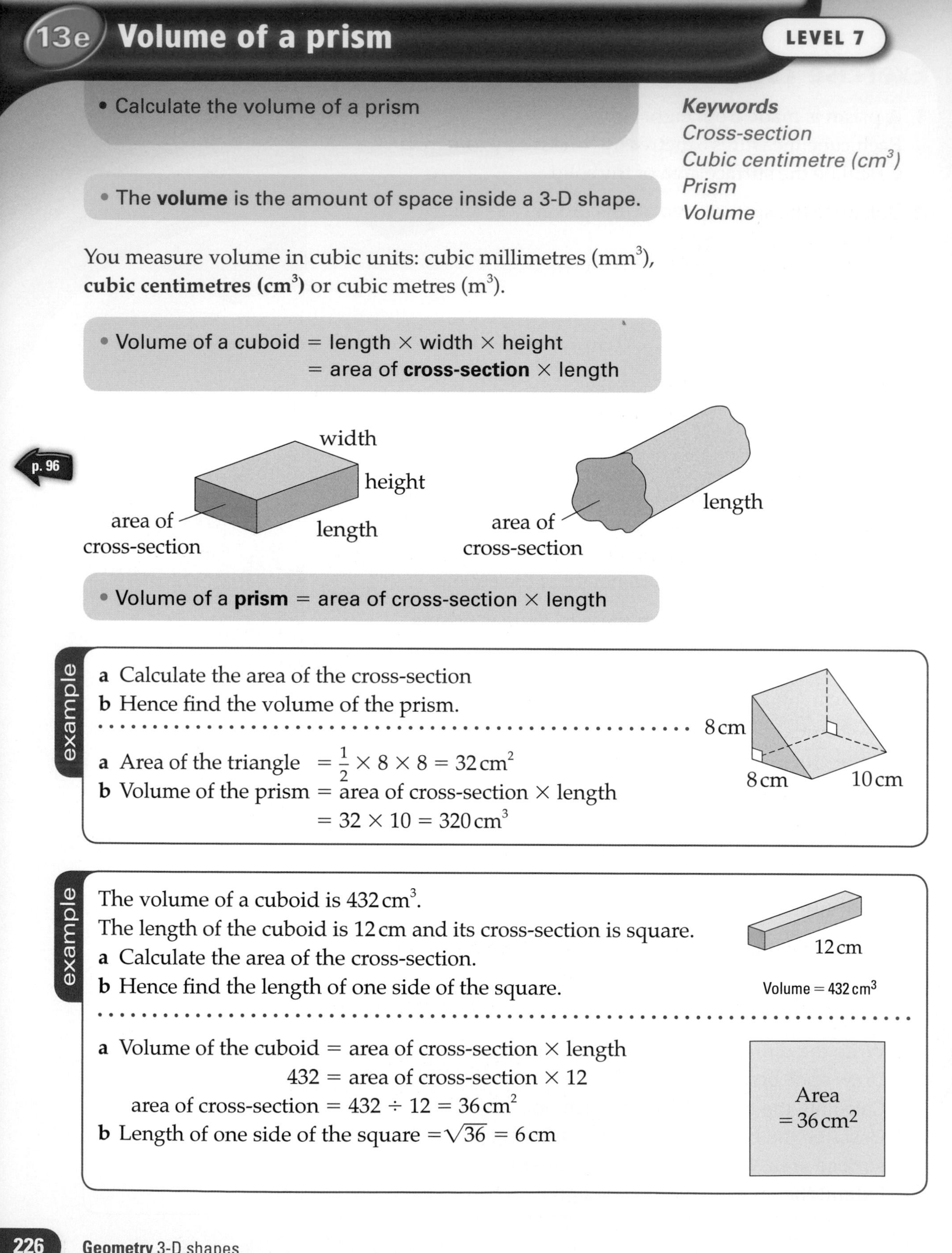

13e Volume of a prism

LEVEL 7

- Calculate the volume of a prism

Keywords
Cross-section
Cubic centimetre (cm³)
Prism
Volume

- The **volume** is the amount of space inside a 3-D shape.

You measure volume in cubic units: cubic millimetres (mm^3), **cubic centimetres (cm^3)** or cubic metres (m^3).

- Volume of a cuboid = length × width × height
  = area of **cross-section** × length

p. 96

- Volume of a **prism** = area of cross-section × length

example

a Calculate the area of the cross-section
b Hence find the volume of the prism.

a Area of the triangle $= \frac{1}{2} \times 8 \times 8 = 32\,cm^2$
b Volume of the prism = area of cross-section × length
$= 32 \times 10 = 320\,cm^3$

example

The volume of a cuboid is $432\,cm^3$.
The length of the cuboid is 12 cm and its cross-section is square.
a Calculate the area of the cross-section.
b Hence find the length of one side of the square.

a Volume of the cuboid = area of cross-section × length
432 = area of cross-section × 12
area of cross-section $= 432 \div 12 = 36\,cm^2$
b Length of one side of the square $= \sqrt{36} = 6\,cm$

Exercise 13e

1 The trailer of a lorry is a cuboid with length 2 metres, width 2 metres and height 4 metres.
What is the volume of the cuboid?

2 The cross-section of a prism of length 5 m is divided into three areas, A_1, A_2 and A_3.
Calculate the volume of the prism when
a $A_1 = 1.5\,m^2$, $A_2 = 5\,m^2$ and $A_3 = 2\,m^2$
b $A_1 = 0.5\,m^2$, $A_2 = 4\,m^2$ and $A_3 = 1\,m^2$

3 a Calculate the area of the triangle.
b Hence find the volume of the prism.

4 A ramp is made in the shape of a prism.
The cross-section is a trapezium.
a Calculate the area of the trapezium.
b Hence find the volume of the ramp.
State the units of your answers.

. 96

5 The volume of this prism is $127.5\,cm^3$.
The area of the cross-section is $15\,cm^2$.
Calculate the length of the prism.

6 The volume of a box with a square cross-section is $540\,cm^3$.
The length of the box is 15 cm.
a Calculate the area of the cross-section.
b Hence find the length of one side of the square.

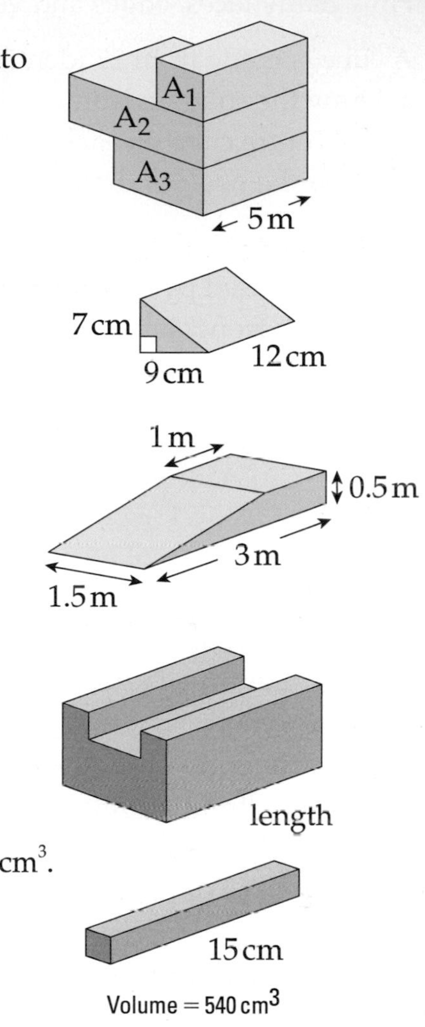

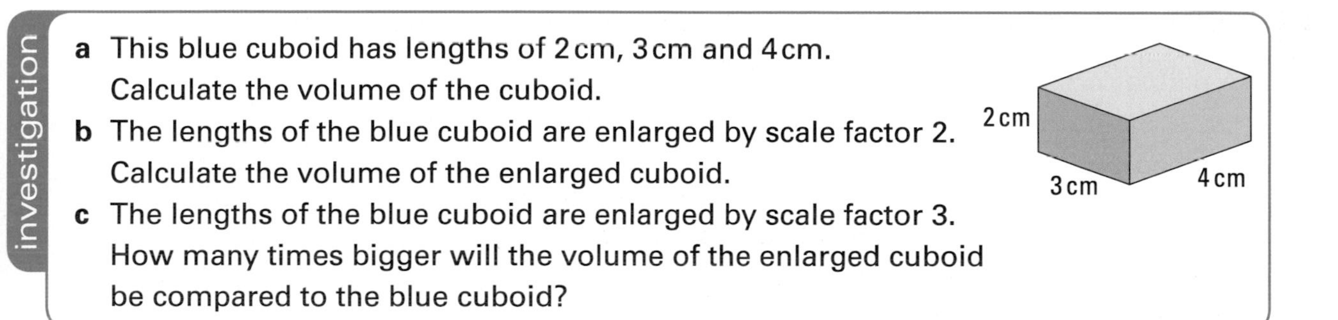

investigation

a This blue cuboid has lengths of 2 cm, 3 cm and 4 cm.
Calculate the volume of the cuboid.
b The lengths of the blue cuboid are enlarged by scale factor 2.
Calculate the volume of the enlarged cuboid.
c The lengths of the blue cuboid are enlarged by scale factor 3.
How many times bigger will the volume of the enlarged cuboid be compared to the blue cuboid?

13 Consolidation

13a

1 A regular tetrahedron is made from four equilateral triangles.
How many faces, edges and vertices does this solid have?

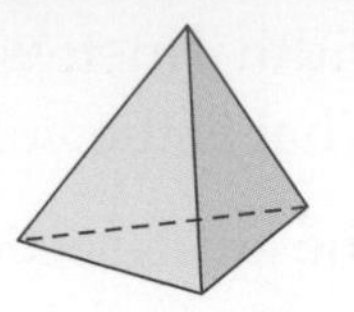

2 A cube is made from 27 identical small cubes.

a Draw the solid on isometric paper.

The centre cube on each face of the solid is now removed.

b Draw the new solid on isometric paper.

13b

3 A square-based pyramid is joined to a cube.
Sketch the front elevation (F), the side elevation (S) and the plan (P) of this solid.

4 The diagram shows the plan of a solid made from cubes.
The number in each square represents the number of cubes in that column.

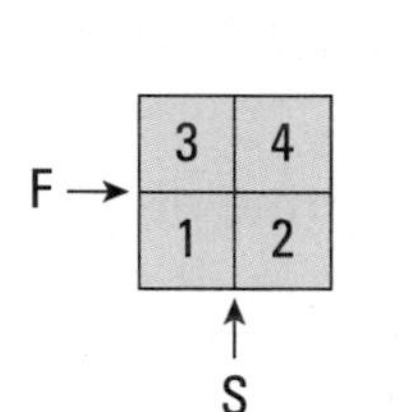

a Draw the solid on isometric paper.

b Draw the front elevation (F) and the side elevation (S) of the solid.

13c

5 A square-based pyramid is sliced horizontally.
Describe the shapes of the cross-section at different heights.

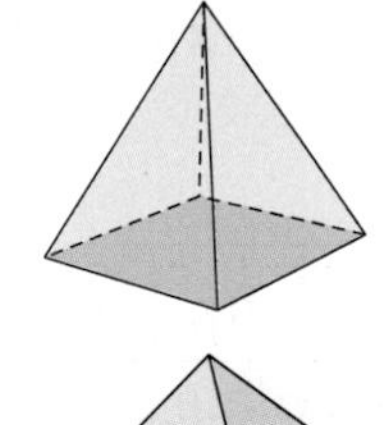

6 A regular octahedron is made from eight equilateral triangles.
Draw diagrams to show all the planes of symmetry of a regular octahedron.

7 Calculate the surface area of this prism.

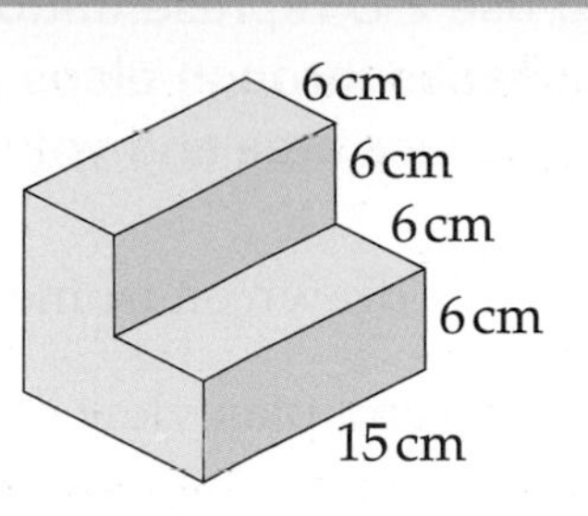

8 A box is made in the shape of a hexagonal prism. The length of the box is 10 cm and the dimensions of the hexagon are shown in the diagram.

a Calculate the area of the hexagon.

b Hence find the volume of the prism.

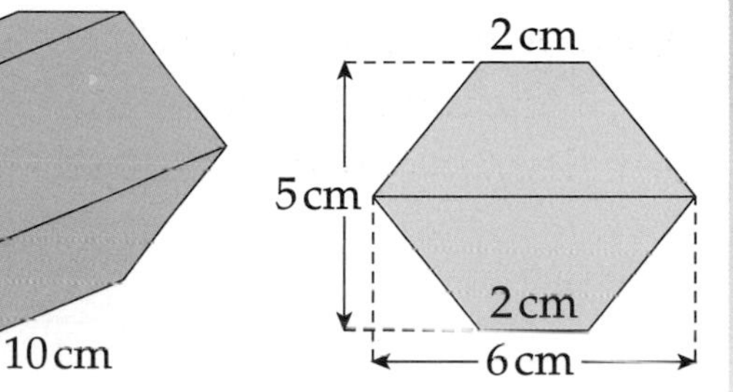

9 A tent is in the shape of a triangular prism. The length of the tent is 5 metres.

a Calculate the area of the triangle.

b Hence find the volume of the tent.

State the units of your answers.

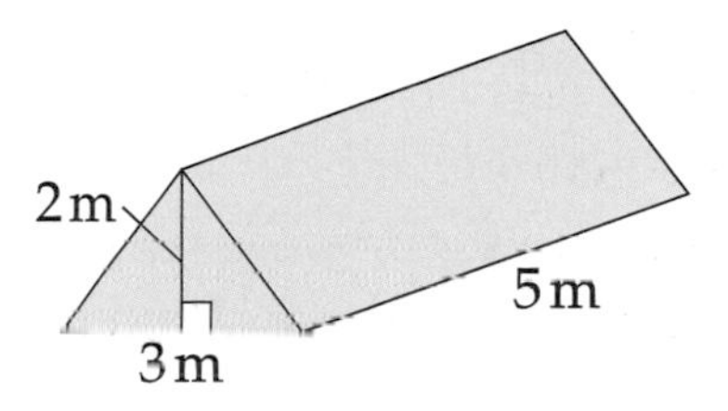

10 A cuboid is made from a rectangular sheet of card 30 cm long and 25 cm wide. The cuboid is 9 cm high. The diagram shows the net of the cuboid.

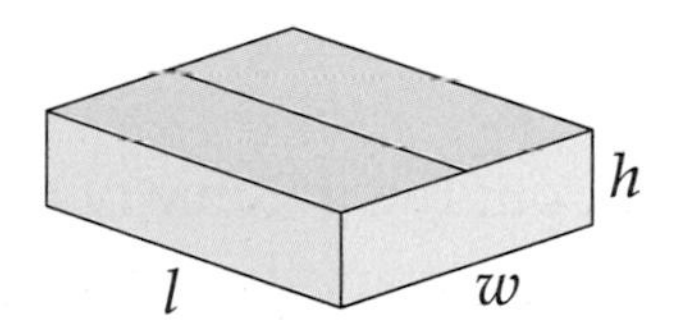

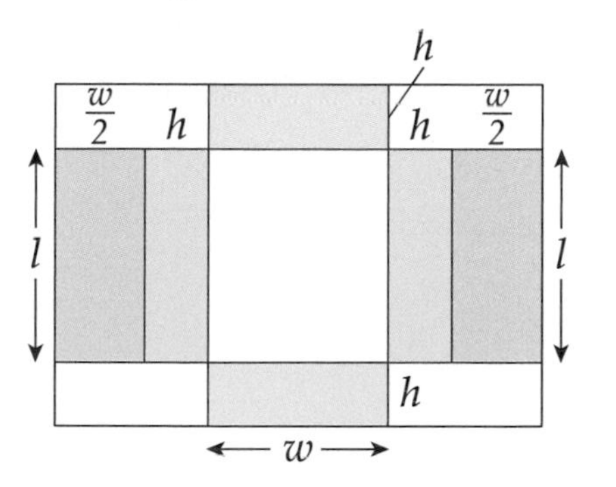

Calculate the volume of the cuboid.

13 Summary

Assessment criteria

- Visualise and use 2-D representations of 3-D objects **Level 6**
- Analyse 3-D shapes through plans and elevations **Level 6**
- Calculate the surface area and volume of a prism **Level 7**

Level 6

1 A triangular prism is drawn on isometric grid paper.

Draw the elevations and plan view of the prism on square grid paper.

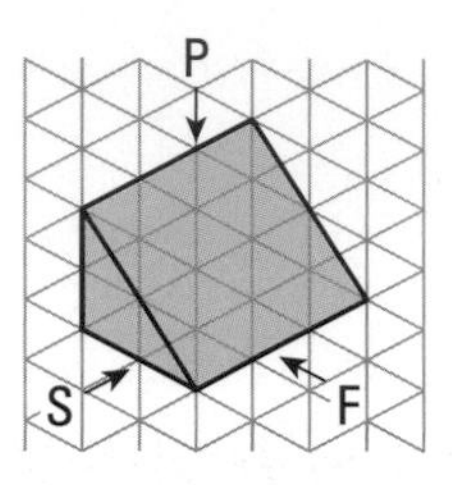

Jack's answer ✔

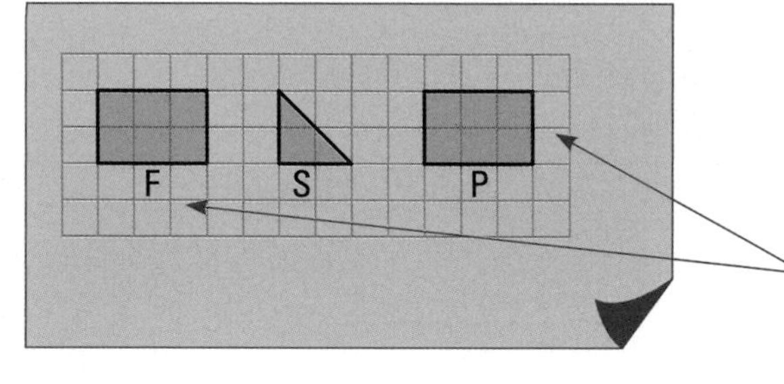

Jack finds the front elevation and the plan to be the same, because of the symmetry of the prism.

Level 7

2 a Look at the triangular prism.

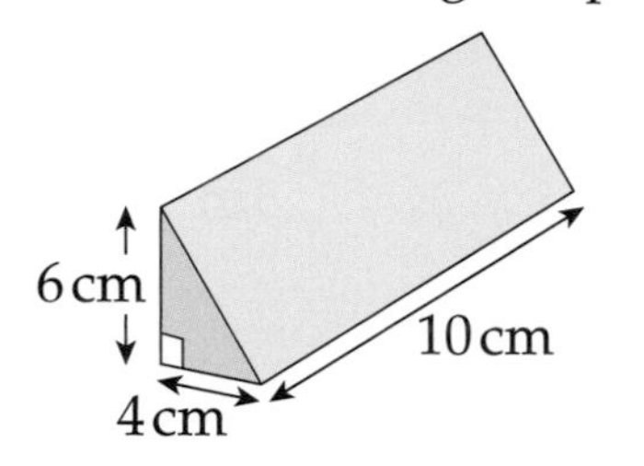

Work out the volume of the prism.

b One face of another prism is made from 5 squares. Each square has side of length 3 cm.

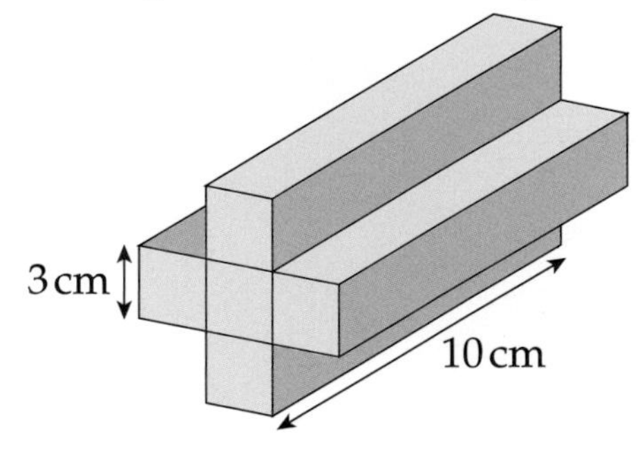

Work out the volume of the prism.

Key Stage 3 2007 5–7 Paper 2

14 Number

Calculation plus

You are doing calculations in your head all the time, probably without realising it. You could be washing out how much money you need to save to buy a new DVD, how many hours of study you need to do in each subject to get you best marks, calculating costs of fruit and vegetables in the supermarket, or ever dividing up your birthday cake into equal portions!

What's the point? A good knowledge of maths can help you in many different situations.

Check in

Level 5

1 Convert these fraction into percentages using an appropriate method.

a $\frac{3}{5}$ **b** $\frac{17}{20}$

c $\frac{5}{8}$ **d** $\frac{3}{7}$

2 **a** Increase £35 by 15%

b Decrease $220 by 8%

3 **a** 5 miles is the same as 8 km. How far in km is 12 miles?

b 6 pizzas cost £15. What is the cost of 7 pizzas?

4 Round each of these numbers to the nearest

i 100 **ii** 1 **iii** 2 decimal places

a 482.65

b 98.073

c 0.7878

14a Percentage problems

LEVEL 6/7

- Choose an appropriate representation of an answer: fraction, decimal or percentage
- Choose an appropriate method of calculation
- Calculate a percentage increase or decrease

Keywords
Percentage
Proportion

- You can represent a **proportion** as a fraction, decimal or **percentage**.

example

p. 26

Last year the Jones family earned £32 453 and spent £2543 on a holiday.

The Hussain family earned £25 000 and spent £2000 on a holiday.

Which family spent proportionately more on their holiday?

	Jones Family	Hussain family
% spent on holiday	$= \frac{2543}{32453}$	$= \frac{2000}{25000}$
	$= 2543 \div 32453$	$= \frac{2}{25}$
	$= 0.078359\ldots$	$= \frac{8}{100}$
	$= 7.8359\%$	
	$= 7.8\%$	$= 8\%$

This is a calculator method.

This is a mental calculation.

Write the answers as percentages so that they can easily be compared.

The Hussain family spent a greater percentage of their earnings on their holiday

- You can calculate a percentage increase or decrease using a single multiplier.

example

p. 24

Talan receives a monthly allowance of £30.
His father increases Talan's allowance by 22%.
What is Talan's new allowance?

New allowance = (100 + 22)% of the old allowance
= 122% of £30
= 1.22 × £30
= £36.60

Increase by 22%

100% 122%

Convert the percentage into a decimal which you can then multiply using a calculator.

Exercise 14a

1 Here is some information about A levels.
How many more students gained a grade A in Maths compared to in English?

Subject	English	Maths
Number of students	75 000	58 000
% with a grade A	22%	36%

2 Last year the Kane family earned £46 275 and spent £2962 on a holiday.
The Walton family earned £20 000 and spent £1700 on a holiday.
Which family spent proportionately more on their holiday?

3 Jack invests £1200 in the National Bank for 1 year.
At the end of the year he receives £78 in interest.
Deidre invests £1650 in KRP bank for 1 year.
At the end of the year she receives £99 in interest.
Who had the better rate of interest, Jack or Deidre?
Explain your answer.

4 Here are two offers.
Which offer is the better value for money?
Explain your reasoning.

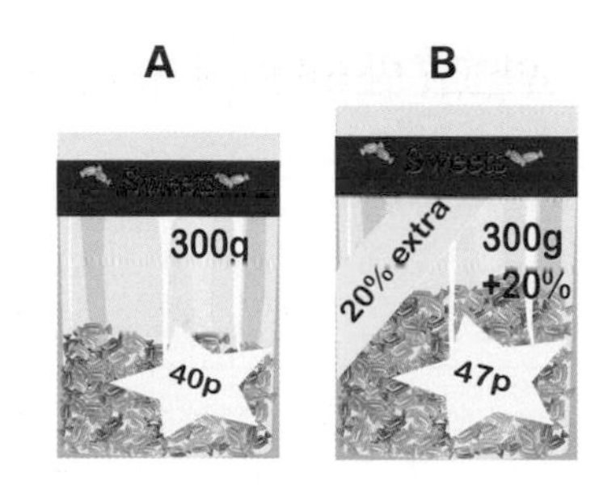

5 **a** A chocolate bar normally has a mass of 240 g.
This week the mass of the bar is increased by 15%.
What is the new mass of the chocolate bar?

b A shirt normally costs £30.
In a sale all the prices are reduced by 18%.
What is the sale price of the shirt?

6 When measuring distances, Jenny knows that her instruments have an error of ±5%.
She measures the length of a room as 450 cm.

a What is the greatest possible length the room could be?

b What is the least possible length the room could be?

7 Jack buys a computer on the internet.
He has to pay an extra 15% of the price advertised in VAT.
What percentage of the total price is the VAT?

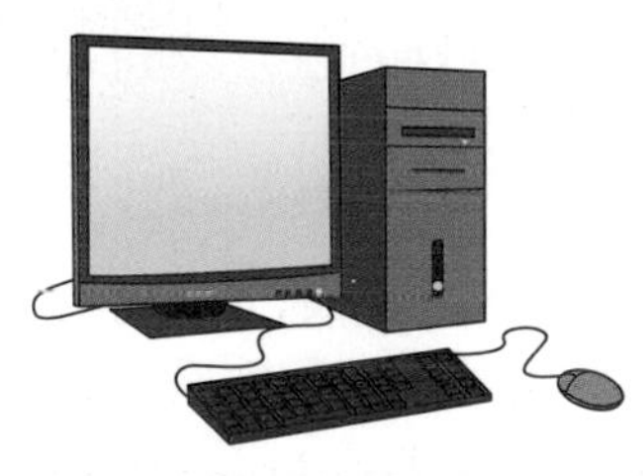

problem

In a sale all prices are reduced by 12%.
A quick way of calculating the sale price is to multiply the original price by a number.

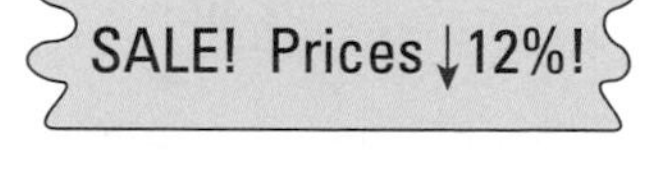

a What is the number?

After three weeks the sale price is reduced by another 12%.

b Show that the original price has been reduced by 22.56%.

14b Proportional reasoning

LEVEL 6/7

- Identify when proportional reasoning is required in a problem
- Calculate the result of any proportional change using a single multiplier

Keywords
Multiplier
Proportional reasoning

- When two quantities are in direct proportion, if one of them increases the other one increases by the same proportion.

This table shows the amount of flour needed to make different numbers of buns.
The amount of flour is directly proportional to the number of buns.

Number of buns	Amount of flour
2	80 g
4	160 g
5	200 g
10	400 g

If you double the number of buns, you double the amount of flour.

If you halve the number of buns, you halve the amount of flour.

- When two quantities are in direct proportion, you can calculate a proportional change using a unitary method or a single **multiplier**.

example

p. 32

How much flour is needed to make 13 buns?

Using a unitary method

Find the amount of flour for one bun by dividing by 2 buns.

Multiply the amount of flour for one bun by 13 to calculate the amount of flour for 13 buns.

Using a single multiplier

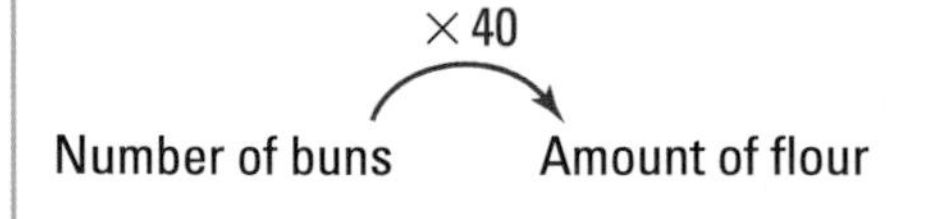

Find the single multiplier by dividing the amount of flour by the number of buns, e.g. $80 \div 2 = 40$

13 buns will need $13 \times 40 = 520$ g of flour.

Multiply the number of buns required by the single multiplier.

Exercise 14b

1 Here are two offers for memory sticks.
Which offers have the numbers in direct proportion?
In each case explain and justify your answers.

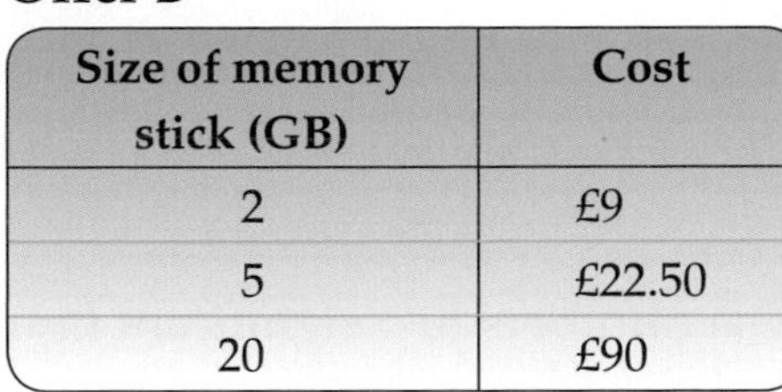

Offer A

Size of memory stick (GB)	Cost
2	£8
4	£14
10	£32

Offer B

Size of memory stick (GB)	Cost
2	£9
5	£22.50
20	£90

2 Vernon has been investigating direct proportion on a spreadsheet. Here are his results.

a Are the numbers in direct proportion?

b What is the single multiplier that connects the number of packets and the cost?

c What formula has Vernon typed into cell B3?

	A	B
1	Number of packets	Cost (£)
2	1	£0.65
3	2	£1.30
4	3	£1.95
5	4	£2.60
6	5	£3.25
7	6	£3.90
8	7	£4.55

3 In these questions the quantities are in direct proportion.
For each question calculate the single multiplier that connects the pair of quantities.

a 5 miles is the same as 8 km.

b 6 pizzas cost £15.

c 10 cm is the same as 100 mm.

d 5 people can eat 350 g of rice.

4 Solve these problems.

a 45 g of breakfast cereal contain 108 calories.
How many calories are there in 150 g of cereal?

b A recipe for eight people uses 1080 ml of stock.
What amount of stock is needed for the same recipe for five people?

c 400 g of cheese costs £6.80.
What is the cost of 1 kg of the cheese?

investigation

Use **direct proportion** to complete this conversion table for inches and centimetres.

Inches	Centimetres	Inches ÷ Centimetres	Centimetre ÷ Inches
1			
	20		
12	30		
20			

What do you notice?

14c Estimating and approximating

LEVEL 7

- Round numbers to 1 significant figure
- Use rounding to make estimates

Keywords
Estimate
Round
Significant figure

- To **round** a number to 1 **significant figure** (1 sig fig), you look at the value of the first non-zero digit in the number.

example

p. 108

Round each of these numbers to 1 significant figure.

a 2456 **b** 38 **c** 0.673

a The first digit is in the thousands column so round to the nearest 1000.
2456 ≏ 2000 (1 sig fig)

Look at hundreds digit: 4.
Round down to nearest 1000.

b The first digit is in the tens column so round to the nearest 10.
38 ≏ 40 (1 sig fig)

Look at units digit: 8.
Round up to nearest 10.

c The first non-zero digit is in the first decimal place so round to 1 decimal place.
0.673 ≏ 0.7 (1 sig fig)

Look at second dp: 7.
Round up to 1 dp.

- You can use rounding to make **estimates** in real-life situations.

example

Siobhan buys and sells cheese.
In October she buys 5252 cheeses at a price of £3.29 a cheese.
Estimate the amount of money Siobhan spends on cheese each day.

Write the problem as a calculation.

There are 31 days in October.

$$= \frac{5252 \times 3.29}{31}$$

Round each number to 1 significant figure.

$$\simeq \frac{5000 \times 3}{30}$$

≏ £500 per day

Exercise 14c

LEVEL 7

Grade C

1 Round each of these numbers to 1 significant figure.

a 128 **b** 2437 **c** 94 **d** 18 372

e 4.56 **f** 0.379 **g** 138.7 **h** 17.363

2 Work out an estimate for each calculation.

Start by rounding to 1 significant figure.

a 237×29 **b** $29.8 \div 4.77$ **c** 2863×0.71

d 196×11.23 **e** $\frac{17.8 \times 235}{9.6}$ **f** $\frac{0.289 \times 978}{5.8}$

3 Work out an estimate for each of these problems. Show all the numbers you have rounded and the calculations you have worked out.

a Nina spends £3511 on her shopping each year. Estimate her weekly shopping bill.

b At High Hill Language School the average height of a Year 9 boy is 1.64 m and the average height of a Year 9 girl is 1.49 m. There are 68 boys and 79 girls in the school. Estimate the total height of the students in Year 9.

Did you know?

You can estimate the size of a dinosaur from a single bone by assuming the ratio of bone length to total length is the same as for better known dinosaurs in the same family.

4 The Run4fun club want to raise money for Children in Need by organising a sponsored run.

Their target is to raise £44 444. There are 187 runners in the club.

The runners would like to run 874 miles between them.

This is the distance from Land's End to John O' Groats.

Each runner can complete a mile in 6 minutes 45 seconds.

a About how far will each of the club members need to run?

b About how much money per mile will the runners need to raise?

c If the runners take turns, about how long will it take them to complete the sponsored run?

investigation

Here are the daily, weekly, monthly and yearly costs of some household bills. Use estimation to complete the table.

Item	Daily cost	Weekly cost	Monthly cost	Yearly cost
TV licence				£139.50
Mobile phone			£24.99	
Food shopping		£88.95		
Newspaper	£0.85			
Total				

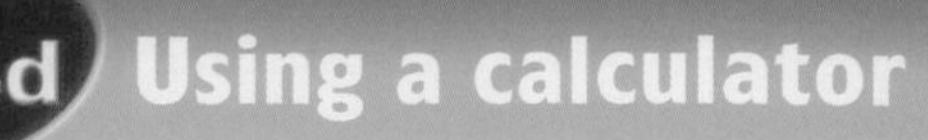

14d Using a calculator

LEVEL 7

- Use a calculator efficiently and appropriately to perform complex calculations
- Know not to round during the intermediate steps of a calculation

Keywords
Calculation
Calculator
Rounding errors

- You should only round an answer at the end of a **calculation** to avoid making **rounding errors**.

example

p. 120

Ciara and Celine convert $\frac{6}{7}$ into a percentage, giving their answer to 1 decimal place.
Explain why their answers are different.

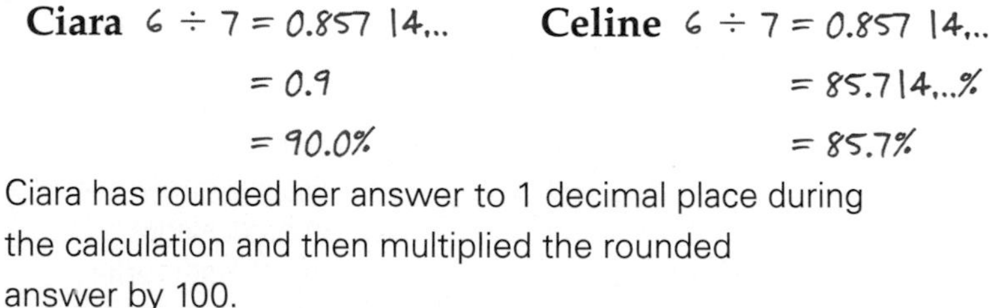

Ciara $6 \div 7 = 0.857\,14\ldots$
$= 0.9$
$= 90.0\%$

Celine $6 \div 7 = 0.857\,14\ldots$
$= 85.714\ldots\%$
$= 85.7\%$

Ciara has rounded her answer to 1 decimal place during the calculation and then multiplied the rounded answer by 100.
Celine has rounded at the end of the calculation.
Celine's answer is more accurate.

Change a decimal into a percentage by multiplying by 100.

- Always write a problem as a set of calculations.
Then you can use your **calculator** correctly.

example

p. 100

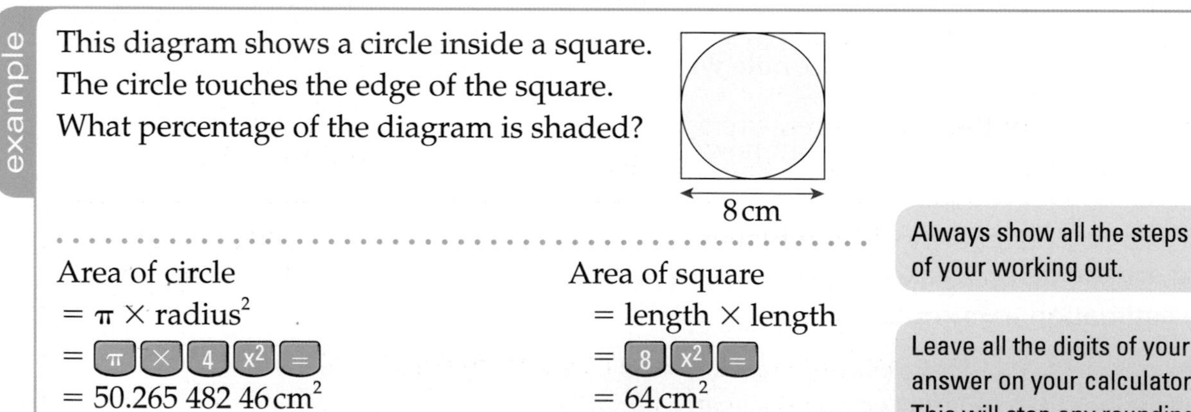

This diagram shows a circle inside a square.
The circle touches the edge of the square.
What percentage of the diagram is shaded?

Area of circle
$= \pi \times \text{radius}^2$
= [π] [×] [4] [x^2] [=]
$= 50.265\,482\,46\,\text{cm}^2$

Area of square
$= \text{length} \times \text{length}$
= [8] [x^2] [=]
$= 64\,\text{cm}^2$

Fraction shaded $= \dfrac{\text{area of circle}}{\text{area of square}} = \dfrac{50.265\,482\,46}{64}$

p. 118

Percentage shaded $= 0.785\,398\,163 \times 100\%$
$= 78.5\%$

Always show all the steps of your working out.

Leave all the digits of your answer on your calculator. This will stop any rounding errors.

Round your answer to 1 dp at the end of your calculation.

Exercise 14d

1 Convert these fractions into percentages using your calculator.
Give your answers to 1 decimal place.

a $\frac{2}{3}$ **b** $\frac{5}{16}$ **c** $\frac{3}{7}$ **d** $\frac{8}{11}$

2 Calculate the percentage of these diagrams that is shaded.

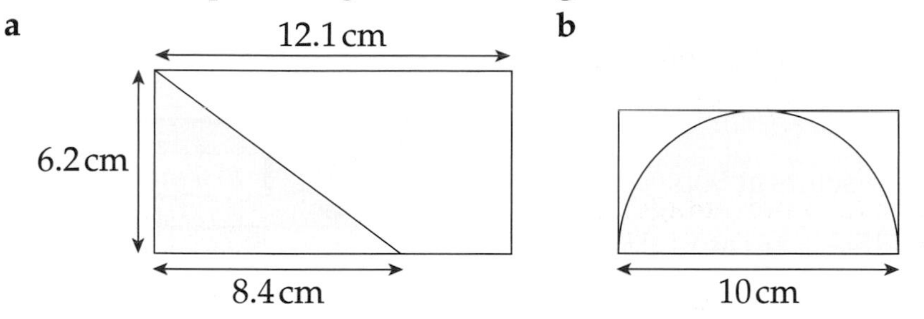

3 For these calculations work out
- **i** the exact answer (rounded to 1 decimal place at the end of the calculation).
- **ii** the answer if you round (to 1 decimal place) after **each step** of the calculation.

a Monty buys three packets of seeds at £2.72 per packet.
Altogether he has 33 seeds.
How much does each seed cost, in pence?

£2.72 / packet

b Saleem drives 324 km each week.
His car travels 71 km for each gallon (4.546 litres) of petrol.
A litre of petrol costs £0.95.
How much does Saleem spend on petrol each week?

c Mixi the rabbit eats 22% of a 3 kg bag of food each day.
How much food does Mixi eat in a year?

d Allana used $\frac{3}{5}$ of a 1.4 kg bag of rice.
Sean used $\frac{1}{3}$ of the rice that remained.
How many grams of rice were left in the bag?

investigation

Harry is playing a game of Countdown.
He explains how he got the target number of 784.
'First I multiplied 6 by 7, which makes 42.
Then I subtracted 3 and multiplied my answer by 2 to make 78.
I multiplied 78 by 10 and added 4 which makes 784.'

TARGET = 784

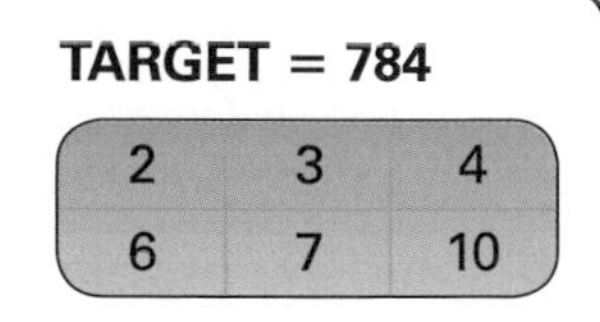

2	3	4
6	7	10

a Write Harry's calculation using the correct order of operations so that you can type it into your calculator as one calculation.

b Use Harry's numbers to make a different target number and write this using the correct order of operations.

14 Consolidation

1 Basil's salary last year was £32 600.
He had to pay £8234 in tax.
Mohinder's salary last year was £44 321.
He had to pay £12 765 in tax.
Who had to pay the higher percentage of their salary in tax?

2 Here are two offers.

Offer A	A 400 g pack of biscuits at 90p
Offer B	A 400 g pack + 15% extra at £1.02

Which offer is the better value for money?
Explain your reasoning.

3 **a** A bag of crisps normally has a mass of 150 g.
This week the mass of the bag is increased by 22%.
What is the new mass of the bag of crisps?

b A pair of trousers normally costs £76.
In a sale all the prices are reduced by 35%.
What is the sale price of the trousers?

4 **a** Kelvin is choosing between two different offers for firewood.
In which of these offers are the numbers in direct proportion?
In each case explain and justify your answers.

Offer A

Mass of wood (kg)	Cost
3	£7.68
5	£12.80
10	£25.60

Offer B

Mass of wood (kg)	Cost
10	£28
50	£135
100	£260

b Kelvin decides to buy 50 kg of firewood.
How much cheaper is offer A?

Assume the cost is in direct proportion.

5 For each of these problems
i find the single multiplier that connects the quantities
ii solve the problem.

a 75 g of cheese contains 30 g of fat.
How many grams of fat are there in 120 g of cheese?

b A recipe for six people uses 420 g of flour.
How much flour is needed for the same recipe for 11 people?

c 1.5 litres of fruit drink cost 87p.
What is the cost of 5 litres of fruit drink?

14c

6 Round all of the numbers in each calculation to 1 or 2 significant figures. Then work out an estimate for each calculation.

a 503×31 **b** $15.16 \div 2.97$ **c** 5673×0.388

d $\frac{19.3 \times 415}{11.4}$ **e** $\frac{0.482 \times 317}{4.9}$ **f** $\frac{38.2 \times 6.39}{0.783}$

7 Work out an estimate for this problem.
Show all the numbers you have rounded and the calculations you have worked out.
Debbie is trying to save money.
She spends £4.89 on a coffee and a sandwich each working day.
Her friend suggests that she could save some money by making a sandwich and bringing a flask of coffee from home.
Making her own sandwiches and flask of coffee costs £1.08 per day.
Debbie works 5 days a week for 46 weeks of the year.
How much money could she save each year if she takes her friend's advice?

14d

8 Calculate the percentage of each of these diagrams that is shaded.

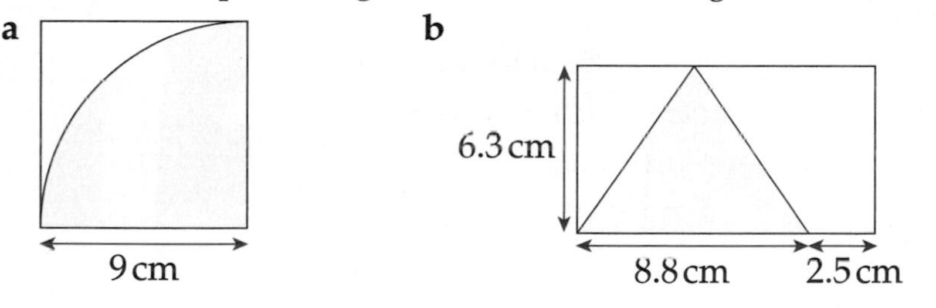

9 For each of these calculations work out
i an approximation by rounding.
ii the exact answer.

a A plane travels from England to Austria at 324 miles per hour for 3 hours.
Another plane travels the identical route but takes 4 hours.
What is the speed of the second plane?

b Stefan drives 388 km in his car each week.
His car travels 61 km for every 5 litres of petrol.
Petrol costs 98p per litre.
Stefan decides to try to save money by driving more slowly and reduces his petrol consumption by 18%.
How much money does Stefan now spend on petrol each year?

Maths Life

Perspective in Renaissance art

The Renaissance is the name given to the period of history starting in the 14th century and carrying through to the 17th century. During the Renaissance, artists tackled the problem of representing the 3-dimensional world in a 2-dimensional painting. They tried to show things so that they looked the same as they do in real life. It was during this time that perspective became widely used in art work.

Compare these two paintings:

- *Which picture do you think looks most realistic?*
- *What has the artist done to make it look more realistic?*

To make their paintings more realistic, Renaissance artists used the idea that lines on an object converge as they go away from the viewer. They also used the related idea that the further away objects are, the smaller they appear to be.

Although perspective is used to make things look real, the essence of perspective is not showing things as they actually are, but showing them as they seem to be when you look at them.

Look at these two representations of a cube: A B

- *Which do you think looks more like a cube?*
- *Measure the edges of the drawing. What do you notice?*
- *What else has changed in B compared with an actual cube?*
- *Why do the changes make it look more like a cube?*

Single point perspective

Renaissance artists began to use the way that lines meet at a single vanishing point to add realism to their work. The vanishing point is clearly seen in this photograph.

Check the perspective in the two paintings on the left hand page. Do either of them have a vanishing point?

As the eye tends to be drawn to the vanishing point, many artists placed the vanishing point near the main subject of their painting.

A famous example of this is The Last Supper by Leonardo da Vinci.

The vanishing point is set at the height of the eye-line. In this drawing, the green cuboid appears to be above the viewer and the blue cuboids below.

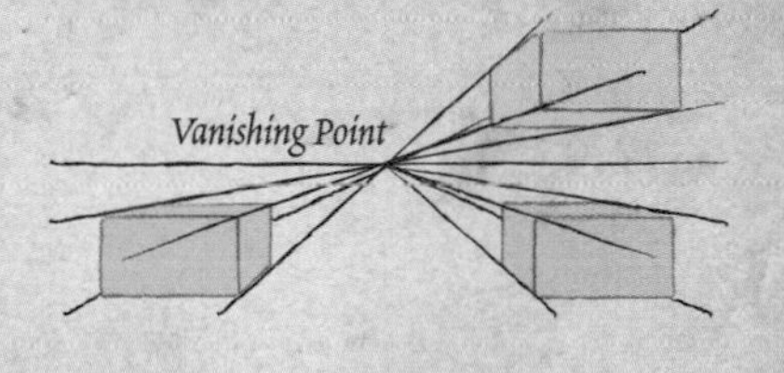

- *Make your own drawing of cubes using single point perspective. Draw at least 3 cubes in different places to see how they look. Include one fairly close to the vanishing point and one quite a long way to the left or right of the vanishing point.*
- *What do you notice about cubes that are a long way to the left or right of the vanishing point?*

Two point perspective

Single point perspective works well when objects are square on to the viewer. However, when objects are edge on to the viewer a single vanishing point no longer works as the parts of the object each side of the edge taper away in different directions.

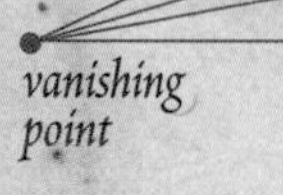

When an object is edge on, two point perspective gives a more realistic impression, using two vanishing points, both on the same horizontal eye line, as in the picture.

- *Use two point perspective to draw a cube edge on, as if looking at it from above.*
- *Now add a second cube edge on, this time as if looking at it from below.*

14 Summary

Assessment criteria

- Solve problems involving direct proportion **Level 6**
- Calculate the outcome of a percentage increase or decrease **Level 6**
- Use a calculator efficiently and appropriately **Level 7**

Level 6

1 Gillian rents a room for £4200 per year.
The landlord increases the rent by 4%.
a How much is the rent increase?
b What is the new monthly payment for rent?

Diana's answer ✔

$4\% = \frac{4}{100} = 0.04$

4200 —(× 0.04, 4%)→ ?

a 4200 × 0.04 = £168

b New rent = £4200 + £168
= £4368 per year
= £4368 ÷ 12 per month
= £364 per month

Diana finds 4% by using the multiplier 0.04

Diana checks 4200 × 1.04 = 4368

Level 7

2 You can buy jars of the same jam in two sizes.

A

454g for £1.59

B

340g for £1.25

Which jar is better value for money?
You must show your working to explain your answer.

Key Stage 3 2008 5–7 Paper 2

15 Functional maths

Real life, functional maths relies on using mathematical processes and applications.

The AfriLinks project links schools in Europe with schools in Africa.

Six British students travel to Kangera in East Africa.

Greg Ella Imran Maxine Josh Wah Wah

The local school has been destroyed in a mudslide. The students will help build a new school.

Before they depart, the students find out about the Kangera region.

1 The population is 9953.
The table shows the population by age.

Age group	0 – 20	21 – 40	41 – 60	60+
Number	3490	2988	2450	1025

a Round these numbers to the nearest 100.

b Draw a pie chart to display the rounded data values.
Make sure you provide a key.

2 The graph shows average temperature and rainfall over a 30 year period in the Kangera region.

a What is the range of temperatures?

b What is the range of rainfall measurements?

c What is the median average rainfall for a year?

d What is the mean average temperature for a year?

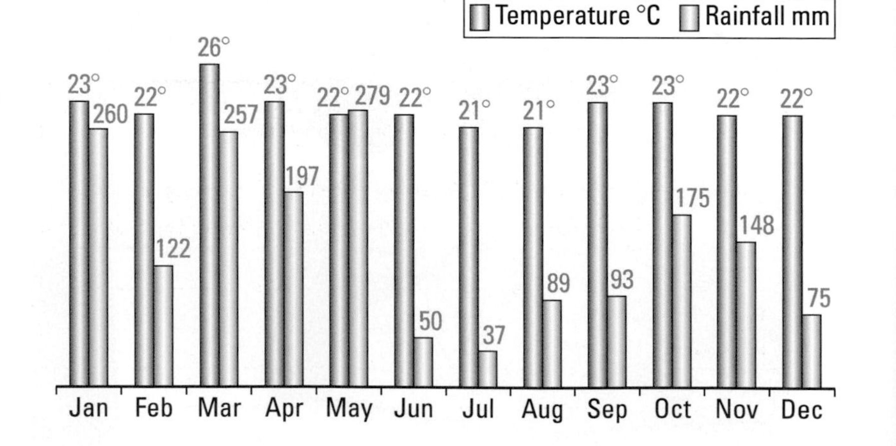

3 The table shows rainfall measurements for the first five months of this year.

Month	Jan	Feb	Mar	Apr	May
Rainfall (mm)	180	242	368	492	481

a What do you notice when you compare these figures with the average rainfall?

b Explain why you think the school building was destroyed.

Most pupils walk to school in Kangera.
The map shows some of the pupils' journeys.

4 Work with a partner to copy and complete this table.

Name	Distance (km)	Bearing in ° from school to home	Bearing in ° from home to school
Albert			
Constance			
Michael			
Mary			
Frieda			

Give the directions as three-figure bearings.

15b Building the schoolhouse

LEVEL 5/6

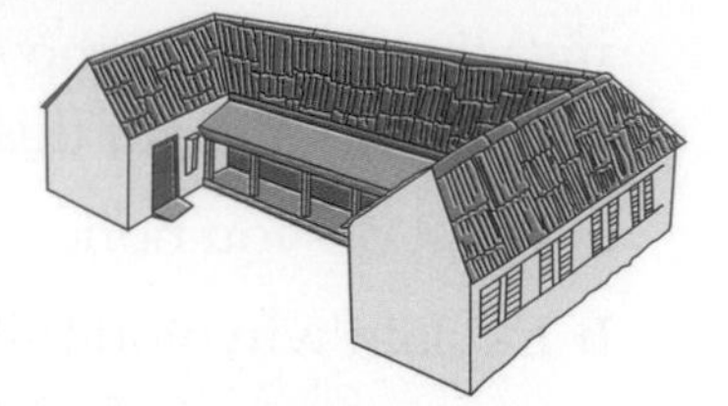

Josh and Maxine are making draft plans for the schoolhouse.

They make a rough sketch of the building and the floor space that it will need.

1 Redraw the plan neatly to a scale of 1 : 200.

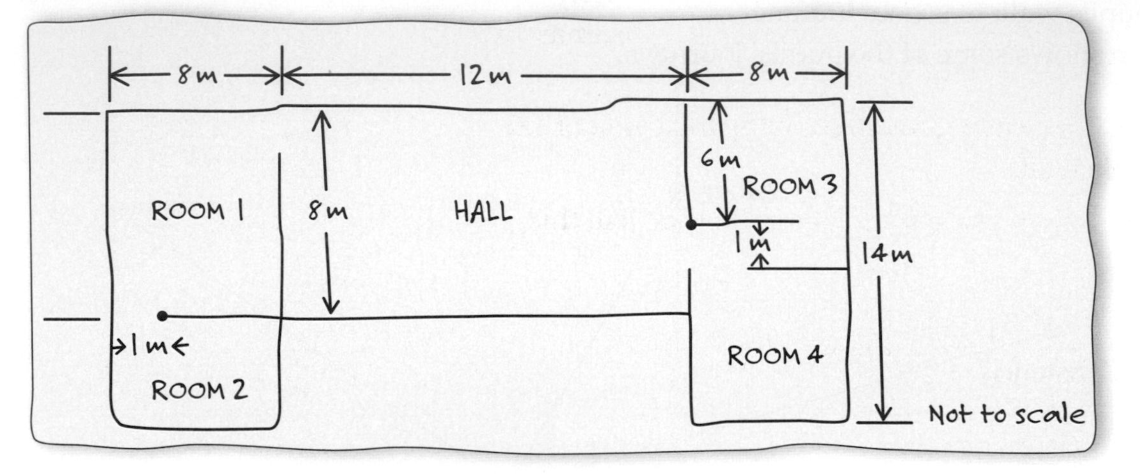

2 **a** Use your plan to calculate the total area of the floor space.

b The headteacher wants the classroom areas to have 1 m^2 for each pupil. If there are 210 pupils in the school, will there be enough floor space for them?

c As an estimate, to the nearest 10% what percentage of the total floor space is the classroom space?

3 To make sure that the building is strong they dig foundations for all of the outer walls.
They dig trenches 80 cm deep and 40 cm wide.

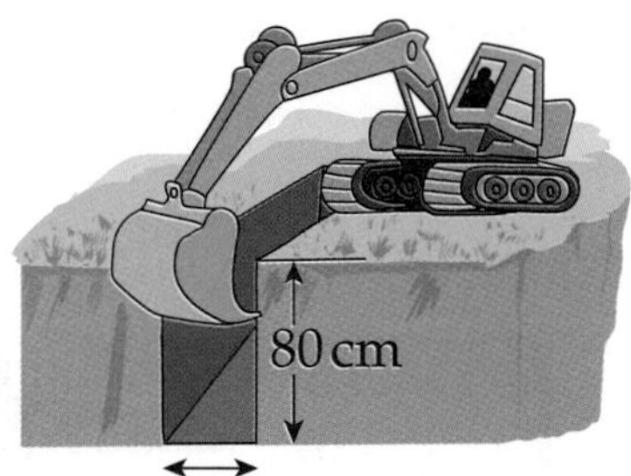

a What is the volume of soil removed from the ground? Give your answer to the nearest whole m^2.

b To make the foundations strong, concrete is poured into the trench.
The concrete costs \$45 per cubic metre plus \$15 delivery cost.
How much will the foundations cost?

4 To cope with the rain during tropical storms Josh says that the roof has to slope at an angle of 35°.

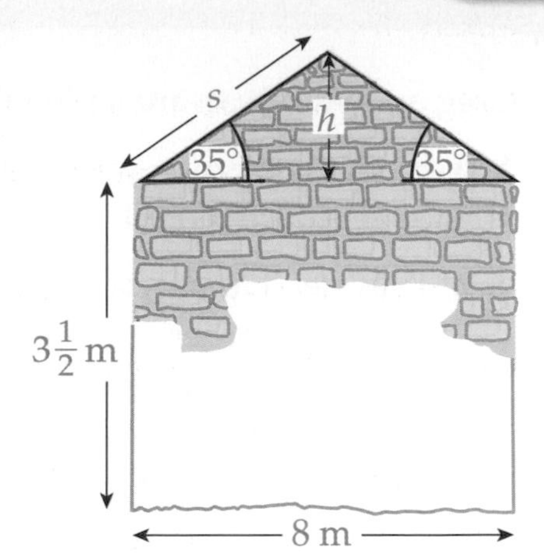

a Make a scale drawing of the roof section using a scale 1 cm : 1 m.

b Use your drawing to measure

i the height, h, of the triangular roof section (write your answer to the nearest 1 decimal place)

ii the length, s, of the slope.

c Use the drawing to calculate the total area of this gable wall.

The wall is made from 'Breeze-blocks' like this.

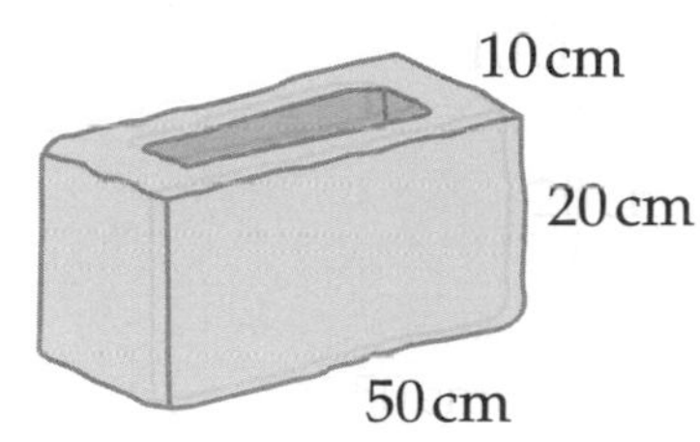

They measure 10 cm × 20 cm × 50 cm.

d Maxine estimates the number of blocks needed for the wall. She ignores the gaps for mortar and estimates that they will need 500 blocks.
Use your answer to part **c** to say exactly by how many blocks she is wrong. Has she overestimated or underestimated?

The blocks are held together by a cement mortar. The mortar is made by mixing sand, cement and water. Stronger mortar uses more cement, weaker mixtures use more sand.

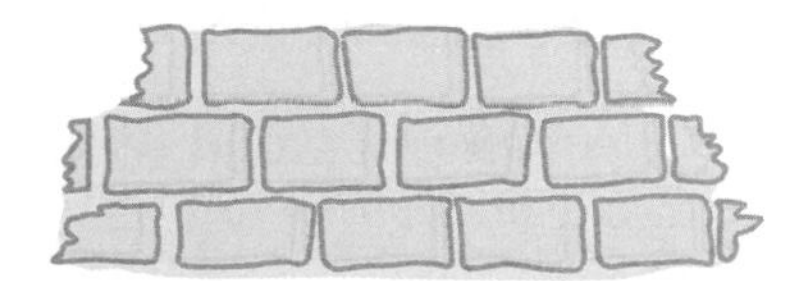

The label shows the ratio of three mixes.

5 **a** What strength of mix are each of these?

i 28 parts of sand and 8 parts of cement.

ii 24 parts of sand and 9 parts of cement.

iii 4 parts of cement and 20 parts of sand.

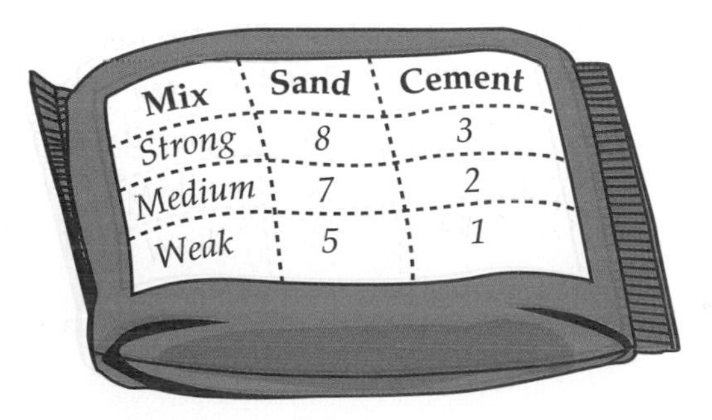

Mix	Sand	Cement
Strong	8	3
Medium	7	2
Weak	5	1

b Maxine uses 16 parts of sand to make a strong mix.
How much cement will she need to use?

c A weak mix is needed for the path. Josh mixes a total of 360 kg. How much sand and how much cement will he need?

15c Laying the path

Greg and Wah Wah are laying the path.

1 **a** From the picture, what is the ratio of yellow to red tiles?

b They need to use 24 yellow tiles. Imran has ordered 142 red tiles.

i Will they be able to complete the path?

ii If they have not ordered enough red tiles, how many more will they need?

2 The red tiles are packed on pallets.

a Make an equation from the information below.

3 pallets and 16 tiles weigh the same as 1 pallet and 166 tiles.

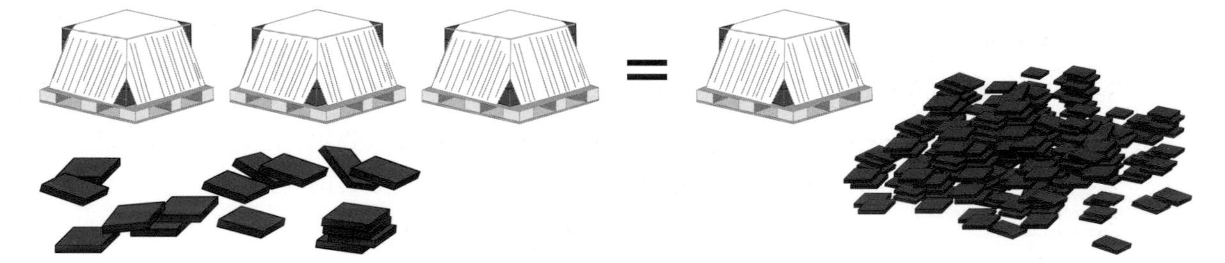

b Solve the equation to calculate the number of tiles on a pallet.

c The total weight of a full pallet and tiles is 126.5 kg.

An empty pallet weighs 14 kg. How much does each tile weigh?

3 A collection of red blocks and green slabs are laid in a pattern like this.

a How many green slabs will be laid before the pattern begins to repeat itself?

b What will be the ratio of slabs to blocks in the pattern?

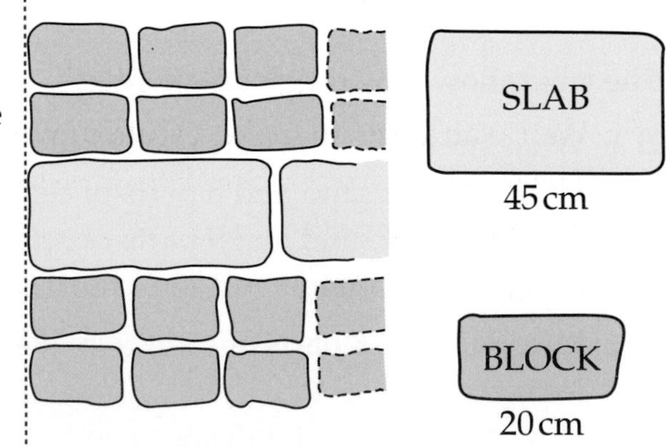

4 Wah Wah wants to make a circular flowerbed.
The flowerbed is surrounded by a path.
The outer radius of the path is 4.5 metres and the inner radius is 1.2 metres.

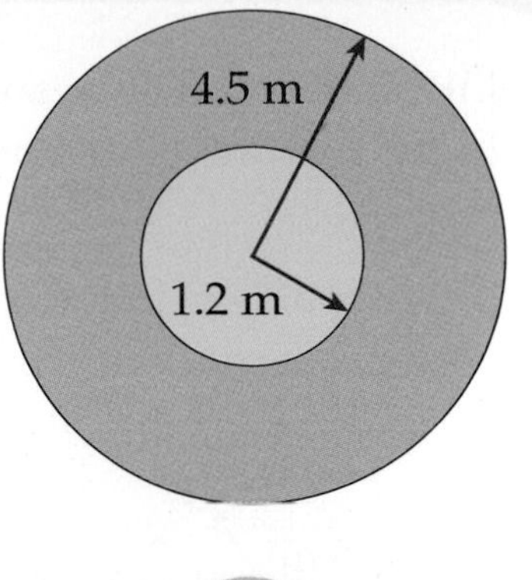

The outside and inside of the path have a plastic border.
The border is sold in 5 metre rolls.

a How many rolls should Wah Wah buy?

b To the nearest 10 cm, how much border will be wasted? (use $\pi = 3.14$)

c What is the area of the path?

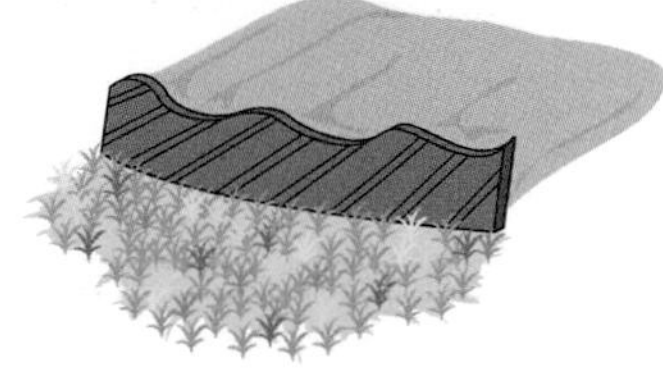

5 Greg wants to use different patterns in the play areas.
He tries different shaped slabs to see if they will tessellate.

Here is an example of Greg's first tessellation made from rectangles in a 'herring-bone' pattern.

a Sketch two other ways of tessellating using rectangles which are twice as long as they are wide.

b Make a sketch for these shapes to show that Greg will be able to tessellate them.
Repeat the shape at least eight times for each sketch.

i

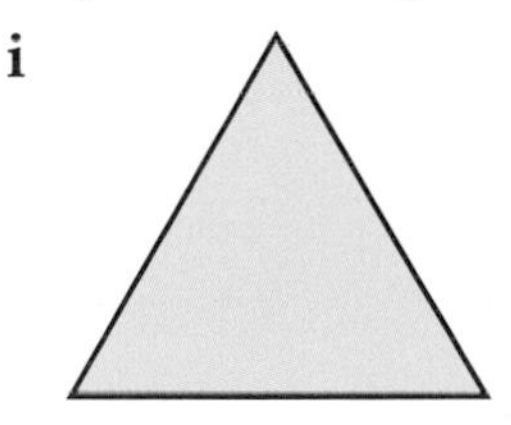

ii

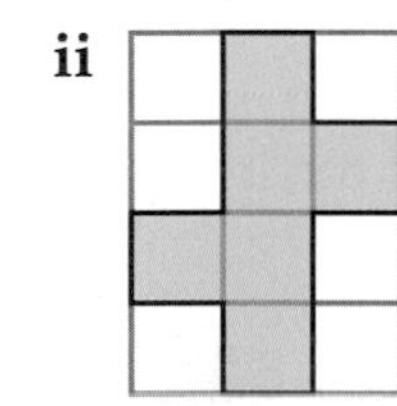

iii

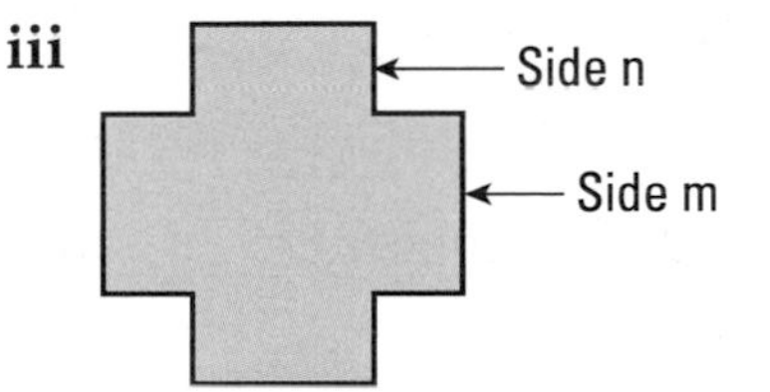

c Wah Wah starts to make a scale drawing of the cross-shaped slab.
The shape will only tessellate if the sides n and m are designed in a certain ratio. What is the ratio?

d If side n is 8 cm, calculate the perimeter of the whole shape.

15d The basketball court

LEVEL 6/7

Ella, Imran and Greg are going to mark out a basketball court. Imran can only find a piece of rope, two sticks and a tape measure.

1 Write a description to explain how they should use these items to mark the circles and semicircles on the court?

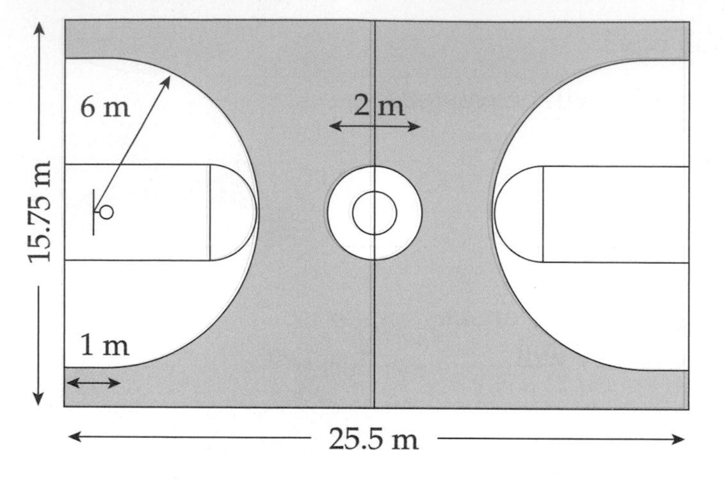

2 **a** What is the area of the court?

b There is a 'D' shape at each end of the court. The semicircle has a radius of 6 m and the straight lines are 1 m long. What is the area of the 'D' shape.

Use $\pi = 3.14$ and give the answer to three significant figures.

3 Ella marks the boundary of the court with tape. If the tape is sold in 20 m rolls, how many rolls will she need to buy? Allow an extra 10% for wastage.

4 The students have a school team. They are asked to choose their own kit from these colours.

a Greg says that there are 13 different combinations of kit using these colours. Draw a probability table and hence explain why he is wrong.

b What is the probability that the kit will be all the same colour?

To celebrate the opening of the court the students arrange a basketball tournament with the locals.

The score keeper records the performance of each competitor.

Here are the statistics for six players. The table records the number of baskets scored during their games.

Baskets scored in a game	Number of games					
	Isaac	Imran	Veronica	Jacob	Oilolay	Maxine
0	0	0	0	0	2	0
1	1	0	2	0	1	0
2	0	0	3	2	0	1
3	6	0	1	0	1	0
4	3	12	3	4	4	1
5	1	0	2	0	0	0
6	4	4	0	3	0	3
7	0	4	0	1	0	6

5 **a** Which player scored the most baskets?

b What is the modal number of baskets scored in a game?

6 **a** Which of the three averages – mode, median or mean – gives you the best idea of the players' performances? Explain your choice.

Discuss your ideas with a partner before answering this question.

b Using the mean, rank the players from strongest to weakest.

7 Based on his current average, if Isaac played three more games predict his new total score.

8 From the table above chose a set of data which, in your opinion, can be best displayed as a pie chart.

This pie chart shows how Isaac performed. Draw a pie chart showing your own data.

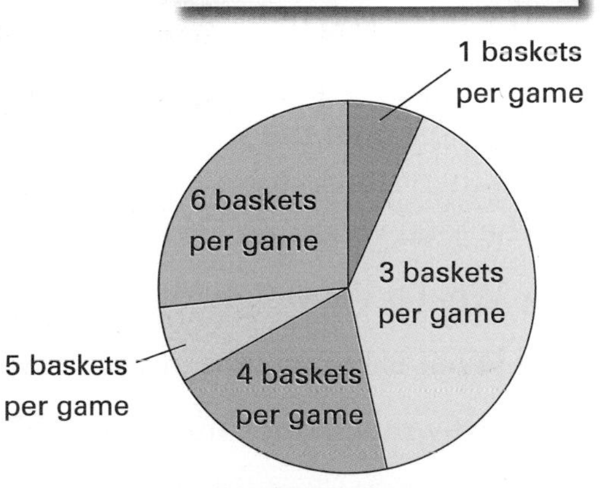

15e The school garden

The students are working in the school's garden.

They find some old gardening items in a shed.

A ruler that measures inches.

A watering can that measures pints and gallons.

A weighing scale that measures pounds and ounces.

Some useful conversions

1 inch ≡ 2.5 cm

1 ounce ≡ 30 g

1 pint ≡ 0.6 litres

1 lb (pound) ≡ 0.45 kg

All their instructions are in metric measures; they will have to convert units into imperial measures to complete the task!

Mix 7 kg of compost with 3 kg of sharp sand.

Mix 600 g of fertiliser with 4.5 litres of water.

Dig a trench 15 cm deep and 70 cm long.

1 **a** How many pounds of compost will be measured?

b How many pounds of sharp sand will be measured?

c How many ounces of fertiliser will be measured?

d Imran says that he needs 3.5 pints of water. Show that his answer is not right.

e Ella dug the trench 6 inches deep. Will it be the right depth?

f How many inches long is the trench?

2 Imran puts 3 bags of soil and 2 bags of compost onto the weighing scales. The total weight is 79 kg.

Imran puts 1 bag of soil and 3 bags of compost onto the weighing scales. The total weight is 52 kg.

Imran puts 2 bags of soil and 4 bags of compost onto the weighing scales. He then sits on top of the bags. The total weight is 135 kg.

a What is the weight of each bag of soil?

b What is the weight of each bag of compost?

c How much does Imran weigh?

Work with a partner to solve these problems.

3 Josh has some seeds to plant

8 onion seeds	10 tomato seeds
6 pepper seeds	12 chilli seeds.

Josh sneezes and the seeds are mixed up.
If he picks up one seed at random what is the probability it will be

a a pepper seed?

b not a chilli seed?

Josh cannot tell the difference between the seeds.
He plants a seed in each of 90 flowerpots.

c Estimate the likely numbers of each of the four types of plants.

4 The school is to have a goat in the garden.
Ella, Wah Wah and Maxine have to build a pen for the goat.
They have these 10 fence panels to make the four walls of the rectangular pen.

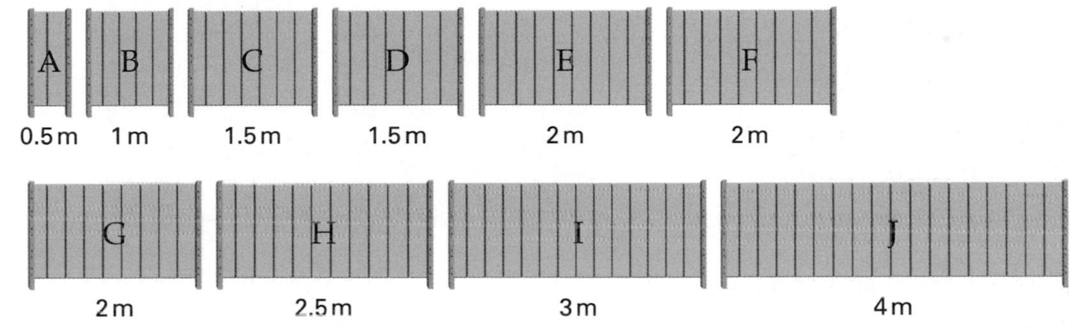

What is the biggest area that can be enclosed with these panels?
Draw a sketch to show how the panels should be fitted together.

5 Greg goes to collect the goat. He meets the three Makale brothers who are arguing about how to divide up the 11 goats given to them by their family.

- The eldest brother is given $\frac{1}{2}$ of them.
- The middle brother is given $\frac{1}{3}$ of them.
- The youngest brother is given $\frac{1}{12}$ of them.

Greg had a great idea. He lent them his goat.

a Calculate how many goats each brother received.

b Show that Greg had his goat returned to him.

c Explain how Greg's great idea works.

15

Assessment criteria

- Solve demanding problems and check solutions; explore connections between different parts of mathematics; find more general solutions — Level 7
- Explain why you chose to solve a given problem in a particular way — Level 7
- Justify generalisations, arguments and solutions — Level 7
- Recognise the difference between a mathematical explanation and experimental evidence — Level 7
- Solve problems by breaking them down into smaller tasks and using a range of methods, including ICT; give solutions to an appropriate degree of accuracy — **Level 6**
- Interpret, discuss and combine information presented in a variety of mathematical forms — **Level 6**
- Give short, reasoned arguments using mathematics and explanatory text — **Level 6**
- Use logic to establish the truth of a statement — **Level 6**

Check in and Summary answers

1

Check in

1 **a** £63 **b** £153

2 **a** 2 **b** 36

3 **a** 24 **b** $7\frac{1}{2}$

4 **a** $C = 2xy + 30$ **b** £90

Summary

2 **a** 55
b 5050

2

Check in

1 **a** 12 **b** 35 **c** 5

2 **a** $\frac{30}{7}$ **b** $\frac{8}{5}$

3 **a** $1\frac{5}{9}$ **b** $5\frac{2}{3}$

4 **a** £2.10 **b** 300 g

5 **a** £4.50 **b** 22 km **c** £23.04

6

Fraction	Decimal	Percentage
$\frac{13}{20}$	0.65	65%
$\frac{5}{8}$	0.625	62.5%
$\frac{2}{25}$	0.08	8%

7 **a** 3:14 **b** 9:13

8 16

Summary

2 2

$\frac{3}{4} \div \frac{1}{8} = 6$

3

Check in

1 **a** 63° **b** 54° **c** 49°

2 **A** rectangle
B rhombus
C isosceles trapezium
D parallelogram
E kite
F square
G arrowhead

Summary

2 $x = 74°$ because triangle ABD is isosceles.
$y = 32°$ because angles in triangle ABD add to 180°.
$z = 46°$ because angles in triangle ABC add to 180°.

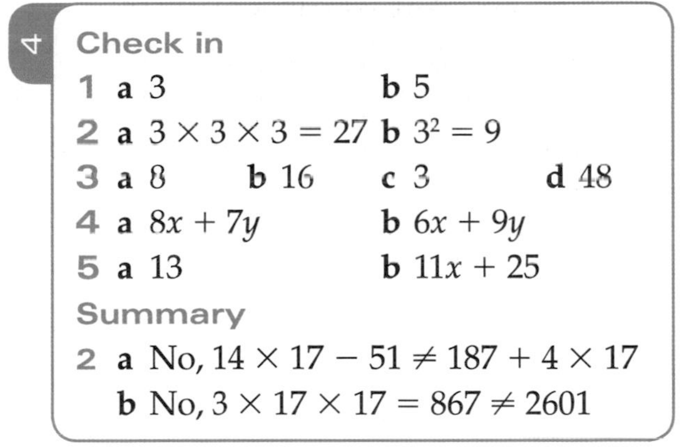

4

Check in

1 **a** 3 **b** 5

2 **a** $3 \times 3 \times 3 = 27$ **b** $3^2 = 9$

3 **a** 8 **b** 16 **c** 3 **d** 48

4 **a** $8x + 7y$ **b** $6x + 9y$

5 **a** 13 **b** $11x + 25$

Summary

2 **a** No, $14 \times 17 - 51 \neq 187 + 4 \times 17$
b No, $3 \times 17 \times 17 = 867 \neq 2601$

5

Check in

1 The most popular channels are BBC1 (with just under a quarter of the total audience) and ITV (about 15% of the total). BBC2, Channel 4 and Channel 5 have smaller shares, and all the other stations have a combined share of about 40%.

2 In 1981 there were only three stations – ITV (with about a 50% audience share), BBC1 (40%) and BBC2 (10%). Since then, both BBC1 and ITV steadily decline to about 20%, with BBC2 remaining steady at about 10%. Channel 4 (from 1982) maintained about a 10% share, and Channel 5 (from 1996) reached around 5%. The other big change is the growth of 'others' from 1990 onwards – rising steadily to more than 35% of the audience.

Summary

2 **a** 11 pupils **b** 12 pupils

6

Check in

1 **a** 30 cm, 50 cm^2 **b** 24 cm, 36 cm^2
c 36 cm, 48 cm^2

2 36 m^3

3 **a** 5500 **b** 40

Summary

3 **a** 9.42 cm
b 9100 ÷ 9.42 = 970 to the nearest ten

7

Check in

1 **a** 290 **b** 3.86 **c** 420 **d** 4.2

2 **a** **i** 2500 **ii** 2460 **iii** 2456.8
b **i** 900 **ii** 930 **iii** 928.3

3 **a** 9.5 **b** 6.4 **c** 18.7 **d** 8.9

4 **a** 143 **b** 1075 **c** 7406 **d** 30.8

5 **a** 15.8 **b** 16 **c** 18.9 **d** 29.4

6 **a** 28 **b** 8

Summary

2 **a** $\frac{1}{10}, \frac{1}{100}$ **b** 11% **c** $\frac{2}{9}$

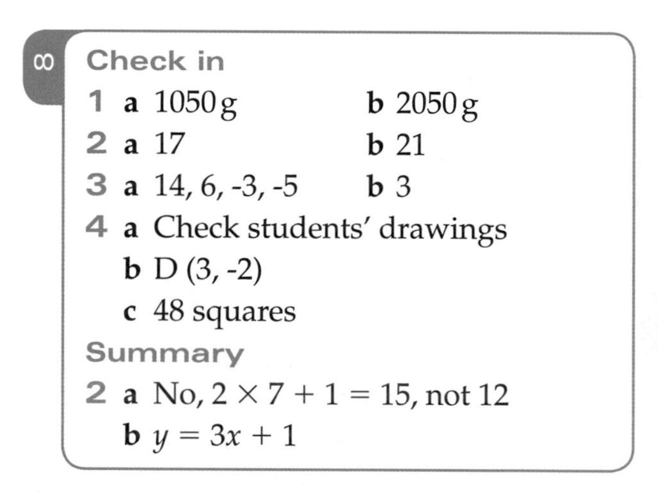

8

Check in

1 **a** 1050 g **b** 2050 g

2 **a** 17 **b** 21

3 **a** 14, 6, -3, -5 **b** 3

4 **a** Check students' drawings
b D (3, -2)
c 48 squares

Summary

2 **a** No, 2 × 7 + 1 = 15, not 12
b $y = 3x + 1$

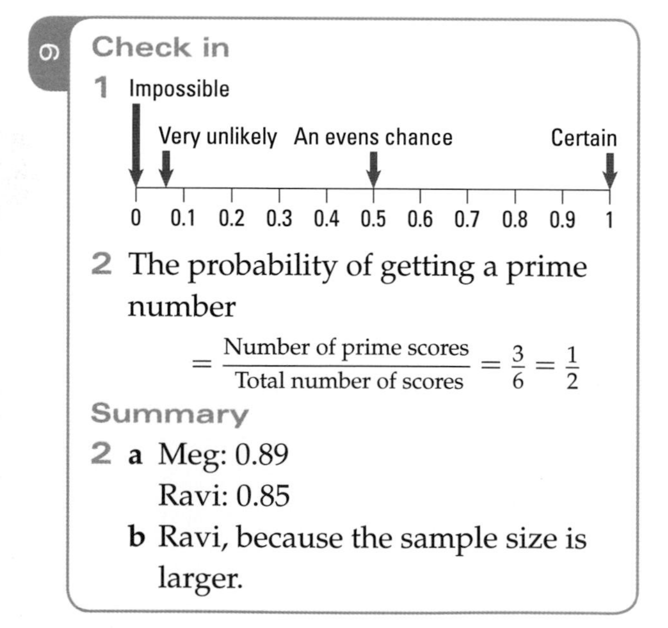

9

Check in

1 Impossible, Very unlikely, An evens chance, Certain (number line 0 to 1)

2 The probability of getting a prime number

$$= \frac{\text{Number of prime scores}}{\text{Total number of scores}} = \frac{3}{6} = \frac{1}{2}$$

Summary

2 **a** Meg: 0.89
Ravi: 0.85
b Ravi, because the sample size is larger.

10

Check in

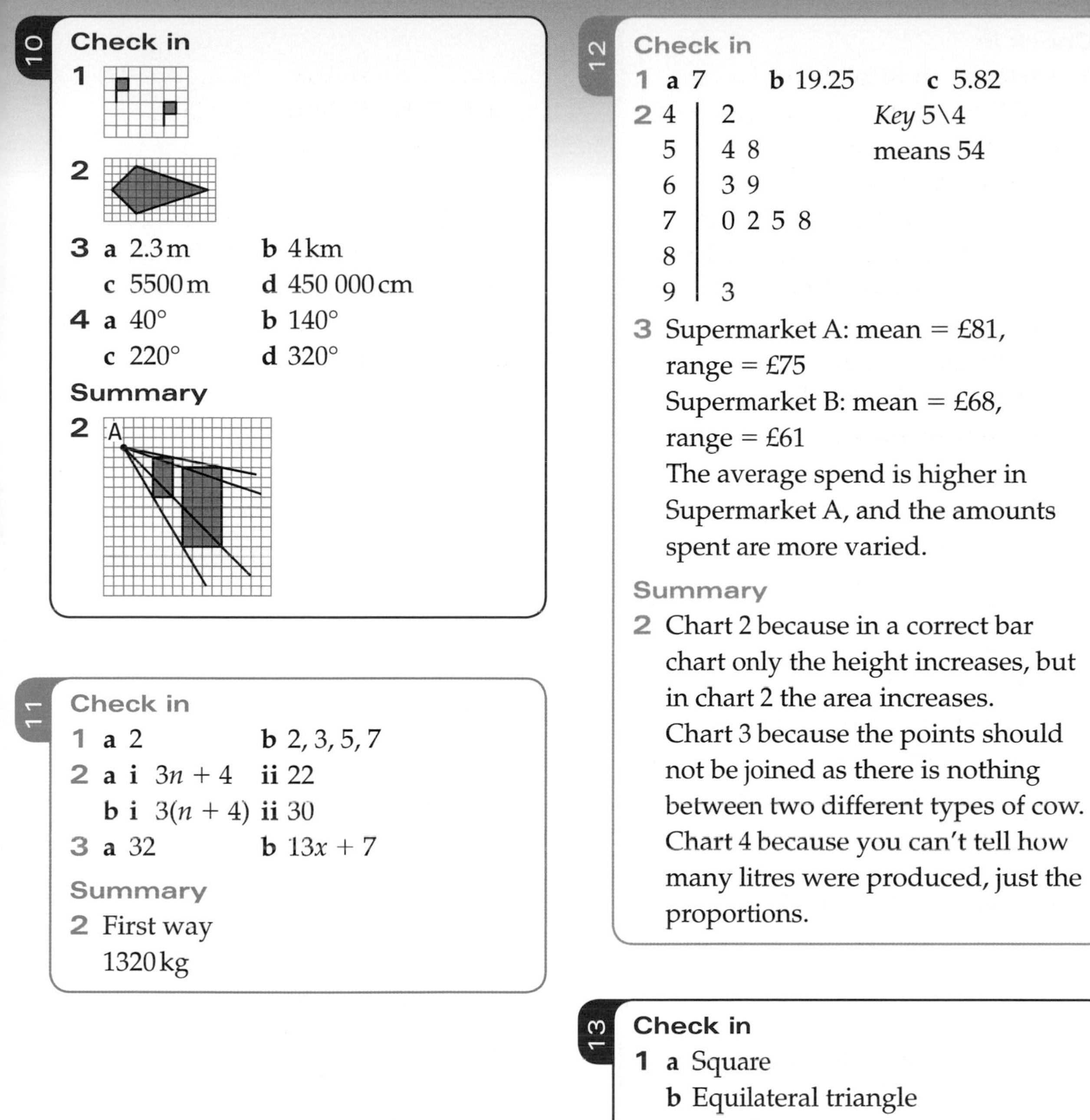

1

2

3 **a** 2.3 m **b** 4 km
c 5500 m **d** 450 000 cm

4 **a** 40° **b** 140°
c 220° **d** 320°

Summary

2

11

Check in

1 **a** 2 **b** 2, 3, 5, 7

2 **a** **i** $3n + 4$ **ii** 22
b **i** $3(n + 4)$ **ii** 30

3 **a** 32 **b** $13x + 7$

Summary

2 First way
1320 kg

12

Check in

1 **a** 7 **b** 19.25 **c** 5.82

2

Stem	Leaf
4	2
5	4 8
6	3 9
7	0 2 5 8
8	
9	3

Key 5\4 means 54

3 Supermarket A: mean = £81, range = £75
Supermarket B: mean = £68, range = £61
The average spend is higher in Supermarket A, and the amounts spent are more varied.

Summary

2 Chart 2 because in a correct bar chart only the height increases, but in chart 2 the area increases.
Chart 3 because the points should not be joined as there is nothing between two different types of cow.
Chart 4 because you can't tell how many litres were produced, just the proportions.

13

Check in

1 **a** Square
b Equilateral triangle
c Regular pentagon
d Regular hexagon
e Regular octagon

2 **a** $40\,cm^2$, $16\,cm^3$ **b** $42\,cm^2$, $18\,cm^3$

3 **a** $405\,cm^2$ **b** $50\,cm^2$

Summary

2 **a** $120\,cm^3$ **b** $450\,cm^3$

14

Check in

1. a 60% b 85%
   c 62.5% d 42.9%
2. a £40.25 b $202.20
3. a 19.2 km b £17.50
4. a i 500 ii 483 iii 482.65
   b i 100 ii 98 iii 98.07
   c i 0 ii 1 iii 0.79

Summary

2. 454 g ÷ 159 p = 2.86 g per 1 p
   340 g ÷ 125 p = 2.72 g per 1 p
   Jar A is better value for money.

dex